Practical Design of
Digital Circuits

For Timothy

Practical Design of Digital Circuits

Basic Logic to Microprocessors

Ian Kampel, C.Eng., M.I.E.R.E.

Newnes Technical Books

Newnes Technical Books
is an imprint of the Butterworth Group
which has principal offices in
London, Boston, Durban, Singapore, Sydney, Toronto, Wellington

First published 1983

© I. J. Kampel, 1983

British Library Cataloguing in Publication Data

Kampel, Ian
  Practical design of digital circuits
  1. Digital integrated circuits
  I. Title
  621.381'73   TK7874

  ISBN 0-408-01183-1

Typeset by Butterworths Litho Preparation Department
Printed in England by Whitstable Litho Ltd, Whitstable, Kent

Preface

As the title of this book suggests, the aim of this work is to demonstrate the *practical* aspects of digital circuit design. For this reason the amount of pure theory has been kept to an absolute minimum and the primary objective has been one of showing the reader the most direct route to 'thinking' about digital design in the manner of an experienced designer. The intention is to give the reader sufficient confidence to embark upon his own design projects utilising digital integrated circuits as soon as possible.

The word *practical* is emphasised, for there can be quite a gap between a practical design approach and a purely theoretical one. Most courses on digital electronics spend quite a considerable time describing how particular integrated circuits function internally. There is no need for the designer to know this, for he uses them as 'black boxes'. There is also a tendency to over emphasise techniques for minimising logic networks in order to achieve the minimum number of gates. These make good academic exercises and allow the student to really get to know Boolean algebra and Karnaugh maps, but they do not reflect the true design environment where low component count and cost minimisation are the most important factors. The minimum number of *used gates* does not automatically give the minimum number of *devices*, and is unlikely to do so where many different types are demanded. All the former may lead to is an unreasonable number of under-utilised devices.

Minimising – or simplifying – one logic network to produce another with less gates also assumes that you are starting with a wasteful network in the first place. Since good design practice should not create such a situation, this is rather like concentrating on how to compensate for shortcomings rather than how to avoid them. The experienced designer always has certain good design principles in mind when he sets about designing a digital circuit, and the purpose of this book is to show what these are.

For those having a reasonable familiarity with linear design but no knowledge of digital design, I would like to assure them that digital design should present them with few problems once they get some 'hands-on' experience. For a digital design is far easier to analyse on paper than a linear design. It is always possible to overlook an important factor or parameter in a complex linear design, but with careful thought, it should always be possible to complete a digital design with a much higher degree of confidence. It is a reasonable proposition to consider all possible conditions within a digital circuit, but such may not be the case for a linear circuit.

There is no doubt about it that digital electronics is here to stay. With the advent of the microprocessor its future is assured, and since any microprocessor needs to interface with fairly conventional digital devices, there will always be a call for digital design engineers. As the range of components increases year by year, and as the price of such components continues to stay at reasonable rates – or even drops – despite ever present inflation, more and more equipment is likely to go digital. There will always be the need for linear circuitry where any form of input or output transducer is concerned, but the system designer is finding it more efficient, cost-effective, and reliable to convert to or from digital circuitry at the earliest opportunity. In complex systems his aim will be to convert from digital circuitry to or from microprocessor software at the earliest opportunity as well.

This book concentrates on digital design techniques using the basic building blocks of such circuits. These devices will always be around simply because they are so basic. Even allowing for the most sophisticated microprocessors of the future, any particular system inevitably has its own particular input/output interface problems, and these devices will always be needed for such purposes. Therefore despite the rapid advancement in microelectronics and in microprocessor technology, I am confident that the techniques described in this book will remain relevant for the foreseeable future.

This book is aimed at a fairly broad market: it is intended to aid the linear design engineer to cross the barrier into digital electronics; it should provide interesting supporting reading for students studying digital electronics from the more academic viewpoint; it should enable the enthusiast to design much more ambitious and sophisticated projects than he could otherwise attempt if restricted to linear devices. The great advantage that digital circuitry can offer is high reliability, and this should be the ultimate aim of any electronics designer.

My own background is in both linear and digital design, and my current occupation involves me in many large and complex systems designed by a wide variety of manufacturers. This viewpoint is a useful one in observing current trends, and one that is reflected in the pages to follow.

You cannot learn faster about anything than by becoming personally involved. My recommendation to the aspiring digital designer is to read through this book in order to get an idea of how to go about designing digital circuits – be they large or small – and then to have a go at a simple design straight away. Electronic games provide an ideal excuse for such an exercise, and digital electronics can provide reasonable sophistication at moderate cost and with minimal complexity. Here is an ideal proving ground.

Good luck!

I.J.K.

Acknowledgements

The author is indebted to the staff of Texas Instruments and RCA for their kind permission to reproduce certain illustrations relating to their products. He would also like to extend his particular thanks to RCA for validating material relating to the 'COSMAC' microprocessor.

Contents

Using this book

This book is intended to be read in the order presented: it then offers the reader a course in the *practical design of digital circuits*. Like any other course, it is necessary to introduce new concepts gradually, and to start with basics and to gradually advance to more and more complexity as the student progresses. Thus the book cannot be effective unless read in this manner; random dipping into later chapters may do no more than give the impression of greater difficulty than should otherwise be experienced.

There are many books on digital electronics, but very few on the techniques of digital design. This is probably because any form of design is essentially creative, and it is always difficult to teach creativity. This does not mean that it is impossible. For example, it is possible to teach someone the basic principles of painting, but once they have learned these, the field is wide open for them to express themselves in their own particular and individual way. The same applies with digital design.

Part 1 of this book teaches the basic principles of practical design, and introduces the designer to his 'tools' – or rather, the range of devices he has to call upon. Part 2 shows him how to put these together into viable designs. The only way to learn how to design is to study how others approach it, and then to have a go for yourself. For this reason, Part 2 of the book includes two detailed descriptions of actual design exercises. The first of these is an exercise in CMOS design, and is fairly simple. The second is a much more complex design for an electronic game, using TTL devices. The reader is urged to keep studying these design examples until he fully understands them. Once he reaches this stage, he may progress towards his own designs with confidence.

A book on digital design would not be complete today without some coverage of microprocessors. Microprocessors represent a further stage of advancement in terms of technology, and the modern tendency is to replace special-to-purpose digital circuitry by microprocessors wherever possible. Since all microprocessors have their special features, it is impossible to adequately cover the subject in one section of this book – or even in one entire book. Each microprocessor is worthy of one or more books to itself! What this book does do, however, is to provide sufficient information about microprocessors for the reader to appreciate their advantages *or disadvantages*, as the case may be. The application and the circumstances dictate whether a particular design is best suited to ordinary logic or to a microprocessor.

The book culminates in a practical illustration of how a particular design problem changes emphasis when a microprocessor is introduced, by reflecting on how the electronic game discussed in Part 2 might have been tackled using a microprocessor.

This book has to cover a vast amount of ground as efficiently as possible. This has been achieved by careful integration of subject matter within the text. The main text is supported by various appendices at the rear of the book, and these provide the aspiring designer with abridged design data, in order to get him off the ground without further expense or delay. It is strongly recommended, however, that the reader purchase a good data book on digital devices as soon as possible. Perhaps the best source of TTL data is: 'The TTL Data Book for Design Engineers', published by Texas Instruments. Such a wide selection of devices can be rather confusing – and daunting – therefore the appendices to this book do reduce the problem to a manageable level during the learning process.

The abbreviation 'App. C2' – or similar – is to be found throughout the text. This refers to entries in Appendix A, and guides the reader to device data. In the example given, 'App. C2' refers to the 7476 device, reference C2 on page 274. No text references are made directly to any of the other appendices, unless specified in full.

The logic symbols used throughout this book comply with MIL-806B standards. This choice has been made because engineers recognise these symbols worldwide, and these are the symbols most frequently found in manufacturer's data. Further information on drawing standards is to be found within Appendix E, together with an explanation of why the MIL standard has been chosen rather than a more recent standard. This appendix also contains equivalent symbols for various gates. It is worthwhile adding that the MIL standard symbols are also much more popular with engineers in general, and do have a great advantage over the more recent rectangular symbols for the purposes of this book: they require far less explanation and are easier for the novice – and engineer (sic!) – to understand.

Everyone knows that this is the age of the silicon chip. If you are interested in electronics, then you will want to come to grips with it as soon as possible. The aim of this book is to place it within your *practical* grasp.

Part 1 – Basic logic

Give us the tools, and we will
finish the job.

Sir Winston Churchill (1874–1965).

1

The ubiquitous silicon chip

It does not seem long ago that the word 'transistor' was bandied around by all and sundry as the description for a transistor radio. It was not generally appreciated then that a 'transistor' was merely one component within such a device. In a similar manner the media has now latched onto the phrase 'silicon chip' to describe anything which is electronic, rather sophisticated, and contains *any* sort of semiconducting device. Since this word has only really been discovered by the masses since the advent of the microprocessor, the phrase tends to be used synonymously with the word 'microprocessor'. Once again the wrong image has been created, for the 'silicon chip' has been around for a great deal longer than the microprocessor.

The first switching circuits which were the forerunners of modern digital circuits were formed from discrete components such as transistors and diodes. These were all very well for simple circuits, but they very quickly became large and unwieldy as soon as the logic began to get complicated. This ushered in the *integrated circuit* which incorporated several devices onto a single chip. This was the birth of the silicon chip.

By this time the techniques of fabricating silicon planar devices were well understood and it was possible to produce large quantities of reliable silicon transistors. The usual practice was to manufacture a large number of discrete transistors on a single chip, so it was a natural development to manufacture simple transistor circuits onto a single chip instead. Passive components such as resistors or small value capacitors could equally well be incorporated into the circuits. Such devices were subsequently referred to as *Small Scale Integration* (SSI) devices, and these still form the basis of simple logic gates today.

As digital circuitry gained ground there came the need for set circuit configurations to be repeated more and more often. Particular arrangements of gates form the building blocks of digital circuits, and in order to improve system reliability, minimise the number of

3

interconnections concerned, and to miniaturise the circuitry involved, *Medium Scale Integration* (MSI) devices were born.

The basis of such circuits was a fairly basic switching transistor, although improvements such as Schottky clamping diodes were introduced to improve switching speed. The transistor does require a fairly large area in microelectronic terms, and it was found that the metal oxide silicon field effect transistor (MOSFET) could be fabricated in much smaller areas, allowing thousands of transistors and resistors to be packed into one tiny chip area. Inevitably these high density circuits came to be known as *Large Scale Integration* (LSI).

The particular requirements of different systems demands different predominant features such as high speed, low power, or simply a compromise between the two, for these features do tend to conflict. The most common devices at present are formed from conventional transistors and are known as transistor transistor logic (TTL) because of their form of interconnected transistors. The speed of these is adequate for most applications but the power consumption does require mains originated supplies unless the component count is quite small. Schottky barrier diodes are used in conjunction with certain families of these TTL circuits to prevent the transistors saturating, and thereby increases their switching speed, but the current consumption is still a problem. MOSFET devices get over the problem of power consumption, but these have the disadvantage of being comparatively slow and of also being somewhat prone to damage due to electrostatic charge if they are mishandled.

More will be said about the various families of devices in a later chapter, but it will be seen that there are several different families to choose from according to the designer's needs. For most applications the designer will choose conventional TTL devices which compromise between speed and cost. It is these devices that we shall chiefly be concerned with in this part of the book. Apart from current levels and switching speeds, and also the available power supply range, there is no functional difference between these various families so far as their logical significance is concerned. For this reason we shall concentrate upon logic functions before introducing the confusion of family variants.

This brief review of the development of the ubiquitous silicon chip cannot be complete without considering the latest innovation: the microprocessor. The sophistication of conventional integrated circuits brought about computers of modest proportions compared with the first valve efforts, and even great improvements over the early transistor versions, but the microprocessor was the greatest step forward of all. It came about as a result of the expertise which developed in the production of LSI circuits, and it was inevitable that the end result would be a computer on a chip: for this is really what a microprocessor is.

The main differences between a microprocessor and a conventional computer are speed and computing capability; the computer wins on both counts. A computer operates with *data words* comprising a set number of *bits*. A *bit* represents the smallest single piece of digital data, and it can indicate either one of two logic states. The most common powerful computers operate with 24-bit words. Microprocessors are most commonly arranged to handle only 8-bit data words. This fact, combined with lower operating speeds, is the main reason why computers are not immediately threatened by their smaller brethren. Computers use faster devices.

We have seen tremendous advances in microelectronics over the past decade. Already 16-bit microprocessors are a reality, and 24-bit microprocessors can only be over the horizon. That only then leaves us with the speed limitation, but modern innovation should find a way round that. Already it is quite common to use several microprocessors in a single system, and it is not inconceivable that several microprocessing elements might be interconnected on a single chip to provide means of carrying out parallel processing in such a manner that the speed limitations of the material might be compensated for. This is only speculation, but it does remind us that we are by no means at the end of the road just yet. A faster material might even be discovered!

Just because microprocessors are versatile, this is not sufficient justification alone for incorporating them into a given system. If the system would require a tremendous amount of conventional logic then there is obviously justification for a computer or microprocessor, but for smaller systems and less demanding applications, a microprocessor might not be the most cost-effective solution. For every microprocessor requires supporting software, and software takes time to write and debug. In commercial terms this can prove to be very costly in a development program, and unless the volume of subsequent sales can justify it, then conventional logic might be a better bet.

The size of a system is not the only deciding factor: rather, it is the cost of software development. Time is of little significance to the hobbyist, for example. Therefore the microprocessor does offer *him* the means of designing some very sophisticated systems which have relatively low costs in hardware terms. Microprocessors can be purchased very cheaply now.

It will be seen that the development of modern electronics has led to three discrete areas of technology: linear electronics, digital

5

electronics, and now software, the latter forming an integral part with the innovation of the microprocessor.

The innovation of digital electronics led to specialist designers and placed a technological barrier between two different branches of hardware design. Computer technology allowed mathematically-minded programmers to program computers with no real knowledge of computer hardware, and hardware engineers were able to work on computer hardware with little real knowledge of software. The microprocessor brought an end to this cosy situation, for it is essentially a digital device and needs to be built into a digital circuit.

A microprocessor system raises the question of how much should be handled by the software and how much by the hardware, and the solution to this hardware-software trade-off can only adequately be answered by someone able to understand both. It has led to a new kind of engineer: a *microprocessor engineer*.

All this may sound rather formidable, but it need not be so if grass roots are returned to and the history of the silicon chip is remembered. For digital electronics is no more than a *restricted* branch of linear electronics. Circuit performance is more predictable because we are only dealing with circuits which switch between two voltage levels: high or low. The microprocessor is only a special kind of digital integrated circuit. True, it does require supporting software, but even here there are different levels at which it may be approached. At the lowest level there is machine code, where specified codes produce particular hardware manipulations, and this is no more frightening than the function of any other LSI device. At the next level there are programming languages such as BASIC, which as the name suggests, is very easy to understand.

It would be a difficult task for a mathematician to get to grips with digital design unless he had some understanding of electronics, but it is an easy task for him to understand programming. Anyone capable of undertaking hardware design can fairly soon pick up microprocessor programming. Equally, anyone familiar with linear design can soon pick up the principles of digital design. Clearly they cannot expect to become instant experts, for any new technology takes time, but it is hoped that this assurance might spur on any doubtful linear designers. My belief is that it is an easier path for a linear design engineer to become an *effective* microprocessor engineer than it would be for a programmer with no electronics experience: for only he can see any electronic short-cuts.

This is the history of the silicon chip. It has had a spectacular past and has an assured future. Without a doubt it will have drastic changes on our life-style over the coming years and it is up to us to see that it is a change for the better. It can be. If we can show just a small proportion of the versatility and innovation that the physicists who have developed it have shown, the silicon chip can release man from a great deal of drudgery, and give him the time for more worthwhile pursuits. After such development, this is surely the only logical conclusion.

2

From linear to digital electronics

Digital electronics tends to *sound* much more sophisticated than linear electronics, and the very *sound* of it is sometimes enough to put off many otherwise very competent designers. Linear designers will sometimes produce very elaborate designs to achieve what amounts to a simple logic function; had they familiarity with digital electronics as well, that same requirement might have needed no more than a small number of digital integrated circuits (ICs). The aim of this chapter is to show that the barrier between the two technologies is little more than a 'sound barrier', and to emphasise that the way to approach digital design from a background of linear design is to regard it as *a restricted form of linear electronics*. It is because of these restrictions that it has been possible to introduce special symbols to represent repeatedly used circuit blocks. Once this has been truly appreciated, the mystique of digital electronics should be removed.

Simple diode logic

In order to understand the basic principles of logic, there is no better place to start than with the simplest logic circuits possible. Diodes give us the essential features of a logic gate, as illustrated in Figure 2.1. This shows three diodes connected to a common pull-up resistor tied to +5 V. A, B and C are the circuit inputs, and Q is the output.

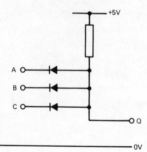

Figure 2.1. A simple logic circuit using diodes

If all the inputs are taken to the supply rail of +5 V (i.e. *high*), no potential difference occurs across any of the diodes, therefore no current flows through the resistor; as a consequence, the output Q is also high. If any of the inputs is taken to 0 V (i.e. *low*), the diode in series with this input is forward-biased, and current flows through the resistor. Assuming a silicon diode with a forward voltage drop of nominally 0.7 V, this has the effect of pulling the output Q down to approximately +0.7 V.

It does not matter if more than one input is taken low, for in this situation the diodes with grounded cathodes simply share the current which is limited by the resistor. *This is a simple logic gate.*

Logic circuits (or *gates*) are so named because they are capable of representing logic conditions. The above circuit represents the logic condition described by the following statement: A AND B AND C true gives Q true. If we separate the input conditions from the output by the equivalence sign, and replace the 'AND' statements by the shorthand notation of a dot, the above logical statement can be rewritten as follows:

A.B.C = Q

Because of the logical significance of this circuit it may be referred to as an 'AND' gate. In practice, a circuit as simple as this would not be used, but it does show the basic concept of digital logic, *where only two signal levels are considered*: either *high* or *low*. Digital circuits do not employ voltage levels between the conditions described as high or low, hence my earlier description of digital electronics as a restricted form of linear electronics.

Logical statements are expressed in the form of terms which may be either *true* or *false*. Given two possible conditions to represent electronically, we require only two voltage levels, hence the high/low circuit conditions. This only leaves us with one permutation to consider: which level represents what? From the logical point of view the choice is purely arbitrary, and both systems are employed. This has given rise to two logic conventions: *positive logic* and *negative logic*. The positive logic convention represents the true condition by the more positive voltage, whereas the negative logic convention represents the true condition by the more negative voltage; this is therefore easy to remember.

Because logic circuits represent only two different states, all arithmetic processes are carried out in *binary arithmetic*, which uses only the numbers 0 and 1. Logical statements are also described in terms of 0 for false, and 1 for true. Thus a logic 1 is the more positive voltage in positive logic, or the more negative voltage in negative logic.

If the concept of positive or negative logic is confusing, not to worry! Most modern designs employ only positive logic, therefore to avoid confusion, this book only considers positive logic.

The transistor in logic circuits

Logic requires both true and false conditions to be easily represented. False logic terms are represented by placing a bar over the term, e.g. $\overline{Q}$, pronounced 'bar-queue'. In electronic terms, $\overline{Q}$ is simply the *inverse* of Q; thus if Q is high, $\overline{Q}$ must be low, and if Q is low, $\overline{Q}$ must be high. Obviously an inverter is therefore an essential requisite of logic circuits, and the reason why transistors play an important role. Consider now the circuit shown in Figure 2.2: this is basically the diode logic circuit previously discussed, but followed by a transistor inverter stage. This is a diode transistor logic (DTL) gate.

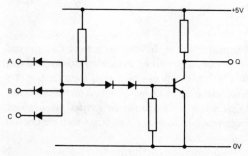

Figure 2.2. A diode transistor logic (DTL) gate

The introduction of transistors gives us an immense improvement, both logically and electrically. Logically, it provides the means of inverting or *complementing* a term (e.g. $\overline{Q}$ is the complement of Q); without this facility, all logic conditions could not be represented. Electrically, the transistor has two advantages: it provides a buffer, enabling more inputs to be connected to an output (known as 'fanout'), and by providing all gate outputs with a transistor stage, it gives a wider voltage swing between logic levels. Where a silicon diode can only give a low level of +0.7 V, a silicon transistor in the *bottomed* condition (i.e. driven hard on by sufficient base current) can present a low level of around +0.2 V.

The circuit shown in Figure 2.2 is logically the same as that shown in Figure 2.1, except that the output is inverted by the transistor. If all the inputs are high, no current flows through any of the input

10

diodes, which allows current to flow through what now becomes the base resistor, thereby biasing the transistor hard on, and producing a low at the Q output.* If one or more of the inputs is taken to 0 V, current flows through the base resistor and diverts to flow through the input diode/s. The two diodes in series with the transistor base ensures that the transistor is cut off with a potential of only +0.7 V at the input resistor-diode junction, therefore the Q output is high.

The logic condition represented by the gate shown in Figure 2.2 can be expressed as follows:

$$\overline{A.B.C} = Q$$

This is read as: 'NOT (A AND B AND C) gives Q'. To interpret the expression, ignore the bar initially, and note the AND condition which applies to A AND B AND C; finally take the bar into account, which signifies an inverse form. Thus Q is *low* for the input condition A.B.C. Because the bar signifies 'NOT', this gate might be called a not-AND; in fact this is abbreviated to 'NAND'.

This form of diode transistor logic was the type of gate used in early SSI components. Note that the circle around the transistor has been omitted in order to distinguish this from a discrete transistor encapsulation, because the entire circuit is formed on a single integrated circuit. The next stage in the development of logic circuits was to introduce a new kind of multi-emitter transistor, thereby minimising the number of chip interconnections, saving space, and simplifying the manufacturing requirements. Because the input diodes were replaced by transistors, these devices became known as transistor transistor logic, or as we shall refer to them hereafter: 'TTL'.

The TTL gate

By diffusing a number of separate emitter n-types into the base p-type of the input transistor shown as TR1 in Figure 2.3, the same logic inputs can be derived within a single transistor. The diode D1 is a 'distributed' diode, but it is shown as a separate diode in this circuit in order that the operation may be better understood. This

---

* *In order to ensure that a transistor is bottomed, the base current must be at least as high as the maximum collector current divided by the d.c. current gain of the transistor in the bottomed state. Whilst modern silicon transistors can achieve current gains of 100–800 when not saturated, this figure is dramatically less when the saturated (or bottomed) condition is reached; figures of 10–20 are typical. Thus the maximum base resistance must be the collector resistance multiplied by the maximum current gain; a factor of ×10 is a good rule of thumb.*

figure shows input C connected to 0 V, and therefore at logic 0, and the inputs A and B connected to +5 V, and therefore at logic 1. Only a negligible leakage current flows into A and B since these are reverse-biased diodes, but current I_b flows out of the emitter connected to input C. This current is derived from the base current plus the larger current I_a, flowing through R1 and D1. The input transistor bottoms as a result of this current and the collector of TR1 is at about +0.2 V, i.e. the saturation level for the collector-emitter.

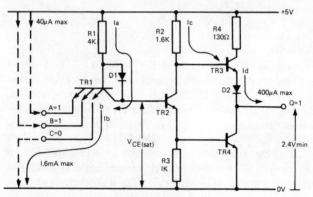

Figure 2.3. A TTL gate with one input low

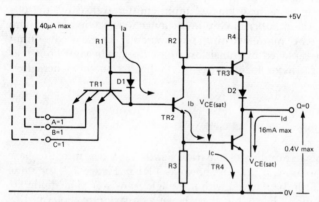

Figure 2.4. A TTL gate with all inputs high

This condition cuts off TR2 and allows current I_c to flow through R2, so biasing TR3 into conduction, and allowing the larger emitter current I_d to flow through D2 and *out* at Q. This causes Q to be high, i.e. at logic 1. The characteristics of the standard 7400 series of TTL gates specifies that the maximum high level current which can be drawn from the output (I_{OH}) is $400\,\mu A$. Since the maximum high level input current (I_{IH}) for any gate connected to an output is specified at $40\,\mu A$, this allows up to ten input gates to be connected to an output. The output voltage level in the high state (V_{OH}) is specified as $+2.4\,V$ minimum, which means that a logic 1 output should always be equal to or greater than this voltage.

Figure 2.4 shows the same gate with all the inputs high. Now no current flows out of the emitters of TR1, and the current I_a diverts to form the base current of TR2. Emitter current I_b, comprising both I_a and current drawn through TR2 collector, flows as base current I_c through TR4. This causes TR4 to switch hard on, and current I_d flows *into* the output Q. The transistor bottoms to give an output voltage equal to $V_{CE(sat)}$ for TR4, thereby producing a logic 0. With TR2 bottomed in this condition, diode D2 ensures that TR3 is cut off.

The characteristics of the 7400 series gates in this condition specify that the maximum low level output current (I_{OL}) is 16mA. Since the maximum low level input current (I_{IL}) for any gates connected to an output is 1.6mA, this allows up to ten gates to be connected to any output. Thus for any logic conditions, this series of devices allows what is termed as *fanout* of ten, i.e. ten inputs may be connected to any output. The specifications also state that the maximum low level output voltage (V_{OL}) shall be $+0.4\,V$.

One characteristic worth bearing in mind is that whilst multi-emitter transistors provide a load for each emitter in the high state, they do not do so in the low state. Thus if several inputs *to the same logic gate* are tied together, they only appear as a single low level load to the driving gate, since the current flowing *out* of the inputs is simply *shared* between the various emitters. In the high state each separate junction contributes its own leakage current. This is worth remembering, for unused inputs on gates can often be conveniently tied to neighbouring inputs. All inputs should be taken either high or low.

Noise margins

So far the output voltage levels have been discussed, but in order to provide safety margins within the specifications, the input requirements are made to overlap the output guaranteed levels to provide a noise margin of at least 0.4 V. Figure 2.5 depicts the noise margins.

The output high level is guaranteed to be at least $+2.4\,V$, but input gates accept a logic 1 above $+2.0\,V$ to provide a high state noise margin of 0.4 V. The output low level is guaranteed to be

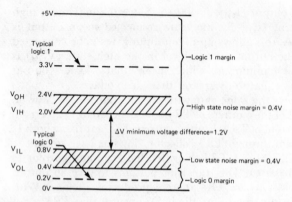

Figure 2.5. TTL noise margins

+0.4 V or less, but input gates accept a logic 0 below +0.8 V, again ensuring a low state noise margin of 0.4 V. The minimum voltage difference between logic states must therefore be at least 1.2 V, and typical logic 1 and logic 0 levels are +3.3 V and +0.2 V respectively.

3
Logic gates

The previous chapter described a typical TTL gate in terms of its linear components. The gate shown in Figures 2.3 and 2.4 is a 3-input NAND gate. Like other gates in this family the output consists of a *totem-pole* arrangement with two output transistors. This ensures that a low impedance current source can be maintained in either logic state, and that adequate loading can be achieved with minimum risk of noise interference.

Having shown the typical internal structure of a basic gate in order to bridge the gap between linear and digital electronics, we shall now only consider logic *gates* as functional blocks. The background knowledge of how inputs and outputs are implemented is of value, however, in understanding device characteristics.

Figure 3.1 shows the logic symbol for a 3-input NAND gate, where A, B and C are the inputs, and Q is the output. An 'AND' function gives A.B.C, but a 'NAND' function modifies this to $\overline{A.B.C}$.

Truth table

A	B	C	Q
0	0	0	1
0	0	1	1
0	1	0	1
0	1	1	1
1	0	0	1
1	0	1	1
1	1	0	1
1	1	1	0

$\overline{A.B.C} = Q$

Figure 3.1. A 3-input NAND gate and truth table

The output from any logic gate is dependent upon the state of all its inputs. In order to fully specify all possible output states it is therefore necessary to consider all possible input states. The usual way to do this is to prepare a *truth table* for the gate. This is also given in the figure.

15

The truth table comprises a column for every input and output. Although it does not matter in what order the various input permutations are considered, it is a good idea to enter these in the form of an ascending binary count. The binary system has a base of 2, and comprises only the digits 0 and 1, therefore each line of the table in question shows the binary equivalent of the decimal numbers 0 to 7.* In this way it is possible to ensure that no input combination is either missed out or duplicated. The truth table shows that the Q output is always at logic 1 *unless* all of the inputs are at logic 1; when all the inputs are at logic 1 the output is at logic 0.

This description of the NAND gate summarises its action more concisely than the lengthy truth table, and the essence of 'thinking like a designer' is to simplify gate descriptions in this manner. There is then less to remember, and you more quickly come to instinctively know how a particular logic network functions at a glance.

One method of simplifying gate actions is to introduce what is known as the *don't care* condition into truth tables. This technique uses the cross symbol 'X' to indicate 'don't care' conditions: this implies that the output is unaffected by the logic state of any don't care terms. Figure 3.2 is an alternative truth table for the 3-input NAND gate previously considered. It may be seen that the truth table has now been condensed to four lines from eight lines in the original. It is not practical to produce a truth table for every possible input condition for a logic network if there are a great many inputs, and in such cases the don't care symbol is invaluable as a method of simplifying the truth table.

Truth table

A	B	C	Q
1	1	1	0
X	X	0	1
X	0	X	1
0	X	X	1

Figure 3.2. Truth table for 3-input NAND gate using 'don't cares'

The idea of utilising an increasing binary count must be discarded in truth tables utilising don't cares, but a sensible pattern should be maintained. A good method is to start with the *unique condition* of the gate which produces a particular output for only one input condition. In the example given in Figure 3.2 this is the condition where all *true* inputs (logic 1) give a *false* output (logic 0). We know that any change to any input affects the output, therefore any input at logic 0 produces a logic 1 at the output. This can be shown in the truth table by considering each input at logic 0 and entering all the

---

* *Binary arithmetic is considered in more detail in Chapter 8.*

other inputs as don't cares – they can be at logic 0 or at logic 1 without affecting the output.

Any logic gate can be described fully by two statements which refer to the two possible output states, and this is what a prospective designer would do well to remember. It is not possible to remember full truth tables, and it is impossible to get a true 'feel' for a circuit if you have to constantly refer to a truth table. In discussing the various logic gates, this method of remembering a gate's function will be emphasised as well as describing it in the more traditional fashion. Figure 3.3 depicts the most common gates. For simplicity, it is usual to consider only 2-input gates.

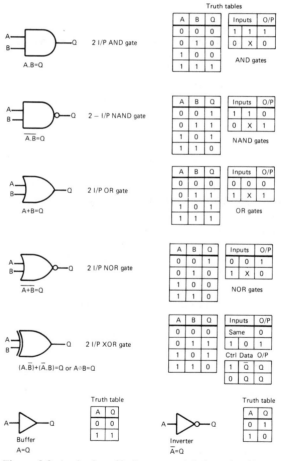

Figure 3.3. A selection of logic gates and their truth tables

The upper section of the figure shows the logic symbol for a 2-input AND gate. The expression: A.B = Q describes the function of the gate in algebraic form. This is known as Boolean algebra, and utilises the following symbols:

.   represents AND
+   represents OR
=   may be read as 'gives'.

Thus 'A.B = Q' may be read as: 'A AND B GIVES Q'.

The unique condition for this gate is when both inputs are true, giving the output true. The larger of the two truth tables given for the gate is the normal way of representing all logic conditions. This is all very well for a 2-input gate, but a 4-input gate would require 16 lines to fully represent it in this manner. The smaller of the two truth tables introduces don't cares, and this principle is applicable for *all* AND gates, no matter how many inputs. The *inputs* side of this truth table shows in the first line that the unique condition of *all* inputs at logic 1 produces a logic 1 at the output. The second line indicates that if *any* input is at logic 0, the output is at logic 0, irrespective of the state of any other inputs, as indicated by the don't care symbol.

The simple way to remember AND gate action is to think of it as follows:

AND GATE: ALL INPUTS AT 1 GIVES OUTPUT AT 1
             ANY INPUT AT 0 GIVES OUTPUT AT 0.

The NAND gate is like an AND gate followed by an inversion. The small circle on the output side of the symbol is the method used to indicate an inversion. The truth table for the NAND gate is identical to that for the AND gate except that the output is inverted (or *complemented*), as shown in the larger truth table for the gate. The Boolean expression $\overline{A.B}$ = Q should be read as: 'NOT (A AND B) GIVES Q'. The simplified truth table has the same input condition for the unique case, but this time the output is at logic 0. This time any input at logic 0 produces a logic 1 at the output. This gate should be remembered as follows:

NAND GATE: ALL INPUTS AT 1 GIVES OUTPUT AT 0
             ANY INPUT AT 0 GIVES OUTPUT AT 1.

The OR gate has a different distinctive symbol, and is described by the Boolean expression: A + B = Q, read as: 'A OR B GIVES

18

Q'. As the larger truth table shows, if any input is at logic 1 then the output is at logic 1. This gives rise to the unique condition of logic 0 at the output when all inputs are at logic 0. Note the simplified don't care truth table representation. This gate should be remembered as follows:

OR GATE: ALL INPUTS AT 0 GIVES OUTPUT AT 0
ANY INPUT AT 1 GIVES OUTPUT AT 1.

The NOR gate symbol is identical to the OR gate symbol except for the inverting circle on the output line. Like the NAND gate in relation to the AND gate, the NOR gate truth table is similar to the OR gate truth table; the difference is simply that the output is complemented. The Boolean expression is: $\overline{A + B} = Q$, read as: 'NOT (A OR B) GIVES Q'. The unique condition is both inputs at logic 0 producing an output at logic 1. This gate should be remembered as follows:

NOR GATE: ALL INPUTS AT 0 GIVES OUTPUT AT 1
ANY INPUT AT 1 GIVES OUTPUT AT 0.

The exclusive-OR gate, abbreviated as 'XOR', is similar to the OR gate, except that it distinguishes the difference between one input at logic 1 and more than one input at logic 1. The distinctive symbol has the double-curved input to signify its 'exclusive' function. Compare the full truth table with that of the OR gate, and it will be seen that the only difference is in the bottom line. With the XOR gate, more than one input at logic 1 produces an output at logic 0. The name can now be appreciated, for the gate detects one input OR another *exclusively*, as opposed to *simultaneously*. The simplified truth table has been modified in form to more easily depict this, and relates directly to the easy way of remembering the function of the gate, given below. The Boolean expression: $(A.\overline{B})$ + $(\overline{A}.B) = Q$ represents this gate, and may be read as: '(A AND NOT B) OR (NOT A AND B) GIVES Q'. As with ordinary algebra, it is possible to transform this expression into another form which is logically equivalent, but the form given is probably the easiest to understand at this point. The symbol $\oplus$ can be used to indicate exclusive-OR directly. This gate can most easily be remembered as follows:

XOR GATE: ALL INPUTS THE SAME GIVES OUTPUT AT 0
ONE INPUT AT 1 GIVES OUTPUT AT 1.

The XOR gate has a most useful function in logic circuits, in that it may be used to either invert or not invert a *data bit* in accordance with a *control* input. Consider the A input as a control, and the B input as a data input, for example. By studying the full truth table, it may be seen that when A is at logic 0, the Q output is a direct copy of the B input. Thus a control input at logic 0 produces no inversion. When A is at logic 1, however, the Q output is the inverted form of the B input. Thus a control input at logic 1 produces an inversion. This feature is summarised by the lower right truth table for the gate, where the output of 'Q' is obtained from a data input 'Q' when not inverted, or '$\overline{Q}$' when inverted.

The lower portion of the figure shows simple *buffer* and *inverter* gates. No logical change occurs between the input and output of the buffer gate, hence the Boolean expression A = Q. The gate is useful where it is required to connect more inputs to a particular output than are allowed as direct connections. If a particular gate is limited to a fanout (i.e. loading) of 10 gates, then if a buffer gate forms one of the loads, 9 inputs can be connected directly to the output in question, and a further 10 to the buffer gate, without any logical modification.

The inverter gate has a similar symbol, but with the addition of the now expected inverting circle on the output. This gate complements the logic state applied to the input, hence the Boolean expression: $\overline{A}$ = Q. Thus a logic 0 *in* produces a logic 1 *out*, and a logic 1 *in* produces a logic 0 *out*.

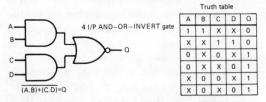

Figure 3.4. A 4-input AND-OR-INVERT gate and truth table

Another logic function which can be quite useful is performed by what is known as an AND-OR-INVERT gate. This is shown with its truth table in Figure 3.4. $\overline{(A.B) + (C.D)}$ = Q is the Boolean expression read as: NOT ((A AND B) OR (C AND D)) GIVES Q. Because there are four inputs, a full truth table would require 16 lines. For this reason only the simplified truth table is given. This shows that the unique condition of logic 0 out results from either (or both) of A AND B OR C AND D being at logic 1. If any input is low

20

in both input pairs then the output is at logic 1. Remember this gate as follows:

AND-OR-INVERT GATE: EITHER INPUT PAIR AT 1 GIVES OUTPUT AT 0
ALL INPUT PAIRS WITH A 0 GIVES OUTPUT AT 1.

Appendices at the rear of this book give a selection of the most useful digital devices in the SN7400 series, where several of the above gate types can be obtained on a single integrated circuit. The smallest of these dual-in-line encapsulations has 14 pins, as illustrated in Figure 3.5. Two of these pins are required for the power

Figure 3.5. The 14-pin dual-in-line plastic encapsulation

supplies, leaving 12 functional pins. This conveniently allows for four identical 2-input logic gates.

Many of the more popular logic gates are also available with open-collector outputs instead of the push-pull or *totem-pole* arrangement shown in Figure 2.4; with reference to this figure, such devices do not include R4, TR3 and D2. The logic 0 output condition is therefore unchanged, but the logic 1 condition simply presents a high impedance output, and an external connection must employ a pull-up resistor to +5 V. Such gates can be useful for driving loads,

Figure 3.6. Examples of 3-state gates: (a) enabled with control high; (b) enabled with control low

or several such gates can be linked to a common pull-up resistor to give what is termed a wired-OR connection.

Another form of output available with certain devices is known as *three-state**. As the name suggests, such devices present three alternative forms of output: logic 1, logic 0, and also a high impedance state. The high impedance state or the logic states are output in accordance with a control line C, as shown in Figure 3.6. The high impedance state allows any number of these gates to be

* *The name 'tri-state' is also used, but this is a manufacturer's trade mark.*

commoned in order to route different data lines to a common destination or destinations. A number of associated data lines connected in this manner are known as a *data highway*; thus data highways link multiple data sources to one or more destinations.

The examples given in the figure show the two options available; in Figure 3.6(a) the control input must be high to enable the gate, and in Figure 3.6(b) the control input must be low to enable the gate. When the gates are not enabled they present a high impedance output. The control circuitry must ensure that only one gate is enabled at once in each group of gates with commoned outputs.

It may therefore be seen that there is a wide variety of devices for the designer to choose from, and invariably a particular type will suit his needs.

Different packages are available for different applications, such as the ceramic encapsulation for military environments. Most commercial systems employ the cheaper plastic dual-in-line (DIL) encapsulations, as illustrated. More complex devices utilise similar packages with more pins. In all cases, however, pinning is always from pin 1 at the top left-hand side of the device, when viewed from the top with the identification mark farthest away from you. This is generally a notch or central mark, as shown, but replaced sometimes by a dot next to the number 1 pin. The pins are then numbered *down* the left-hand side and back *up* the right-hand side, as shown in Appendix A.

There is a preferred standard for the power supplies, which places ground as the bottom left-hand pin, and V_{cc} as the top right-hand pin, but there are numerous exceptions to this, and this should never be taken for granted.

Commercial devices containing logic gates discussed in this chapter are included in Appendix A as follows.

Gate	Number in package	Type number	Appendix ref.
2 i/p AND	4	7408	A7
2 i/p NAND	4	7400	A1
2 i/p OR	4	7432	A8
2 i/p NOR	4	7402	A6
2 i/p XOR	4	7486	B5
Buffer	6 (with open-col)	7417	A2 (note)
Inverter	6	7404	A2
4 i/p AND-OR-INVERT	2	7451	B3
3-state buffers	4	74125/6	B7
Schmitt inverter	6	7414	A4

Schmitt triggers

The previous chapter described the internal structure of a typical TTL gate, and emphasised that all inputs and outputs switch between high and low states. Certain gates may contain quite a number of stages, and if an input is held at some intermediate voltage level the internal circuit may not switch to one of the two logic states: this could lead to transient conditions and internal oscillations. For this reason it is important that switching times are always very fast. These should typically be of the order of 10 ns (10^{-8} s).

This may sound an enormous problem to the person more familiar with linear circuits of a slower variety, but it should be remembered that logic gates naturally achieve the switching time requirements, and the only problem comes where it is necessary to interface a logic circuit with a slower section of discrete circuitry, as with a transistor input, for example. This is where the Schmitt trigger comes in. The linear designer will be familiar with discrete versions of the Schmitt trigger, but in logic terms, it is simply another gate, as shown from the last entry in the table of gate types given above.

Slow inputs should not be connected to ordinary logic gate inputs, except under special conditions, which will be discussed in Part 2. Slow inputs may be connected to Schmitt triggers, since these provide fast output switching between logic states once the input has crossed upper or lower threshold voltages. Figure 3.7 shows the symbol for a 4-input Schmitt trigger arranged as a NAND gate (7413 is a dual 4-input version). The waveform diagram shows how the output changes in relation to an input, assuming that the other inputs are at logic 1. The typical positive-going threshold voltage (V_{T+}) is 1.7 V and the negative-going threshold (V_{T-}) is typically 0.9 V. The hysteresis between these two figures prevents oscillation at an intermediate voltage level.

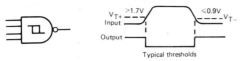

Figure 3.7. A 4-input Schmitt trigger (NAND) gate

Schmitt triggers are available as 4 or 2-input NAND gates, or as simple inverters (as listed in the preceding table). The hysteresis symbol within an ordinary gate outline distinguishes it as having Schmitt inputs. Because these gates will accept slow edges, they can be used after small CR type delays.

23

Logic networks

Figure 3.8 depicts a very simple logic network: a combination of logic gates connected together to form a logic circuit. If it is required to determine the output conditions for all input conditions, then one method of achieving this is to prepare a truth table. In the figure this has been done by considering every possible input condition. The 1's and 0's written above the lines indicate the *sequence* that these conditions have been considered in. Thus A = 0 and B = 0 is the first condition considered, which produces logic 0 at the OR gate output, logic 1 at the NAND gate output, logic 0 at the AND gate output, and logic 1 at the inverter output. This is a useful circuit to study since it contains most of the gate types. Satisfy yourself of the validity of the truth table by considering all the conditions.

Once this has been done, it is interesting to note that the circuit without the inverter is the equivalent of the exclusive OR gate. Compare the truth table with that shown in Figure 3.3. Here is a simple method of obtaining an XOR function without using an XOR gate.

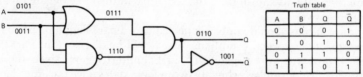

A	B	Q	Q̄
0	0	0	1
1	0	1	0
0	1	1	0
1	1	0	1

Figure 3.8. Considering all possible states for a logic network

So far we have only considered logic gates in terms of meaningless A, B, C and Q terms. It is perhaps a little more inspiring at this stage to consider a simple logic circuit which has a practical application. In this way it may be better appreciated how useful logic can be. Figure 3.9 shows some indicator logic for a combined burglar and fire alarm system. It drives an alarm buzzer if a window is opened, a door is opened, or if smoke is detected. A light emitting diode (LED) indicates the nature of the alarm, and two outputs are provided to drive other equipment in order to give alarms to the police station for an intruder, or the fire station for a fire.

Logic lines are best labelled with a mnemonic which suggests their function. Thus the inputs are labelled WINDSHUT to indicate that all windows are shut, DOORSHUT to indicate that all doors are shut, and NOSMOKE to indicate that a smoke detector has not detected any smoke. IC3 provides three open-collector buffer gates (App. A2 note) for driving the LEDs; these are non-inverting gates. If any of the inputs goes false*, i.e. to logic 0,

---

* *Positive logic is used throughout this book.*

24

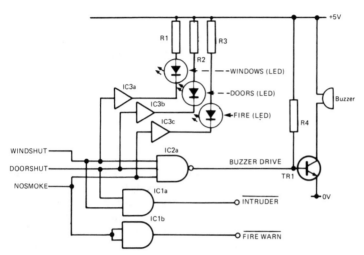

Figure 3.9. A practical application of logic gates

the output of the appropriate buffer gate also goes low, thereby drawing current through the LED-resistor combination to indicate the nature of the alarm.

All inputs at logic 1 provide a logic 0 output at IC2a NAND gate, which holds off TR1, but if one or more of the inputs goes false, the output goes high, allowing current to flow through R4 into the base of TR1, so switching on the alarm buzzer. R4 provides for a higher base current than the NAND gate could provide in its high state. If WINDSHUT or DOORSHUT goes false, the output of IC1a AND gate also goes false, making the INTRUDER output go active; the bar indicates that this output line is active low. If NOSMOKE goes false then FIREWARN goes active low. IC1b is simply used to provide a buffer between the output line and the NOSMOKE input line, but it has no logical significance because the gate is non-inverting. The two inputs of this gate are tied together purely for convenience: all unused gate inputs should be taken to a logic level, and an alternative would be to tie one input to logic 1. As explained in the previous chapter, when inputs to a single gate are tied together as shown, they only form a single gate load to a low-driving input.

The integrated circuits used in this circuit are included in Appendix A as follows:

IC1 – 7408 – quad 2 i/p positive AND gates (App. A7).
IC2 – 7410 – triple 3 i/p positive NAND gate (App. A3).
IC3 – 7417 – hex buffers/drivers with open collector high voltage outputs (App. A2).

25

4

Optimisation versus minimisation

The previous chapter showed how *Boolean algebra* lends itself to expressing logic circuits in mathematical terms. Like ordinary algebra, by following certain rules it is possible to manipulate the terms and obtain equivalent but different expressions; it is also possible to simplify logical expressions. Another method employed to simplify logical conditions is to draw what are termed *Karnaugh maps*; these allow all possible logical permutations to be displayed in graphical terms.

Both the above methods lead to what I have termed *minimisation* of a logical requirement, in that they produce the simplest *logical* solution. These techniques are extensively documented in other literature, and are the subject matter of the more traditional digital courses, therefore this chapter will only describe them in sufficient detail to show their usefulness – and limitations. Whilst such techniques lead to minimisation, this is not the same thing as *optimisation* of a logic circuit, in practical terms; this chapter aims to show the difference.

Boolean algebra

George Boole devised an algebraic method of converting logical statements into mathematical terms; it was intended as a tool for the logician. It was Shannon who recognised its use when analysing circuit conditions as long ago as 1938. He used it to analyse mechanical switching, but today it is the perfect mathematical method of expressing logic circuits. We shall now look briefly at the rules of Boolean algebra, for it will be appreciated that by simplifying a Boolean expression we can simplify the associated logic network.

Below are given the basic laws of Boolean algebra. Many see these purely in mathematical terms, but the reader is encouraged to visualise them in terms of their gate equivalents. In this way their significance – and truth – will be better understood.

Laws of Boolean algebra

Gating

	AND	*OR*	*NOT*
	$0.0 = 0$	$0 + 0 = 0$	$\overline{1} = 0$
	$0.1 = 0$	$0 + 1 = 1$	$\overline{0} = 1$
	$1.1 = 1$	$1 + 1 = 1$	Complements
	$A.0 = 0$	$A + 0 = A$	$A.\overline{A} = 0$
	$A.1 = A$	$A + 1 = 1$	$A + \overline{A} = 1$

Identity

$A.A = A$ $\qquad$ $A + A = A$

$A(A + B) = A$ $\qquad$ $A + A.B = A$

$A(\overline{A} + B) = A.B$ $\qquad$ $A + \overline{A}.B = A + B$

Double negative $\qquad$ $\overline{\overline{A}} = A$

Commutative laws $\qquad$ $A.B = B.A$ $\qquad$ $A + B = B + A$

Associative laws $\qquad$ $A + (B + C) = (A + B) + C$

$A.(B.C) = (A.B).C$

Distributive laws $\qquad$ $A.(B + C) = (A.B) + (A.C)$

$A + (B.C) = (A + B).(A + C)$

De Morgan's Theorem:

First Rule: $\qquad$ negation of logical sum

$$\overline{A + B} = \overline{A}.\overline{B}$$

Second Rule: $\qquad$ negation of logical product

$$\overline{A.B} = \overline{A} + \overline{B}$$

Taking just a few examples will show how the above rules may be visualised in terms of their equivalent gates. Once you have learned how the gates behave (and it is essential that you do), the above expressions make immediate sense. By relating the expressions to gate equivalents you obtain a practical grasp instead of learning arbitrary laws in the more usual parrot-fashion.

Firstly consider an AND gate. By definition, this requires all inputs to be at logic 1 for a logic 1 at the output, therefore the first three gating AND terms are seen to be true. If we now consider an unknown input represented by A, it is equivalent to a don't care input if the other input is at 0, therefore the output is also 0. If the A input is combined with a 1 input, however, the output will be the same as the A input, hence $A.1 = A$. If in doubt, study the truth table given in Figure 3.3. Having satisfied yourself of this much, carry out a similar exercise with the OR gate terms.

Since there are only two logical states, 0 and 1, then clearly $\bar{1}$ must be equivalent to 0, or conversely, $\bar{0}$ equivalent to 1. The complementary expressions are also self-evident. If A and $\bar{A}$ are inputs to an AND gate, they must always differ, therefore the unique condition of all 1's producing an output of 1 can never be achieved, the output always being 0. If A and $\bar{A}$ are applied to an OR gate, one of them must always be at 1, therefore the output is always at 1.

The Identity laws are simpler than they look, if you think about them. For example, if the terms A and A.B are applied to the inputs of an OR gate, the output will be at 1 any time A is true; since A is required in both terms, the output is equivalent to A; if A is false, the output will be at 0. The double negative is obvious, for if something is NOT (NOT A), it must be A. The Commutative laws show that there is no significance in order – apples and pears are the same as pears and apples. The Associative laws remind us of ordinary algebra, as do the Distributive laws, where we are factorising. Draw logic circuits to represent any expressions you are in doubt about and all should become clear (see Figure 3.8 for the technique).

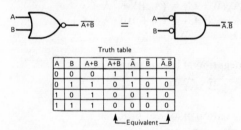

Truth table

A	B	A+B	$\overline{A+B}$	$\bar{A}$	$\bar{B}$	$\bar{A}.\bar{B}$
0	0	0	1	1	1	1
0	1	1	0	1	0	0
1	0	1	0	0	1	0
1	1	1	0	0	0	0

└─Equivalent─┘

Figure 4.1. Interpreting De Morgan's First Rule using a NOR gate

De Morgan's Theorem is a little more difficult to follow, but both rules can be proven by drawing the truth tables for the indicated gates and then comparing them. Figure 4.1 shows this for De Morgan's First Rule: $\overline{A + B} = \bar{A}.\bar{B}$, using a NOR gate on the left for the left-hand term, and an AND gate with 'notted' inputs on the right, for the right-hand term; in the latter case, the inverting circles on the inputs create $\bar{A}$ and $\bar{B}$ from the true A and B inputs. The NOR gate section of the truth table is identical to that seen before in Figure 3.3 (except that an OR column has been added for clarity); the $\bar{A}$ and $\bar{B}$ columns are the complements of the A and B columns, and the far right-hand column is an AND of the negated $\bar{A}$ and $\bar{B}$ columns which immediately precede it.

By comparing the columns representing the outputs of these two gates it can be seen that they are identical, thereby proving the rule. In practical terms it means that a NOR gate can perform an AND function with negated inputs.

De Morgan's Second Rule is similarly proven in Figure 4.2 using a NAND gate for the left-hand term $(\overline{A.B})$, and an OR gate with inverting inputs for the right-hand term $(\overline{A} + \overline{B})$. Once again it may be seen that the outputs from these two gates are identical. In practical terms this indicates that a NAND gate can be used to provide an OR function with inverted inputs.

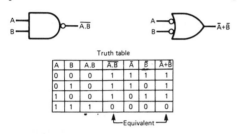

Truth table

A	B	A.B	A̅.B̅	A̅	B̅	A̅+B̅
0	0	0	1	1	1	1
0	1	0	1	1	0	1
1	0	0	1	0	1	1
1	1	1	0	0	0	0

Equivalent

Figure 4.2. Interpreting De Morgan's Second Rule using a NAND gate

Logic circuits frequently produce inverted signals at a point where non-inverted signals are required to perform a particular function directly. For example, if $\overline{A}$ and $\overline{B}$ are directly available and the function $A + B$ is required, the optimum solution is to use a NAND gate, which produces the required result directly; the alternative is to use inverters in series with both $\overline{A}$ and $\overline{B}$, and to follow these with an OR gate. Because NAND and NOR gates provide an inversion, it is possible to use combinations of either of these gates to produce any AND/OR/NAND/NOR function, which can be useful where spare gates are available; clearly either a NAND or a NOR gate can be pressed into service as a simple inverter if required.

Karnaugh maps

Consider the following Boolean expression, which represents a logic circuit requirement:

$$ABC + A\overline{B}C + AB + \overline{B}\overline{C} = Z$$
①   ②   ③   ④

As with ordinary algebra, the absence of a symbol between letters implies '.' (i.e. and AND relationship, in this context). Figure 4.3 is a Karnaugh map for three variables, which in this case are A, B, and C. The first two columns represent A true, the two central columns represent B true, and the upper row represents C true. Thus the top left-hand square represents the logical condition $A\,\overline{B}\,C$, and the bottom right represents $\overline{A}\,\overline{B}\,\overline{C}$.

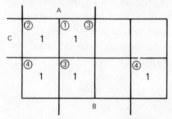

Figure 4.3. A simple Karnaugh map for three variables

If '1' is now marked in the various squares to plot the logical expression given above, the entries shown in the figure will be obtained. The circled numbers beneath the terms in the Boolean expression match the related squares marked by similar circled numbers in the Karnaugh map*. It may be seen that the shorter the term, the more squares it specifies. In this case, the square representing A B C is covered by the first and the third Boolean terms.

The Karnaugh map allows us to see a simplified logical expression. This is derived by grouping together adjacent squares in the map, where it may be visualised that left and right-hand sides bend round and touch, and upper and lower sides do likewise. Thus A describes the four squares in the left-hand block of the map, leaving only one required square not covered. A simplified expression is: $A + \overline{B}\,\overline{C}$.

A combined example

Let us suppose that a circuit is required to produce an output Z from the input conditions as described by the following expression:

$$\overline{A}\overline{B}C + \overline{A}BC + \overline{A}B\overline{C} + AB\overline{C} + ACD = Z$$
$$\text{①} \qquad \text{②} \qquad \text{③} \qquad \text{④} \qquad \text{⑤}$$

By applying the laws of Boolean algebra, this may be simplified as follows:

$$\overline{A}C(\overline{B} + B) + B\overline{C}\,(\overline{A} + A) + ACD = Z$$
$$\overline{A}C . 1 + B\overline{C}.1 + ACD = Z$$
$$\overline{A}C + B\overline{C} + ACD = Z$$
$$C\,(\overline{A} + AD) + B\overline{C} = Z$$

---

* *The circled numbers are purely a teaching aid.*

30

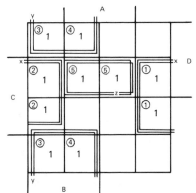

Figure 4.4. A Karnaugh map for four variables

Figure 4.4 shows the same expression plotted on a four variable Karnaugh map in the same manner as before. This then leads to a simplified expression obtained from the borders marked x, y and z on the map, corresponding to the penultimate line in the Boolean simplification (x giving $\overline{A}C$; y giving $B\overline{C}$; z giving ACD). It can also be seen that the final Boolean expression above is equally true by inspection of the Karnaugh map.

One final word about Karnaugh maps. If more than four variables are involved, an extra dimension is needed to cope, and arrays are needed! Things really tend to get out of hand at this point and the designer should be seeking another more practical approach.

Optimisation

Let us now consider whether the techniques of Boolean algebra or Karnaugh maps are the final solution when it comes to effective logic design. It will be appreciated that such procedures lead to *minimisation* of the logic function, but is this the same thing as *optimisation* of components?

The primary objectives of a digital design engineer may be summarised as follows:

a. Minimum component count.
b. Maximum availability of components.
c. Low cost components.

If minimum component count is achieved, we will have won in two ways: firstly on cost, since low component count and low cost go

31

hand-in-hand, and secondly in the reduction of device interconnect-ions. Each and every interconnection is a *potential* source of trouble, therefore the fewer there are, the more inherently reliable the equipment will be. Cost is also reflected in device availability, for maximum availability of component types goes with low cost – the prices of ICs dramatically illustrate the supply and demand equat-ion, with the most popular types being the cheapest, by far. For this reason, the designer should work with preferred types in mind.

The techniques of logic minimisation are obviously useful in reducing a complex logical requirement into its simplest *logical* form, but the designer should then take this as the bare bones of his requirement and optimise his final solution by his manner of implementation. This is best illustrated with a simple example.

Consider the simple alarm/indicator logic circuit discussed at the end of the previous chapter (see Figure 3.9). Ignoring the simple buffer requirements of the LEDs, the logical requirements are as follows:

$$\overline{\text{WINDSHUT.DOORSHUT.NOSMOKE}} = \text{BUZZER}$$
$$\text{DRIVE}$$
$$\text{WINDSHUT.DOORSHUT} = \overline{\text{INTRUDER}}$$
$$\text{NOSMOKE} = \overline{\text{FIREWARN}}$$

The above Boolean expressions describe the circuit requirements, where 'BUZZER DRIVE' is taken to be the input to TR1 base. These three expressions could be used as the basis for three separate Karnaugh maps, but there is little point in drawing these for such simple requirements: the circuit shown in Figure 3.9 can be seen to be the minimum logical solution, for single gates directly implement the above expressions, where:

BUZZER DRIVE is implemented by IC2a
$\overline{\text{INTRUDER}}$ is implemented by IC1a
$\overline{\text{FIREWARN}}$ is implemented by IC1b (providing a required non-inverting buffer).

The original circuit will work using the components listed in Chapter 3, but it can be improved by taking into account the effectiveness with which we are utilising the components. Consider what is used of the original components:

in IC1 only two out of four AND gates are used;
in IC2 only one out of three NAND gates is used;
in IC3 only three out of six buffer/drivers are used.

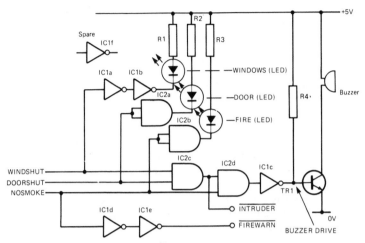

Figure 4.5. A cost-effective version of the alarm/indicator logic previously considered in Figure 3.9

It will be seen that this leaves *seven* unused gates, which is clearly an ineffective use of components. Consider the alternative solution given in Figure 4.5.

At first sight the circuit looks needlessly complex, but the advantages are seen when the component count is considered. In this alternative circuit only two ICs are needed:

IC1 – 7404 – hex inverter/drivers (App. A2), containing *the only unused gate*

IC2 – 7408 – quad 2 i/p AND gates (App. A7).

The first economy is to note that the output required for INTRUDER is a partial decode of the BUZZER DRIVE requirement; thus IC2c provides the INTRUDER output directly, but only needs to be NANDed with NOSMOKE to obtain the BUZZER DRIVE requirement. Since IC2c gate has made us use a quad AND gate, IC2d followed by an inverter (AND inverted) is equivalent to the required NAND function. Inverters are invariably required in any logic circuit, therefore hex inverter ICs are extremely cost-effective. In this circuit the inverters are doubled-up in two places to provide non-inverting buffers (double inversion equates to no inversion), i.e. IC1a/IC1b and IC1d/IC1e. The two AND gates IC2a and IC2b provide the remaining non-inverting buffers required to drive the LEDs (NB this circuit would require LEDs having a forward current requirement of less than 16mA).

33

The percentage effect of *optimisation* techniques such as this grows smaller as the size of a circuit increases – for the more gates of a particular type that are called for, the more gates may be used in a particular device. Part 2 of this book will show how to best approach efficient design from the point of view of component count, but this information should be sufficient to demonstrate that there is a clear distinction between what I have termed *minimisation* and *optimisation*. Optimisation is just as important in a larger circuit, for here the designer is trying to keep down the component count for even more pressing reasons – it could make the difference between needing an extra printed circuit board or perhaps a higher current capability from the power supply, and in these regions the cost difference can be quite considerable.

Thus the need is seen for the designer to appreciate not just the logical significance of his circuits, but the practical aspects as well. It makes no difference whether the enthusiast's pocket or the manufacturer's profitability is being considered, the aim is the same: component optimisation. If you can appreciate the need from the start, it becomes an inner instinct, and an important aid to practical design.

An interesting exercise at this point is to attempt to design a simple circuit optimised for available components. The circuit required in the combined example given earlier is ideally suited to this. Allowing for the fact that the circuit output simplifies to $C(\overline{A} + AD) + B\overline{C}$, and that the circuit inputs are A, B, C and D, attempt to design a suitable circuit using only 6 NAND gates*.

---

* *The few exercises suggested throughout this book should considerably aid the reader's appreciation of the points under discussion. For the book to achieve its objective, they should be attempted.*

5
Timing

The circuits that we have looked at so far have been *static* in nature, i.e. we have only considered them with fixed inputs and outputs. In a practical circuit the sitation is *dynamic* and the inputs and outputs change with time. This may not be an important consideration in simple circuits, but it can become ·of critical importance in more complex circuits, as will be seen later.

In order to allow us to better understand how a circuit performs *with time*, the most convenient method of displaying the changing dynamic situation is to draw *timing diagrams*, sometimes known as *waveform diagrams*. This chapter introduces the timing diagram in order that it may be used in following chapters. It also demonstrates the importance of timing considerations with reference to hazard conditions.

General considerations

It will be appreciated by those familiar with linear electronics that there must be a finite delay due to the switching time of a logic gate. Chapter 2 showed the internal structure of a typical TTL gate, and this was seen to comprise several transistors, each of which must switch from one level to another if a change of state is demanded. The time taken for the output of a logic gate to change as a result of an input change is known as the *propagation delay*, i.e. the time taken for the changed logic condition to 'propagate' through the element. The propagation delay is typically 10ns for a TTL gate (i.e. 10^{-8} second), however, this is reduced to around 3ns for Schottky TTL, where special diodes prevent internal transistors from saturating. The figure of 10ns should generally be borne in mind for design purposes. If good design practices are followed, the actual propagation of any device should not be significant in any calculations, any more than the actual current gain of a transistor should be a linear design; it is the designer's aim to make variable component parameters irrelevant in the performance of this circuit.

Timing diagrams

A simple logic circuit will now be considered in an operational context with varying input and output conditions, and it will be shown how these can be illustrated by means of a timing diagram. Figure 5.1 depicts the circuit, and Figure 5.2 the related timing diagram for particular input conditions. For clarity in this example, the input signals are shown above a horizontal chained line, and the resultant outputs are shown below this line.

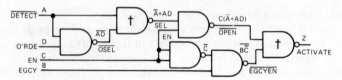

Figure 5.1. A circuit producing an output C $(\overline{A} + AD) + B\overline{C}$ (showing added signal names beneath the lines)

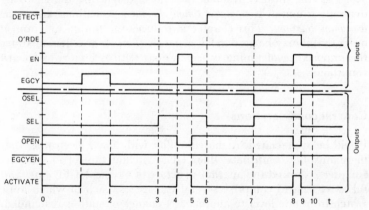

Figure 5.2. Timing diagram for the circuit giving in Figure 5.1 (inputs shown above the chain line)

The reader might be interested to note that the Boolean expressions *above* the lines in Figure 5.1 related to the exercise suggested at the end of the previous chapter – this figure represents the solution to the exercise. To make the circuit more meaningful in an operational context, signal names have been added to inputs and outputs, and have also been shown at intermediate points in the circuit *below* the lines.*

* *Thus Figure 4.4 shows the Karnaugh map for this circuit.*

Let us suppose that an activating mechanism can only be activated when either:

a. an enabling pulse EN occurs when a $\overline{\text{DETECT}}$ line is low, or when an override signal O'RDE is present if $\overline{\text{DETECT}}$ is high;
b. the enabling pulse EN is not present, but an emergency signal EGCY is present.

Meaningful signal names have been added on the circuit as follows:

a. $\overline{\text{OSEL}}$ (override select) goes *low* for: $\overline{\text{DETECT}}$.O'RDE;
b. SEL (select) goes *high* due to selection by either $\overline{\text{DETECT}}$ or $\overline{\text{OSEL}}$ going low (i.e. there is a NAND gate operating as an inverted input OR);
c. $\overline{\text{OPEN}}$ goes *low* if both SEL and EN are true;
d. $\overline{\text{EGCYEN}}$ (emergency enable) goes *low* if EN is low together with EGCY high;
e. ACTIVATE goes *high* if either $\overline{\text{OPEN}}$ or $\overline{\text{EGCYEN}}$ go low (another inverted input OR gate).

As a special aid for the novice, Figure 5.1 – and the remainder of this book – use the symbol † within gates which are used to perform other than their normal function, by virtue of inverted inputs. This is a most useful design aid which the reader may care to use himself.

The timing diagram in Figure 5.2 shows changes in logic states at times marked by vertical lines, these being labelled 0 to 10 for reference purposes; thus t_0 represents the situation at the far left of the diagram, with no inputs active. The first condition illustrated is the emergency condition, with EGCY going true at t_1, and false again at t_2. The second condition illustrated is the normal operation where $\overline{\text{DETECT}}$ goes active (low) at t_3, the enable pulse EN occurs between t_4 and t_5, and $\overline{\text{DETECT}}$ reverts to an inactive state at t_6. Finally the override condition is illustrated, where O'RDE goes high at t_7 until t_9; the special case of EN being true whilst O'RDE is true is shown betwen t_8 and t_9 to show the effects of this perhaps unwanted condition. It is in circumstances like this that the timing diagram can be most useful, for it allows us to analyse circuit effects under all conditions. Finally EN goes false again at t_{10}.

It is not possible to draw the waveform for ACTIVATE directly because there are too many intermediate stages to take into account. We must therefore work through the circuit from the inputs. In this timing diagram, and all that follow, the logic 1 state is shown as the upper voltage level and the logic 0 state as the lower voltage level; the diagrams therefore effectively plot voltages against time.

Let us consider $\overline{\text{OSEL}}$ first. This is a NAND of $\overline{\text{DETECT}}$ and O'RDE; since O'RDE is only high between t_7 and t_9, and because $\overline{\text{DETECT}}$ is also high between these times, $\overline{\text{OSEL}}$ is only low between these times; it is drawn high at all other times.

SEL is an inverted input OR of $\overline{\text{DETECT}}$ and $\overline{\text{OSEL}}$; thus we can only work out this waveform in its entirety after $\overline{\text{OSEL}}$ has been determined. SEL is high between t_3 and t_6 due to $\overline{\text{DETECT}}$ being low, and is also high between t_7 and t_9 due to O'RDE being high together with $\overline{\text{DETECT}}$ high.

$\overline{\text{OPEN}}$ is dependent upon both the former signals, and is a NAND of SEL and EN. It is therefore low between t_4 and t_5 and between t_8 and t_9. Normally it might be expected that it would be low when EN is true, but it is cut off at t_9 rather than t_{10} due to SEL going low at t_9.

$\overline{\text{EGCYGEN}}$ is a NAND of EGCY and $\overline{\text{EN}}$ (since EN is inverted by a NAND gate); thus $\overline{\text{EGCYEN}}$ is low when EGCY is high, providing that EN is low (i.e. between t_1 and t_2). It will be seen that if EN went high whilst EGCY is high, this would force $\overline{\text{EGCYEN}}$ high (not shown).

The output ACTIVATE is the result of the inverted input OR gate, and is high if either $\overline{\text{OPEN}}$ or $\overline{\text{EGCYEN}}$ are low; thus the two waveforms above ACTIVATE on the timing diagram show when ACTIVATE is high, i.e. between t_1 and t_2, between t_4 and t_5, and between t_8 and t_9.

Design practice

The example previously given illustrates several important design practices which the reader is encouraged to follow.

1. Signal names are given to significant points within the circuit to:
   a. be meaningful, in terms of their mnemonics;
   b. allow the circuit points to be identified on a timing diagram.
2. The signal names are always given a name to clearly indicate their *active* level. Thus $\overline{\text{DETECT}}$ is used in preference to DETECT, since 'detection' is signified by the line going *low* when active. Similarly $\overline{\text{OPEN}}$ is better than OPEN, since the line goes low to 'open'. ACTIVATE is used (as opposed to $\overline{\text{ACTIVATE}}$) because this line goes high (i.e. true) to 'activate'.

Much confusion can be caused by not observing the latter rule, especially on inputs and outputs to printed circuit boards; in this respect, many engineers fall down. Whilst there may be no confusion in their minds, there may be in the minds of those who have to interpret their circuits at some later date. Another constant source of confusion is where a line has opposite significance in its two separate states; examples are: READ/WRITE; ON/OFF; STOP/GO. This confusion even exists in manufacturers' data, although there is an unwritten convention that the first of such terms represents the logic 1 condition. This can never be taken for granted. The author strongly advocates the use of a bar over the appropriate term in order that there can be no confusion. The above then become: READ/$\overline{\text{WRITE}}$; ON/$\overline{\text{OFF}}$; STOP/$\overline{\text{GO}}$.

In addition, the author's scheme of using the 'dagger' symbol is a useful one to draw attention to gates not performing their expected function; this can save a lot of puzzlement for those other than the designer, and even for the designer after a few weeks! Where such circuits are liable to be used by others, a '†' footnote should indicate: *gates not used for their primary logic function*.

Start as you mean to go on with conventions such as these, and not only do your designs become clearer to you – they are clearer to others as well.

Race hazard conditions

Figures 5.3 and 5.4 show another logic circuit and its associated timing diagram. These will be used to illustrate what is known as a 'race hazard'.

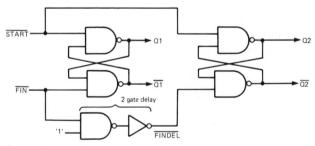

Figure 5.3. A latching circuit demonstrating race hazard conditions

The circuit comprises two *latches*, more of which will be said in the next chapter. For the purposes of this chapter, all that need be said is that two NAND gates coupled as shown provide a means of retaining a particular logic condition *between* controlling input pulses. The controlling inputs $\overline{\text{START}}$ and $\overline{\text{FIN}}$ are lines which are pulsed low (i.e. they are normally high), to change the latch state.

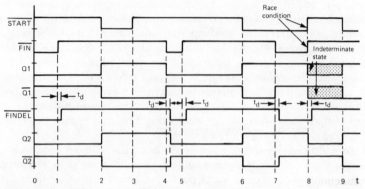

Figure 5.4. Timing diagram showing the results of a race hazard condition in the circuit given as Figure 5.3

Reference to the timing diagram between t_0 and t_5 shows how the latch with outputs Q1 and $\overline{Q1}$ is *set* and *reset*. At t_0 and until t_1 $\overline{FIN}$ is low; at t_1 both inputs are inactive. At t_2 $\overline{START}$ pulses low until t_3. Note that outputs Q1 and $\overline{Q1}$ are always complementary *provided* that both inputs to the latch are never taken low simultaneously. Thus $\overline{START}$ going low forces Q1 high; Q1 high together with $\overline{FIN}$ high forces $\overline{Q1}$ low. When $\overline{START}$ reverts to a high condition at t_3 the outputs do not change because $\overline{Q1}$ low keeps Q1 high, and Q1 AND $\overline{FIN}$ high keep $\overline{Q1}$ low. This condition will remain until t_4, when $\overline{FIN}$ is pulsed low until t_5. This reverses the condition of the latch, forcing $\overline{Q1}$ high, which in itself is combined with $\overline{START}$ high to force Q1 low, and these new conditions are retained after t_5, when the $\overline{FIN}$ pulses finishes.

Under normal circumstances, the two inputs to a latch such as this would never be taken low together, but t_7 shows a case where they are; this forces both outputs Q1 and $\overline{Q1}$ high together, such that they are no longer complementary. All will be well if one input is removed before the other, but if they are both removed at the same time, as shown at t_8, a *race hazard* condition arises. The latch must fall into a stable state with one output high and one output low, but which will it choose? In fact the result depends upon gate propagation delays, a situation which cannot be tolerated in a design.

Such a condition should never be permitted, but for the sake of this illustration of hazard conditions, it will be shown how a delay on one signal can make all the difference. The second latch with outputs Q2 and $\overline{Q2}$ is identical to the first latch. The only circuit difference is that a 2-gate delay is introduced between the $\overline{FIN}$ input and the reset side of the second latch. Thus the waveform shown as

40

$\overline{\text{FINDEL}}$ (i.e. FIND-delayed) is always a small time lagging $\overline{\text{FIN}}$; it is delayed time t_d as a result of two gate propagation delays (i.e. a nominal 20 ns). Thus the setting (i.e. front) edges of the second latch are the same as for the first latch, but the resetting edges lag because of this delay. At t_8, when both inputs go high, the first latch might see either input as last, dependent upon propagation delays, and the latch outputs reach an indeterminate state (shown dotted on the timing diagram); no one can predict which state it will go to, except that the outputs will be complementary. The second latch avoids this *race condition* because $\overline{\text{FINDEL}}$ remains low at t_8, whilst $\overline{\text{START}}$ alone goes high; thus $\overline{\text{Q2}}$ remains high, which with $\overline{\text{START}}$ high forces Q2 low; Q2 is low when $\overline{\text{FINDEL}}$ finally goes high, thereby maintaining $\overline{\text{Q2}}$ high.

Any logic gating which depends upon inputs which nominally change at the same moment in time gives rise to a race condition and a logic hazard; such conditions must never be allowed in circuitry, and indeterminate states cannot be tolerated under normal conditions. It should be noted that the indeterminate conditions at the output of the first latch are removed as soon as normal conditions are restored by *one* input being pulsed low again, as at t_9.

Timing diagrams are a valuable aid towards checking that a particular circuit is fault free. For if all normal input conditions are examined, any possible hazard conditions should be spotted. If they exist, the design must be modified to avoid the situation. The delay shown in this example is for illustrative purposes only, and should not be taken as a method to be employed to counteract all potential race conditions. It is a technique which can be employed in some situations, however, although a 3-gate delay is perhaps more reliable. Later chapters will show alternative methods of introducing a delay.

The best design aim is to avoid any situation which can give rise to possible race hazards, rather than to counteract their effects, and this will be taken further in Part 2.

6

Latch, bistable, monostable and astable circuits

Previous chapters have been primarily concerned with *combinational logic*: circuits in which the output is completely determined by the inputs. The exception so far has been the latch, for this is an element of *sequential logic*: the output is dependent upon the sequence of operation of the inputs. This chapter goes into greater depth on the latch, and also covers bistable, monostable and astable circuits.

The purpose of sequential logic is to *staticise* (i.e. store) particular logic conditions *after* the affecting inputs have been removed. In this way the logic condition arising at one moment in time can be made to affect the logic condition arising at a subsequent moment in time. A short pulse can be detected and converted into a staticised level, or may be 'stretched' in time. Bistables and latches generally form the heart of any control logic, and monstables provide a means of obtaining single pulses of any desired length. Astable circuits provide a source of clock pulses.

Latches

We have already met the NAND gate latch (see Figures 5.3 and 5.4). An alternative is the NOR gate latch. Both are shown in Figure 6.1, together with *function tables* and timing diagrams. Note that a 'function' table is basically the same as a truth table, but whereas a truth table is restricted to logic states, the function table is more versatile; the latter generally utilises the unambiguous 'H' and 'L' symbols to indicate high and low states respectively (thereby independent of logic convention), and incorporates other symbols such as arrows or pulses, where these are convenient in describing *functional* operation. Function tables are generally more popular in manufacturers' data sheets, and will therefore be used extensively throughout this book. The reader should therefore become familiar with interpreting them.

Function table

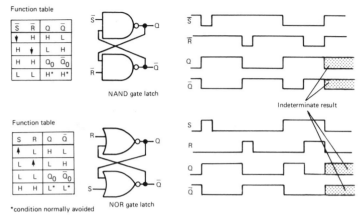

$\bar{S}$	$\bar{R}$	Q	$\bar{Q}$
↓	H	H	L
H	↓	L	H
H	H	Q_0	$\bar{Q}_0$
L	L	H*	H*

NAND gate latch

Function table

S	R	Q	$\bar{Q}$
↑	L	H	L
L	↑	L	H
L	L	Q_0	$\bar{Q}_0$
H	H	L*	L*

*condition normally avoided

NOR gate latch

Indeterminate result

Figure 6.1. Latching circuits with function tables and timing diagrams

The convention with latches and bistables is to say they are *set* when the Q output is high, or *reset** when the Q output is low; the $\bar{Q}$ output is normally complementary to the Q output.

For clarity, the NAND gate latch is shown with inputs of $\bar{S}$ to set, and $\bar{R}$ to reset, i.e. the set/reset inputs must be taken *low* to function, as indicated by the downward pointing arrows in the function table. Thus taking $\bar{S}$ low sets the NAND latch, and taking $\bar{R}$ low resets it. The NOR gate latch offers the reverse action: the set input S is taken high to set the latch, and the reset R input is taken high to reset the latch. The action of the NAND gate latch was explained in the previous chapter, therefore only the NOR gate latch will be explained in detail in this chapter. The reader may care to note that the NAND latch is the most common.

The inputs to the NOR gate latch should normally be low; in this condition the outputs staticise the condition previously applied (represented by Q_o and $\bar{Q}_o$ in the function table). If we suppose that the latch is initially in the reset condition, Q is therefore low, which combined with S low in the lower NOR gate produces $\bar{Q}$; $\bar{Q}$ high maintains Q low via the upper NOR gate. If a set pulse is applied, momentarily taking S high, this forces $\bar{Q}$ low, which combined with R low takes Q high, thereby setting the latch. When output Q goes high it forces $\bar{Q}$ low via the lower gate, thereby maintaining the stable set condition after the setting pulse has gone. The latch is reset in similar fashion. A positive-going reset pulse on R forces Q low, which combined with S low forces $\bar{Q}$ high, thereby restoring the other stable state. Except in special circumstances, S and R inputs should not be taken high simultaneously (see timing diagram).

* or 'cleared'

The NAND gate latch calls for negative-going pulses to set and reset the latch; for this reason the inputs should normally be kept high except to change the latch state, and normally both inputs should not be taken low together. Figure 6.1 shows how an indeterminate result occurs if set/reset inputs are cancelled together.

All the latches shown have used two input gates for simplicity. Some applications call for alternative set or reset inputs, and in such cases gates can be used with more than two inputs. NAND gates are available with a wide variety of inputs, and are generally used for such purposes. The rule in such a case is that only one input should be taken low at once (unless the designer knows what he is about!).

D-type bistables

D-type bistables are similar to latches, except that they are *clocked*. Figure 6.2 shows such a bistable in (a), complete with optional preset (PR) and clear (CL) inputs; these control the state of the bistable in a similar fashion to the set and reset inputs of a latch, respectively, and such inputs override the clock. A function table is provided, together with timing diagrams. The timing diagram at (b)

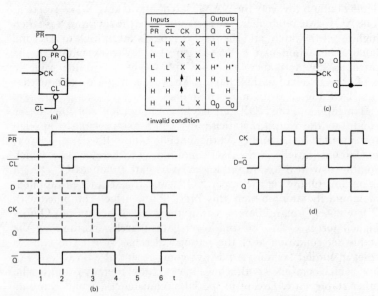

$\overline{PR}$	$\overline{CL}$	CK	D	Q	$\overline{Q}$
L	H	X	X	H	L
H	L	X	X	L	H
L	L	X	X	H*	H*
H	H	↑	H	H	L
H	H	↑	L	L	H
H	H	L	X	Q_0	$\overline{Q}_0$

*invalid condition

Figure 6.2. D-type bistables, function table and timing diagrams

44

shows the various possibilities with all inputs externally controlled. The connections to the bistable shown in (c) show how the element can be *toggled*, and the related waveform for the toggled condition is shown at (d). (See App. C1.)

The type of bistable element we shall now be considering is known as *edge-triggered*. This phrase signifies that it is the (leading) *edge* of the *clock* waveform which *triggers* the device. The state the outputs resume after such a trigger pulse is dependent upon the D input: the Q output will take the condition of the D input when the bistable is triggered, as shown in the left-hand timing diagram.

The timing diagram will now be considered in detail (i.e. Figure 6.2(b)). The preset input $\overline{PR}$ pulses low at t_1 and thereby *presets* the bistable (Q = 1; $\overline{Q}$ = 0). The clear input $\overline{CL}$ pulses low at t_2 and thereby *clears* the bistable (Q = 0). At t_3 the leading-edge of the first clock pulse triggers the bistable, but Q remains at 0 since the D input is at 0. At t_4 the next clock pulse edge-triggers the bistable to give Q = 1, since the D input is now also at 1. At t_5 the situation is simply confirmed, since the D input has not changed. At t_6 the clock pulse clocks the bistable to the reset (or cleared) condition because the D input is now low.

It should be appreciated that the edges of pulses such as the clock pulse will have very fast rise and fall times – typically well below 10 ns – therefore the condition seen at the beginning of the rising edge of edge-triggered bistables dictates what state it will take up; so long as the D input does not change for the typical propagation delay time, the bistable is not affected if the D input then changes. The propagation delay in bistables themselves is more than adequate when coupled to each other to allow simultaneous clocking without any ambiguity of conditions arising. Thus it is possible to couple the $\overline{Q}$ output of a D-type bistable back into the D input, thereby causing the bistable to change state – or *toggle* – at each clock pulse, as shown in parts (c) and (d) of the figure. The $\overline{Q}$ output must be used because it is always opposite to the state that the Q output takes up; since the Q output takes up the state of the D input, linking this to the D input would cause the bistable to remain in one state when clocked: either high or low, depending upon its initial condition.

Another variety of D-type bistable is the *D-type latch*, sometimes known as a *transparent latch*. This is not usually employed singly, but in conjunction with similar latches, usually on parallel data lines. This is shown in Figure 6.3. This is not clocked by the G input, but allows the output (at Q) to follow the D input whilst it is high; when G is taken low, it latches the condition then existing at the D input and retains it until G is again taken high. (See App. C3.)

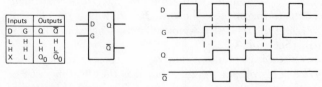

Figure 6.3. A bistable D-type latch (transparent latch)

J-K type bistables

The J-K bistable is available as either edge-triggered or *master-slave*. It is similar to the D-type bistable, except that there are now two controlling inputs (i.e. J and K) rather than one (i.e. D). This means that there are more permutations possible for the output to take with respect to the inputs; as before, this occurs under the control of a clock pulse. This section only describes the master-slave variety, since this is by far the most popular and useful. The edge-triggered variety is identically controlled with respect to J-K inputs, but changes state on a defined edge of the clock pulse (either positive or negative), as opposed to the more complex timing relationship to be described for the master-slave variety. (See App. C2.)

The alternatives of either edge-triggered D-types or master-slave J-K bistables should give sufficient scope for just about all design requirements, and the reader is advised to only use these types, particularly in early designs. As a matter of normal practice, this is generally good advice, for these two varieties are most commonly used by engineers, and circuits are universally easier to follow if edge-triggered J-K bistables are avoided.

Figure 6.4 shows the master-slave J-K bistable, its function table, and an example timing diagram. The optional preset ($\overline{PR}$) and clear ($\overline{CL}$) inputs override clock inputs as before. The J-K inputs control the final output state as shown in the table. The timing of the bistable is referenced to *both* edges of the clock pulse. The element comprises two separate bistables in one: a *master* and a *slave*. Information presented at the J-K inputs is clocked into the master on the rising edge of the clock pulse, and is transferred to the outputs, via the slave, on the falling edge of the clock pulse. It is generally understood that the J-K inputs should not vary for the duration of the clock pulse, for the effects of this vary according to the type of internal circuitry employed. Some devices have a *data lockout* facility which prevents changing inputs having any effect after the front edge of the clock pulse, but other master-slave devices can be affected. The best procedure to adopt with *any* master-slave J-K

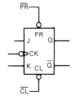

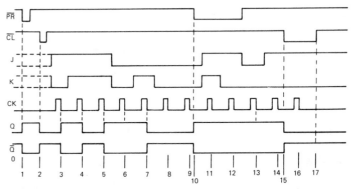

Figure 6.4. A master-slave J-K bistable with function table and timing diagram

bistable is to ensure that the J-K inputs are established *before* the clock pulse occurs, and are maintained until *after* the clock pulse finishes, although they may be safely removed coincident with the trailing edge of the clock pulse.

The J-K inputs affect the bistable as follows:

a. if they are complementary, the outputs take the same levels as the inputs (i.e. $Q = J$; $\overline{Q} = K$);
b. if both inputs are low no change occurs due to clocking;
c. if both inputs are high, the bistable is toggled by a clock pulse (i.e. it changes state). This can be seen from the function table.

The timing diagram is now considered in depth, to fully explain the bistable's actions with respect to changing J-K inputs.

At t_1 a negative $\overline{PR}$ pulse presets the bistable from the leading edge ($Q = 1$). At t_2 a negative $\overline{CL}$ pulse clears the bistable from the leading edge ($Q = 0$). At t_3 the negative edge of the clock pulse CK sets (the same as 'presets') the bistable as a result of complementary inputs with $J = 1$. At t_4 and t_5 the bistable is toggled, since the J-K

47

inputs are both high. At t_6 no change occurs at the outputs since the J-K inputs are both low. At t_7 the clock resets (the same as 'clears') the bistable as a result of the complementary inputs with $J = 0$. At t_8 and t_9 no change occurs since J and K are low. At t_{10} the preset input goes active which overrides any clocked effects at t_{11} and t_{12}. Since the preset signal is then removed, the clock has its normal effect at t_{13}, but no change occurs because both J and K are low. The J-K inputs at t_{14} reassert that the bistable should be set, therefore no change occurs. At t_{15} the clear input goes active to immediately reset the bistable, and the clock pulse at t_{16} is ignored because the clear pulse is still held. The clear is removed at t_{17} and the bistable is then ready to respond to any further clocking.

Various other single J-K type bistables are available incorporating gating on the J-K inputs. The reader is referred to manufacturers' data for types such as the following: 7470, 7471, 7472.

Monostables

It is sometimes required to generate a pulse of predetermined length. This is readily achieved with a monostable, the pulse length being set by means of an external capacitor. The 74121 is the most common device for this purpose (App. J1), or the 74122 (App. J2) when a *retriggerable* version is required. These elements are most simply represented as shown in Figure 6.5. An internal CR is sufficient to provide a nominal 35 ns pulse, but this must be supplemented by the shown external CR in order to achieve times greater than this. These devices are suitable up to about 28 s. For longer times, the 555 timer device is more suited (see p. 50).

Firstly we shall consider the 74121 (non-retriggerable) device. This has two inverted OR inputs (A1 and A2) and one other positive enable incorporating a Schmitt trigger for pulse-shaping purposes (B). The monostable is triggered when the appropriate input conditions are met, as shown in the function table. This may be summarised as follows. The device is triggered if:

a. one or both of the A inputs are *taken* low when the B input is high;
b. the B input is *taken* high when one or both of the A inputs are low.

It is the *initial setting* of these input conditions which triggers a single pulse from the monostable. Because it only produces a single pulse, it is sometimes known as a *one-shot*. The timing diagram shows

48

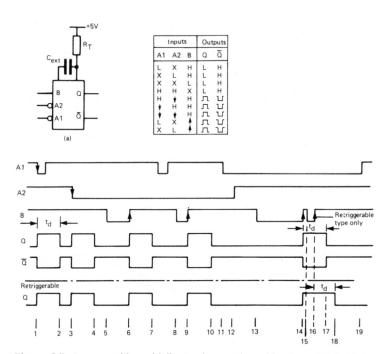

Inputs			Outputs	
A1	A2	B	Q	Q̄
L	X	H	L	H
X	L	H	L	H
X	X	L	L	H
H	H	X	L	H
H	↑	H	⎍	⊔
↑	H	H	⎍	⊔
↑	↑	H	⎍	⊔
L	X	↑	⎍	⊔
X	L	↑	⎍	⊔

(a)

Figure 6.5. A monostable multivibrator (non-retriggerable above the chained line; retriggerable below the chained line)

how it would respond to varying inputs. Arrows on the edges of the inputs signify triggering edges. Each time the device is triggered it produces a pulse of fixed length, i.e. t_d. Thus the leading edge of A1 triggers it at t_1, and a single pulse occurs at Q (inverted form at $\overline{Q}$). This pulse is said to *time-out* at t_2. Similarly, the leading edge of A2 triggers the monostable at t_3, which times-out at t_4. The B input goes low at t_5, which has no effect, but it triggers the monostable at t_6 when it goes positive again (note that A2 is still low); this pulse times-out at t_7. Before t_8 occurs, a negative pulse is shown on A1; this has no effect because A2 is already low. B goes low again at t_8 and triggers the monostable when it goes high again at t_9, the monostable timing-out at t_{10}. A1 and A2 are seen to change over at t_{11} and t_{12} respectively, with no effects, since one is always low. B then goes through another cycle between t_{13} and t_{14} to again trigger the monostable, timing-out at t_{17}. At t_{15} the B input is again taken low, going high at t_{16}, but because this monostable is non-retriggerable, this triggering edge is ignored because the device is *already* triggered; the time-out is the normal time, t_d.

49

In some instances it is desirable to retrigger the monostable in such circumstances, and this is where the retriggerable monostable, the 74122, comes in. This is shown as the bottom line of the timing diagram (only Q is shown; $\overline{Q}$ is complementary as usual). In this case, the edge of input B which occurs at t_{16} *retriggers* the monostable, and it then times-out t_d *from that point*. A retriggerable monostable may be retriggered any number of times during its time-out period; it does not revert to the reset condition until t_d *after the final trigger pulse*. Thus retriggering can be used as a means of extending the time-out, or of ensuring that a delay, t_d, occurs after the *last* triggering pulse.

The output pulse width produced by these two monostables is as follows:

$$t_{w(out)} = K.C_{ext}.R_T$$

For the 74121, $K = 0.7$. For the 74122, $K = 0.3$ when C_{ext} is in excess of $1000\,pF$, but if the capacitance is less than this value, the curve given in App. J2 should be consulted. Curves for both devices are given in App. J1 and J2, and the appendix should also be consulted for details of the limiting values for C_{ext} and R_T.

The 555 timer

Strictly speaking, the 555 timer is not a digital device, but because of its uses in conjunction with digital circuitry as a timing element, not to mention its availability and low cost, all designers should be aware of its uses. It is an extremely versatile device with timing ranges from microseconds to hours. It can be used as a retriggerable

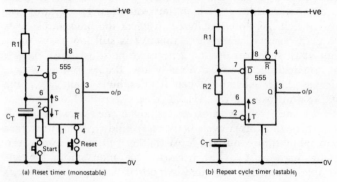

Figure 6.6. The 555 timer in monostable and astable configurations

monostable, or it can be used in an astable mode as a multivibrator (free-running oscillator). Figure 6.6 shows it connected in these two modes, with labels $\overline{D}$, $\uparrow$ S, $\downarrow$ T, $\overline{R}$ and Q appended to various pins. It should be understood that these labels have been given for ease of understanding in this book, and are not recognised labels – although the pins have names (given in brackets below), circuit diagrams usually do no more than show pin numbers; the suggested labels help the user to remember their significance. The pins are as follows:

$\overline{D}$ (Discharge) – shorts *external* capacitor to 0 V via internal transistor;

$\uparrow$ S indicating Sample (threshold) - samples *rising* voltage on C_T;

$\downarrow$ T (Trigger) – taken *low* to trigger the timer;

$\overline{R}$ (Reset) – taken low to reset the timer;

Q (Output) – goes high after trigger and remains high until time-out/reset. Pin 8 is connected to + ve and pin 1 to 0 V.

A further pin (pin 5) is known as the control voltage or Fm input; for usual applications this may be ignored.

The 555 (or its big brother the 556 dual timer) may be operated over a +4.5 V to +16 V supply range; because the time-out period is set by the voltage developed across C_T, and this is related to the 'aiming' potential of the supply rail (through the external resistor/s), it is relatively independent of the actual value of the supply voltage. Taking $\downarrow$ T low momentarily triggers the device, which releases a short-circuit held across C_T via the $\overline{D}$ (discharge) pin. C_T charges, but when it reaches 2/3 of the supply, this is sensed by the $\uparrow$ S terminal. The output Q goes high when the device is triggered, and remains high until the voltage rises to 2/3 of the supply, whereupon it goes low, i.e. similar action to a monostable as previously described. If $\overline{R}$ is taken low momentarily during the time-out period this resets the timer, i.e. it terminates the time-out at once. If $\overline{R}$ and $\downarrow$ T are momentarily taken low simultaneously, this retriggers the device to time-out the full time again (like a retriggerable monostable); the circuit shown in Figure 6.6(a) shows these modes. App. K provides further details of the timer.

When connected as an oscillator, the 'mark' and 'space' may be separately determined by the resistors (R1 + R2), and R2 alone, respectively; this is because timing capacitor C_T charges (during 'mark') through R1 in series with R2, but discharges (during 'space') via R2 and the $\overline{D}$ terminal.

The time period for the monostable configuration is given by:

$$T_D \cong 0.7 \, R1 . C_T$$

The time periods for the astable configuration are given by:

$$T_m \cong 0.7 \ (R1 + R2) \ C_T$$
$$T_s \cong 0.7 \ (R2) \ C_T$$

These timers are capable of driving 200 mA into a load (when high or low at the output). They are therefore very useful as an output device, and can drive relays directly. If the $\overline{R}$ terminal is used as a control in the circuit shown in Figure 6.6(b), the oscillator can be switched on and off by taking $\overline{R}$ high and low respectively. This can be used as an audible output, with a loudspeaker capacitively coupled to the output (see example in Chapter 18). If used in this manner, it should be noted that the first time-out cycle is longer than subsequent cycles because the capacitor has to charge from 0V to begin with.

Astable circuits

One form of astable circuit using the 555 timer IC has already been shown in Figure 6.6(b), but a simple circuit suitable for use with logic circuitry is given in Figure 6.7. Each time the timing capacitor is discharged a short negative pulse occurs at the timer output. This is inverted to produce a positive pulse suitable for clocking digital circuitry. If $\overline{R}$ is taken to +5V the circuit is free-running, but if gated, it can stop the clocking source when taken low. This gives a very elegant and controllable clock source.

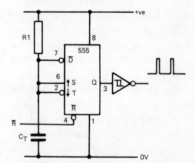

Figure 6.7. A clock pulse generator using the 555 timer

A very similar circuit can be made using an ordinary TTL Schmitt trigger, as shown in Figure 6.8, although the timing range is much more limited. This circuit is often adequate, however, and does give excellent reliability. The maximum resistor value is about

1 kΩ, due to the need to ensure that the high level input current does not swamp the capacitor charging current. When the output of the gate is high, C charges through R until the voltage reaches the Schmitt's upper threshold, whereupon the output goes low; C then discharges through R until the voltage reaches the lower Schmitt threshold, whereupon the output goes high again. As shown, the 'mark' period is slightly shorter than the 'space'.

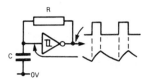

Figure 6.8. A Schmitt oscillator

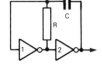

Figure 6.9. A typical TTL oscillator

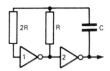

Figure 6.10. A typical CMOS oscillator

It is possible to cross-couple two ordinary inverting type gates as an oscillator, as shown in Figure 6.9, although there is still the limitation on high values of R. This circuit is more suitable for the CMOS families, as shown in the variation as Figure 6.10. In both circuits, gate 1 output goes to the opposite state of the output at gate 2, thereby causing capacitor C to discharge/charge to the opposite polarity; once the threshold level on the input gate (high or low) has been crossed, the circuit switches, and the situation reverses. Thus there is a sawtooth waveform at the input to gate 1, but a square-wave at the output.

Finally, there is a way of producing a very short duration pulse for clocking purposes using a unijunction transistor. Figure 6.11 shows how this is achieved. Capacitor C1 charges through R1 until it reaches the trigger voltage of the device, whereupon it discharges through the emitter (e) and R3. Because R3 is low in value compared with R1, discharge is brief, hence the short pulse. Unijunction transistors are rather more difficult to use than the circuits previously discussed, for if component values are not within fairly critical limits, the circuit will fail to oscillate. The designer unfamiliar with UJTs is therefore advised to use an alternative

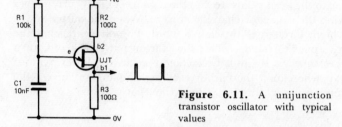

Figure 6.11. A unijunction transistor oscillator with typical values

circuit. This circuit can drive CMOS directly, but a Schmitt buffer is required to speed up the edges and to ensure correct levels when used with TTL (NB the output pulse does not go anywhere near the positive rail).

7
Registers

Single bistables and latches are frequently used in logic circuitry, but there is often the need for quite a number of such logic elements. Thus while it is possible to construct up to two latches from a single quad NAND or quad NOR gate (i.e. 7400 or 7402), or to use a single D or J-K bistable device, it is often more efficient to use multiple devices. Where a number of bistables (also known as *flip-flops*) are used to staticise related data, and can therefore utilise certain common lines (e.g. clock, preset or clear), they are obtainable as single devices known as *registers*. Economy of connections is achieved because of commoned control lines. Before considering the more complex devices, first, dual and quad devices – useful for general purposes rather than as data registers – will be considered.

Quad $\overline{S}$-$\overline{R}$ latches

Quad $\overline{S}$-$\overline{R}$ latch (see App. C4). This is a 16-pin DIL device, and amounts to four independent NAND gate latches of the type shown in Figure 6.1; each latch has $\overline{S}$ and $\overline{R}$ inputs and the Q output accessible from the pins. It follows that an inverter must be used on the output if $\overline{Q}$ is required.

4-bit bistable latch

The 7475 is a 4-bit bistable (transparent) latch of the type shown previously in Figure 6.3 (see also App. C3). This is also in a 16-pin DIL encapsulation, with each of the four latches having individual D, Q and $\overline{Q}$ lines brought out; the enables are combined, with two enables each controlling two latches.

Where several data lines are associated, each individual line is referred to as one *bit*; since the 7475 is capable of staticising four such lines, it is known as a *4-bit* latch.

Dual bistable latches

The 7474 is a dual D-type bistable latch. Each latch is completely independent and incorporates all the requirements that a designer could want. The following lines are brought out for each latch: CK, D, $\overline{PR}$, $\overline{CL}$, Q and $\overline{Q}$. (See App. C1.)

The 7476 is a dual J-K bistable latch. Again, each bistable is independent, with the following lines brought out: CK, J, K, $\overline{PR}$, $\overline{CL}$, Q and $\overline{Q}$. (See App. C2.)

The above devices may be used as 2-bit registers, or could be used for quite different purposes.

Octal D-type bistable

The 74273 is an octal D-type bistable with common clock and clear lines, as shown in Figure 7.1. (See also App. D1.) All eight 'flip-flops' are simultaneously triggered by the positive edge of the CK clock input; a buffer gate is incorporated to ensure that this input only represents one gate load to a driving device, as opposed to eight. The data required to be entered into all eight flip-flops must be presented at the eight D-type inputs (1D to 8D) prior to applying the CK pulse; after the rising-edge of CK, the Q outputs then take on the logic states fed into their respective D inputs. By taking the common $\overline{CLEAR}$ line low, all the flip-flops may be simultaneously cleared (i.e. Q taken low); again a buffer gate is used.

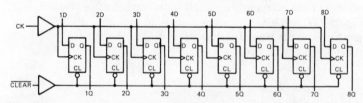

Figure 7.1. Octal D-type bistable with common clear (74273 – App. D1)

It will be shown in Part 3 that 8-bits are used extensively in microprocessor applications for data lines, or for a portion of an address. For this reason, 8-bits of associated data are a common requirement, hence octal bistables. Chapter 10 will show how multiples of 2 are always significant in digital systems, therefore this is another reason why 8-bits should be a useful combination, microprocessors apart.

Shift registers

Binary arithmetic frequently operates with 8-bits, and one requirement often met is the need to *shift* data bits with respect to their
lines. For example, if line (a) below represents an 8-bit data word,
this becomes as (b) when shifted one place to the left, or as (c) when
shifted three places to the right.

(a)   [1 1 0 0 0 1 0 1]   (original data word)
(b) ← 1 0 0 0 1 0 1]0 ←   (original data word shifted left one
                             place)
(c) → 0 0 0[1 1 0 0 0 →   (original data word shifted right
                             three places)

It should be noted that as bits are shifted out of the register –
spilling out to the left in (b) or the right in (c) – they are replaced by
0's from the other end of the register, and the significance of the bits
shifted out of the register is lost.

Sometimes the ends of the register are linked together, such that
data shifted out of one end is fed straight back into the other end:
this is known as *circulatory shift* or *logical shift*. Repeating the previous
process, and causing the data word given in (a) to undergo
circulatory shift, the following results are obtained:

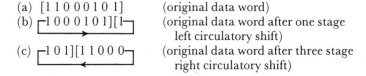

(a) [1 1 0 0 0 1 0 1]   (original data word)
(b) ┌1 0 0 0 1 0 1][1┐   (original data word after one stage
    └───────────→   left circulatory shift)
(c) ┌1 0 1][1 1 0 0 0┐   (original data word after three stage
    └──────────←   right circulatory shift)

The 74199 (App. D2) is an 8-bit shift register which has the
capability of being *parallel loaded* or *serial loaded*, and provides *serial* or
parallel outputs; it is therefore one of the most versatile of shift
registers, if not one of the cheapest! But what do all these terms
mean?

First of all imagine eight individual flip-flops similar to those
shown in Figure 7.1, with each stage of this 8-bit register holding one
bit of our data word. *Parallel loading* refers to the ability to load all
8-bits with parallel data, as 1D to 8D in the figure. *Parallel output*
refers to the ability to 'read' all 8-bits of the register simultaneously
(i.e. in parallel), as 1Q to 8Q in the figure. *Serial data* is data read or
manipulated one bit at a time; thus if a particular data input is
applied to 1D in the figure, and then changed for seven subsequent
clock pulses, and if the Q output of each bistable is fed as the D

input to the following bistable (e.g. 1Q linked to 2D, etc.), this amounts to *serial loading* of a 8-bit register; at each clock pulse the data is shifted one place – or one stage – to the *right*. By reversing the connections (e.g. 8Q to 7D, 7Q to 6D, etc.) the same register gives us *left-shift*, and serial data is input at 8D. Data read at the output end of such a register is termed *serial data output* since each bit appears *serially* (i.e. one bit per clock pulse).

The propagation delay of bistables is more than adequate to ensure that the output of one may feed the input of the next, providing *synchronous clocking* is employed (i.e. all bistables are clocked at the same time by a common control line). The table below lists a variety of shift registers to meet different requirements, and the reader is referred to manufacturers' data. The 74198 and 74199 are covered in the Appendices, however.

Type	Bidirectional	Serial in	Serial out	Parallel in	Parallel out	Bits
74198	yes	yes	yes	yes	yes	8
74195	no	yes	yes	yes	yes	4
74164	no	yes	yes	no	yes	8
74165	no	yes	yes	yes	no	8
74199	no	yes	yes	yes	yes	8

As an example of all relevant features, the 74199 is now considered in depth.

Shift registers may utilise J-K or D-type bistable elements, the only difference being in the input gating. The 74199, shown in Figure 7.2, is of the J-K variety, but note that the K serial input is actually $\overline{K}$. Since the J and K inputs of a bistable must be complementary to enter a logic 0 or logic 1, it is more convenient to provide J-$\overline{K}$ in such a case; this allows the J-$\overline{K}$ inputs to be tied together, thereby entering a 1 when high, or a 0 when low.

Whilst it is possible to wire up shift registers from individual bistable elements and external gating, this is not a practical proposition because of the amount of gating required. This is plain when it is realised that the 74199 is equivalent to 79 individual TTL gates! The circuit of the complete shift register would be too large to show fully, therefore Figure 7.2 shows only three elements. The first element differs slightly from the rest due to the serial input interface, but the remaining seven stages are identical to those stages shown which have outputs Q_B and Q_C.

Firstly, for simplicity, the latter stages will be considered. Note that a common clock line feeds all the *edge-triggered* J-K bistables*, and that they are triggered on the *positive-edge* of the CLOCK input

---

* These are not master-slave J-K flip-flops.

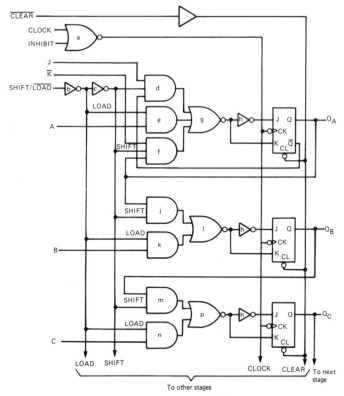

Figure 7.2. Three stages of an 8-bit parallel load, parallel-out shift register with serial J-K input (74199 – App. D2)

pulse; gate *a* inverts this pulse, but the inverting circle on the clock inputs shows that the bistables respond to a negative-going pulse, thereby ensuring that they clock on the positive-edge of the *input* pulse. The inverter gates marked *h* correct the phase for the J inputs after NOR gating on the inputs, hence the K input is fed directly from these NOR gates. A SHIFT/$\overline{\text{LOAD}}$ ('SHIFT/LOAD' in manufacturers' data, but converted to an unambiguous signal name) input is buffered and inverted by *b* to produce a LOAD line, and then further inverted by *c* to provide a SHIFT line; thus with SHIFT/$\overline{\text{LOAD}}$ high, SHIFT is true, and with SHIFT/$\overline{\text{LOAD}}$ low, LOAD is true.

Consider the B input to be high. If LOAD is made true, the AND gate *k* has a high output, which produces a low from NOR gate *l*; hence *h* presents a high to the bistable J input. If a clock pulse

59

occurs, a 1 is loaded into the bistable, producing a high at output Q_B; this has loaded an input logic 1. If the B input is low, gate *k* produces a low output, gate *l* has a high output, gate *h* a low output, and the bistable loads a logic 0. In this manner, all eight stages of the shift register can be parallel loaded with data applied on lines A to H.

If SHIFT is made true, gating is enabled to connect the output of each stage to the input of the following stage; note that Q_A is connected as input to stage B via gate *j*, and Q_B is connected to stage C via gate *m*. If a particular output is high, this is ANDed with SHIFT and then fed to the same NOR gate as before, hence feeding the following gate input lines. It must be remembered that SHIFT and LOAD are complementary since they are obtained from the opposite phases of the SHIFT/$\overline{\text{LOAD}}$ line, therefore it is impossible for both to be true. Hence the NOR gates *g, l* and *p* only receive one operational input.

The serial input to the first stage is via the J-$\overline{\text{K}}$ gating, thus Q_A takes on a logic condition according to the state of these inputs when

INPUTS							OUTPUTS				EFFECTS		
CLEAR	SHIFT/$\overline{\text{LOAD}}$	CLOCK INHIBIT	CLOCK	Serial J	Serial $\overline{\text{K}}$	Parallel A……H	Q_A	Q_B	Q_C……	…Q_H			
L	X	X	X	X	X	X	X	X	X	X	Clear		
H	X	L	L	X	X	X	Q_{A0}	Q_{B0}	Q_{C0}	Q_{H0}	Rest		
H	L	L	↑	X	X	a……h	a	b	c	h	Load		
H	H	L	↑	L	H	X	Q_{A0}	Q_{A0}	Q_{Bn}	Q_{Gn}	Inhibit	'A' bistable	SHIFT
H	H	L	↑	L	L	X	L	Q_{An}	Q_{Bn}	Q_{Gn}	Reset	'A' bistable	SHIFT
H	H	L	↑	H	H	X	H	Q_{An}	Q_{Bn}	Q_{Gn}	Set	'A' bistable	SHIFT
H	H	L	↑	H	L	X	$\overline{Q}_{An}$	Q_{An}	Q_{Bn}	Q_{Gn}	Toggle	'A' bistable	SHIFT
H	X	H	↑	X	X	X	Q_{A0}	Q_{B0}	Q_{C0}	Q_{H0}	Inhibited		SHIFT

Figure 7.3. Function table for the 74199 8-bit shift register

clocked with SHIFT true. This is shown in the function table for the device, given as Figure 7.3.

Examination of the table shows the results of clocking with various input states, or of clearing. The 'rest' state represents the device between other modes. Taking $\overline{\text{CLEAR}}$ low clears all stages. With SHIFT/$\overline{\text{LOAD}}$ low, the positive-edge of CLOCK loads the device (a *broadside load*), with parallel input data. Clocking with SHIFT/$\overline{\text{LOAD}}$ high causes shifts as indicated. Note that the CLOCK is inhibited by taking the CLOCK INHIBIT high; the initial conditions of the outputs are represented as Q_{A0} to Q_{H0}. Shifting shifts data in the direction Q_A towards Q_H. The Q_A stage is controlled by the J-$\overline{K}$ conditions; this is easier to understand in terms of a conventional J-K bistable if you mentally invert the state applied to $\overline{K}$, thereby making it equivalent to K.

A timing diagram for the device is shown in Figure 7.4. This should be studied carefully.

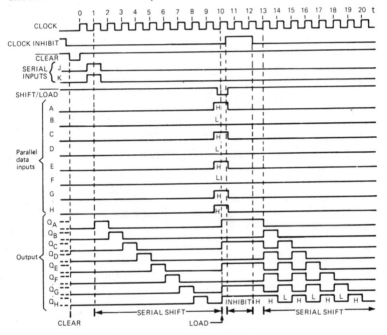

Figure 7.4. Timing diagram for the 74199 8-bit shift register

The timing diagram depicts the following sequence of events:

(a) The $\overline{\text{CLEAR}}$ input is taken low to clear all eight outputs.
(b) A logic 1 is fed into Stage A at the clock pulse marked t_1; eight subsequent clock pulses clock this logic 1 through each stage of the register and out of the end; no further logic 1's are entered because the J-$\overline{K}$ input is low after clock pulse t_1.
(c) After t_9, but before t_{10}, the SHIFT/$\overline{\text{LOAD}}$ line is taken low. The actual load is *synchronous* with respect to the CLOCK, and therefore occurs at t_{10}. Note that the parallel inputs are set up with data prior to the load command, and remain stable until after the clock edge. Note also that only those outputs which

61

have inputs at a high level go high after the loading clock pulse (i.e. A, C, E, G and H).

(d) The CLOCK INHIBIT is taken high after t_{10} until after t_{12}, thereby inhibiting any shifting for the two following clock pulses at t_{11} and t_{12}.

(e) At t_{13} the A stage goes to logic 0 due to the low J-$\overline{\text{K}}$ input, and the other stages go to the state of the previous stage, i.e. shifting occurs, as it does on the following clock pulses.

Because the 74199 can be parallel loaded and has a parallel output, it can also be employed as a *octal register*. In this case the SHIFT/$\overline{\text{LOAD}}$ control line may be permanently tied to 0 V, and each CLOCK pulse then performs a load. No doubt because of the popularity of such a versatile device, it is generally more commonly available than the octal D-type bistable (74273 – App. D1), and as a result, is usually quite a lot cheaper.*

This latter point once again reinforces the need for the designer to take device cost into account; for the most complex device is not always the most expensive. The Appendix to be found at the rear of this book incorporates a *cost factor* to allow the user to take cost into account. Since costs are always varying, actual costs are not given; the cost factor shows relative costs, normalised to a value of 1.0 for the most basic device of them all: the 7400 quad NAND gate.

* *Even the more versatile 74198 (bidirectional) is seldom more expensive.*

8

Number systems and binary arithmetic

The point has now been reached where an appreciation of the various number systems employed in digital electronics makes forthcoming chapters easier to follow. The base or *radix* of a chosen number system comes about through some particular convenience. Doubtless human beings prefer the decimal system – based upon a radix of 10 – because they began by counting on their fingers. Indeed, they still do! A radix of 10 gives 10 different states. Since digital systems are based upon circuitry having only 2 different states, *binary arithmetic* is employed because this has a radix of 2.

Large numbers in the binary system become unwieldy in length, and whilst this presents no problems to the electronics of a system, it does present problems at the human interface. Because of this there are various other number systems in use which conveniently interface with the binary system. These systems express numbers in a more convenient and shorter form, e.g. *octal*, *binary coded decimal*, and *hexadecimal*. These systems are discussed in the present chapter.

The latter part of the chapter outlines binary arithmetic, but only in sufficient detail for the reader to understand the principles involved. For practical purposes it is not necessary to design complicated circuits to perform binary arithmetic. This would require endless gates and would be quite uneconomical. The majority of everyday digital applications do not require binary arithmetic, and those that do can employ arithmetic devices to carry out all the 'number crunching' requirements. If an application calls for considerable mathematics, it is probably best suited to a microprocessor.

Binary system

As earlier chapters have shown, the binary system utilises '0' (nought) and '1' (one) to represent the two stable states. Binary counting is therefore as follows:

Decimal	Binary
0	0
1	1
2	10
3	11
4	100
5	101
6	110
7	111
8	1000
9	1001
10	1010

No matter what the radix of a number system might be, the procedure is identical. The count starts at zero, proceeds through the available digits until all have been used, then introduces a new digit *of higher significance*, starting with the lowest *significant* digit available, then repeating all available lower digits in the count as before. Each time they run out, the higher significant digit is incremented up to the limit, whereupon yet another digit of higher significance is required. Zeros placed to the left of a number in any number system are said to be non-significant, since they do not alter the value of the number. This is why '1' is the first *significant* digit used where a new digit is required.

The decimal system therefore starts at 0, counts through all available digits to 9, then introduces a 1 in the next place of significance, and repeats the count 0 to 9 preceded by the 1. After 19 we have 20, and so the process continues to 99, whereupon we must introduce a digit of higher significance to give us 100. We have names for the 'weightings' of digits in their various places of significance (e.g. tens, hundreds, thousands), but other number systems need not employ names.

The preceding comparison of decimal and binary counting shows that the same procedure is employed. The binary system reaches its limit at a count of 1 and has to introduce a digit of higher significance for the next count of 10; *do not call this ten*, for *ten* is a number in the *decimal* system. The number '10' in the binary system is expressed as 'one-nought'.

Because binary arithmetic is carried out by electronics which calls for a separate stage to be available for each digit in a number, such systems must allow for the maximum number of stages required. These stages are more correctly known as *bits*. Thus a particular system might employ 8 bits, giving the maximum binary capability of 11111111. In such a system it is normal practice to add non-significant zeros to the front of lower numbers, thus the binary equivalent of the decimal number 2 would be expressed as 00000010.

There are many different methods employed on converting between decimal and alternative number systems, but to avoid confusion, this chapter employs the same basic procedure. The procedure chosen is more directly representative of their true form than other procedures, and is also particularly suitable for calculator conversions. Since calculators are so widely available today, it is considered a reasonable assumption that anyone needing to make many number system conversions will have such a facility available.

Conversions to or from the decimal system are greatly assisted by ruling columns on a piece of paper, and heading each column with the decimal *weighting* of the number system in question. This weighting is always the radix to the power of increasing numbers in the decimal system, i.e. 2^0, 2^1, 2^2, 2^3, 2^4 for the binary system. The table given below illustrates this point, and shows various binary numbers with their decimal equivalents.

2^{11}	2^{10}	2^9	2^8	2^7	2^6	2^5	2^4	2^3	2^2	2^1	2^0	Binary
2K	1K	½K	¼K									Decimal
2048	1024	512	256	128	64	32	16	8	4	2	1	
							1	0	0	0	0	16
							1	0	0	0	1	17
							1	0	1	0	0	20
			1	0	0	0	0	0	0	0	0	256
			1	0	0	0	1	0	0	1	0	274
			1	1	1	1	1	1	1	1	1	511
		1	0	0	0	0	0	0	0	0	0	512
	1	0	0	0	0	0	0	0	0	0	1	1025
1	0	0	1	0	0	0	0	0	0	0	0	2304

Examination of the table shows that conversion from binary to decimal is simply achieved by adding together the decimal weightings of each true (i.e. '1') binary bit. Thus the decimal equivalent of the second entry in the table is derived by adding together $16 + 1 = 17$. Similarly, decimal 274 is achieved by adding $256 + 16 + 2$. Obviously this is a very simple procedure for any number using a calculator. If one is to hand, try adding all the necessary bits to give decimal 511.

In order to convert a decimal number into binary, the following procedure is equally simple with a calculator to hand. Enter the decimal number (e.g. 274), deduct the highest weighting lower than this number placing a 1 in the appropriate column, (e.g. place '1' in 256 column and deduct 256 giving 18), then repeat until zero is reached (e.g. place '1' in the 16 column and deduct 16 giving 2, then place '1' in the 2 column and deduct 2, giving 0).

A shorthand notation is employed for large numbers, where the value 1024 is known as '1K'. Thus 2048 is called '2K', etc. Because all digital devices are based upon the binary system, all tend to have number associations with the binary relationships illustrated above, and memory capacity for example, is quoted as having 1K bits (i.e. 1024 bits).

Since digital systems operate with a fixed number of available bits – this bearing a direct relationship to the provision the designer cares to make – a particular system with eight bits is said to utilise 8-bit *words*. Perhaps 16 bits might be required for a particular application, but only 8 bits are catered for in the hardware. In such a case, the 16-word may be divided into two 8-bit *bytes* (think of *bites* of the cherry!). Most popular microprocessors have the ability to address 64K words (or bytes) of store, which needs 16 address bits, as will be seen from the following table.

Binary weighting	Bit number
1	0
2	1
4	2
8	3
16	4
32	5
64	6
128	7
256	8
512	9
1K	10
2K	11
4K	12
8K	13
16K	14
32K	15

Octal system

The octal system has a radix of 8. The octal count is as follows: 0, 1, 2, 3, 4, 5, 6, 7, 10, 11, 12, 13, 14, 15, 16, 17, 20, etc., employing eight digits. It now becomes clear that if there is any doubt about which number system a particular number is based upon, it is necessary to define the radix. The convention employed is to place the radix as a subscript after the number. Thus 275_{10} is a decimal number, but 275_8 is an octal number.

A table is constructed opposite for decimal-octal conversions. To perform these, a memory calculator is ideal. For example, to convert 275_8 to its decimal equivalent, proceed as follows: enter

$2 \times 64 = 128$, then place this sub-total in memory (press $M+$); enter $7 \times 8 = 56$ and add this to the sub-total (press $M+$); enter 5 and add this to the sub-total (press $M+$); the answer 189_{10} is then obtained as the total from memory (press MR).

8^4 4096	8^3 512	8^2 64	8^1 8	8^0 1	Octal / Decimal
		2	7	5	189
			1	0	8
			1	2	10
	7	6	4	0	4000
1	0	0	2	0	4112
	7	7	7	7	4095

To convert from octal to decimal, it is necessary to establish how many times the highest multiple of the next highest weighting goes into the number in question at each stage. For example, to convert 4000 decimal to octal, the first step is to take the next highest weighting below 4000, i.e. 512, and establish how many times this goes into 4000. Using a memory calculator, enter 4000, place this in memory (by pressing $M+$), then divide 4000 by 512, obtaining 7.8125; the decimal portion is irrelevant. Enter 7 in the appropriate column, then multiply 7 by the weighting figure of 512, obtaining 3584; deduct this from the memory (press $M-$); recall the memory total (press MR) to obtain 416, the next number to be converted. Divide by 64 as the next highest weighting, obtaining 6.5. Place 6 in the appropriate column, then multiply 6 by 64 to obtain 384. Deduct this from memory ($M-$), then examine the new total (MR) of 32. Divide by the next highest weighting of 8 to obtain 4.0. Since no decimal portion remains, this finishes the calculation, and 4 is entered in the appropriate column. This gives the octal conversion of 7640 (noughts are significant at the lower end).

Binary to octal conversion could not be easier. Simply group the binary word into 3-bit groups from the decimal point* and convert each group into the corresponding octal digit by inspection, remembering the weightings are 4, 2, 1. Two examples are given below.

421	421	421	421	binary weightings

101	111	010	011	in binary represents 5723 octal
	001	110	000	in binary represents 160 octal

* *The decimal point may be assumed after the least significant digit.*

Binary coded decimal

Binary coded decimal (BCD) is a notation employed as a means of easily converting from the decimal system to a number system which can be simply converted to binary by electronic means; it provides an appropriate man-machine interface. It uses the principle just discussed, involving converting digit by digit, but because the decimal system has ten different states, *four* binary digits are required to specify each BCD digit (leaving 6 redundant binary states). Two 12-bit binary words are shown below with their BCD equivalents; note the grouping of the binary word into 4-bit *bytes*.

8421	8421	8421	binary weightings
1000	0010	0000	in BCD represents 820 decimal
1001	0110	0111	in BCD represents 967 decimal

As the name suggests, this form is decimal coded in binary form. Digital devices are available which accept BCD codes, therefore this is a very useful way of interfacing decimal to binary forms; it could not be much simpler!

Hexadecimal system

The *hexadecimal* system is widely used today because of its convenience when associated with microprocessors, which predominantly utilise 8-bit words. As previously mentioned, addressing frequently requires 16 bits, and this can be readily expressed as four *hex* digits. Since 16-bit addresses are generally divided into two 8-bit bytes, the address breaks down into two pairs of hex digits. Operator error could be high if many 16-bit binary numbers had to be manipulated, therefore the hex notation is of great assistance in minimising this problem. The hexadecimal system has a radix of 16.

At first sight this may sound daunting, especially when it is considered that we are only familiar with ten digits! The hexadecimal system introduces letters above 9, thus the hex count goes as follows: 0, 1, 2, 3, 4, 5, 6, 7, 8, 9, A, B, C, D, E, F, 10, 11 . . . 19, 1A, 1B . . . 1F, 20 . . . 9F, A0, A1 . . . FF, 100, etc.. The extra digits give us shorter representations of larger numbers.

It was seen that 4 bits were used in order to convert decimal to BCD. Since the highest BCD code is 1001 (because 9 is the highest decimal digit), this wastes possible binary combinations that follow, i.e. 1010, 1011, 1100, 1101, 1110, 1111. These six wasted codes are fully utilised in the hexadecimal system. The table below gives the letter conventionally used to represent these additional states.

Decimal	Hexadecimal	Binary
0	0	0000
1	1	0001
2	2	0010
3	3	0011
4	4	0100
5	5	0101
6	6	0110
7	7	0111
8	8	1000
9	9	1001
10	A	1010
11	B	1011
12	C	1100
13	D	1101
14	E	1110
15	F	1111

If a binary number is written down and then divided by vertical lines into 4-bit bytes, each byte can be separately converted into the appropriate hex digit, utilising the table above. Two examples are given below.

$$1100 \mid 1101 \mid 0111 \leftarrow \text{Binary} \rightarrow 1110 \mid 0101 \mid 1010 \mid 0000$$
$$\;\;\;C \;\;\;\mid\;\; D \;\;\;\mid\;\; 7 \;\;\; \leftarrow \text{Hex} \rightarrow \;\; E \;\;\;\mid\;\; 5 \;\;\;\mid\;\; A \;\;\;\mid\;\; 0$$

Hexadecimal-decimal conversions can be achieved via binary (i.e. hex-binary-decimal), or by utilising the methods previously described. A suitable table is given below. In the conversions, which are identical in method to those described for octal conversions, the intermediate decimal numbers in the range 10-15 must be replaced by their hex letter equivalents.

16^3 4K 4096	16^2 ¼K 256	16^1 16	16^0 1	Hex / Decimal
1	0	0	2	4098
	2	1	E	542
	4	0	0	1024

The following table provides a much easier method of converting between decimal and hexadecimal (in either direction). The four main vertical columns indicate decimal weightings for each hex digit in its appropriate significance. To convert from hex to decimal, simply look up the decimal weighting of each hex digit and add the totals. This table should provide sufficient for most needs.

To convert from decimal to hex, find the number equal to or next lowest to the number in the table and take this as the most significant hex digit. Deduct this weighting from the number and then repeat the process for each remaining hex digit. Again the calculator can be used to good effect. For example, to convert 542 decimal to hex, take 512 from the table, giving 2 as the third significant digit; $542 - 512 = 30$. Locate 16 in the table, giving 1 as the second significant hex digit; $30 - 16 = 14$. Locate 14 in the table, giving E as the first significant digit. Thus $542_{10} = 21E_{16}$. The letter 'X' is sometimes written before a hex number as an alternative form of identification. Thus $21E_{16}$ could also be written as X21E (or X'21E).

Hex digit	Decimal weightings			
	4th	3rd	2nd	1st
0	0	0	0	0
1	4096	256	16	1
2	8192	512	32	2
3	12288	768	48	3
4	16384	1024	64	4
5	20480	1280	80	5
6	24576	1536	96	6
7	28672	1792	112	7
8	32768	2048	128	8
9	36864	2304	144	9
A	40960	2560	160	10
B	45056	2816	176	11
C	49152	3072	192	12
D	53248	3328	208	13
E	57344	3584	224	14
F	61440	3840	240	15

The importance of understanding the hexadecimal notation will be better appreciated when Part 3 of this book is reached, and microprocessor systems are discussed. The following table is added with this in mind, for it shows how the hex system easily relates to decimal numbers expressed as 'K' multiples. Note that the two most significant hex digits express the 'K' value in terms of ¼K and 4K weightings, respectively. Intermediate values are easily obtained; for example, adding 4_{16} (i.e. X4 or hex 4) to the third hex digit, adds decimal 1K.

Decimal	Hex	Decimal	Hex	Decimal	Hex
¼K	0 1 0 0	2¾	0 B 0 0	7K	1 C 0 0
½K	0 2 0 0	3K	0 C 0 0	8K	2 0 0 0
¾K	0 3 0 0	3¼K	0 D 0 0	10K	2 8 0 0
1K	0 4 0 0	3½K	0 E 0 0	32K	8 0 0 0
1½K	0 6 0 0	3¾K	0 F 0 0	36K	9 0 0 0
2K	0 8 0 0	4K	1 0 0 0	40K	A 0 0 0
2¼K	0 9 0 0	5K	1 4 0 0	60K	F 0 0 0
2½K	0 A 0 0	6K	1 8 0 0	64K-1	F F F F

Sixteen binary bits provide a count of 64K (i.e. 65536). The highest binary number in this range (1111111111111111) is expressed as FFFF in hex, and is equivalent to decimal 65535 (i.e. 64K-1, as shown in the table above; allowing for the extra count of 0000, this gives a total of 64K numbers).

Alternative methods of conversion

The method of conversion demonstrated in this chapter has been chosen because it emphasises the principle of *weighting factors*, and thereby instills in the newcomer the significance of different bases. Many other methods are used for converting between different number systems, and the following two examples of octal-decimal and decimal-octal conversion show a much more efficient method, also applicable to other base conversions.

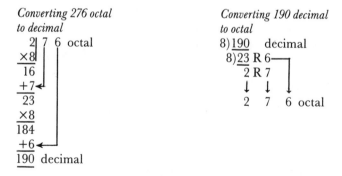

Converting 276 octal to decimal

Converting 190 decimal to octal

These methods utilise the arithmetic *significance* of the radix in order to avoid the use of multiples of the radix. In the octal-decimal conversion, the *larger-based* decimal number is obtained by starting at the most significant digit, *multiplying* it by the octal radix (i.e. ×8), then adding in the next lowest octal digit, before repeating. The decimal-octal conversion obtains the *lower-based* octal number by *dividing* the decimal number by the octal radix as many times as it will go. The final dividend followed by the remainders from the previous stages gives the octal number.

Note that a very simple way of converting a large binary number to a decimal number is to firstly convert it to octal (by the method of grouping the binary number into 3-bit bytes – page 67), and to then convert it by the *explosion method* described above (i.e. repeated stages of multiplication by 8).

Methods such as these are simple to undertake, but the conversion soon becomes a mathematical exercise, and the reason for performing the various mathematical manipulations is easily lost: hence the more laborious, but more basic method described previously.

Binary arithmetic

The foregoing part of this chapter has dealt only with whole numbers, and the majority of design work should only require such numbers. For the sake of completeness, *binary fractions* should be mentioned. Apart from the different radix, binary fractions take exactly the same form as decimal fractions. For example, the decimal fraction 0.542 is really a shorthand form for:

$$(5 \times 10^{-1}) + (4 \times 10^{-2}) + (2 \times 10^{-3}) = \frac{5}{10} + \frac{4}{100} + \frac{2}{1000}$$

$$= \frac{500}{1000} + \frac{40}{1000} + \frac{2}{1000} = \frac{542}{1000}$$

A binary fraction is similarly computed, using powers of two instead of powers of ten. For example, the binary fraction 0.1001 is a shorthand form for:

$$(1 \times 2^{-1}) + (0 \times 2^{-2}) + (0 \times 2^{-3}) + (1 \times 2^{-4})$$

$$= \frac{1}{2} + \frac{0}{4} + \frac{0}{8} + \frac{1}{16} = \frac{9}{16} \text{ (as the decimal equivalent)}.$$

Binary addition is carried out in the same manner as with the more familiar decimal system, except that a carry results after $1 + 1$. The example given below shows binary addition. To prove that it is correct, the decimal equivalents are given alongside.

```
  1 1 0 0 1 (25₁₀)
 +0 1 1 1 1 (15₁₀)
 ─────────
 1 0 1 0 0 0 (40₁₀)
 ─────────
  1 1 1 1 1  ← carry (shifted to next significance).
```

If two binary digits A and B are to be added, the truth table given in Figure 8.1 gives the *sum* and *carry* requirements. Comparison with Figure 3.3* shows that the sum is identical to an exclusive-OR function, and the carry is identical to an AND function. Thus an XOR gate and an AND gate constitute what is known as a *half adder*, when connected as shown in the figure.

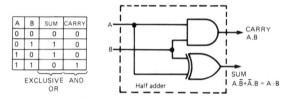

Figure 8.1. A truth table for binary addition, together with a half adder circuit

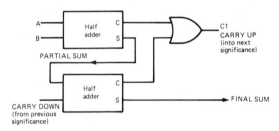

Figure 8.2. A full adder circuit

This circuit is called a *half* adder, because it only copes with 'half' the problem. A practical adder has to allow for any carry from a preceding stage, and in order to do this, two half adders are needed. This gives the *full adder* shown in Figure 8.2. The CARRY UP to the next higher significance is a simple OR of the carries from the two half adders. The PARTIAL SUM from the first half adder is added to any CARRY DOWN resulting from the next lower significant stage, and the result is the FINAL SUM.

Binary subtraction is just like decimal subtraction, except for the radix difference. Our preference for the decimal system does make it more confusing, but this hardly matters in view of the fact that digital circuitry generally carries out subtraction by a method *complementation*. In order to do this, the maximum range of the numbers to be handled must be known. To take a decimal example of complementation, take 1000 as the maximum range, and let us

* *See page 17.*

deduct 729 from 894. This sum can be performed by *adding* what is termed the *ten's complement* of 729 to 894, then deducting the maximum count if the result 'spills over'. The sum thus becomes:

$$894 - 729 = 894 + (1000 - 729) - 1000$$
$$= 894 + 271 - 1000 \qquad \text{OR}$$
$$= 1165 - 1000$$
$$= 165$$

$$\begin{array}{r} 894 \\ +271 \\ \hline 1\!165 \end{array}$$

delete spill-over

This may seem a long way round the problem in view of the fact that 729 will still have to be deducted from *something*. In binary arithmetic, it is a simple matter to obtain the *two's complement* of a number, therefore it is a much more practical proposition.

The two's complement of a binary number is obtained by copying the number from the least significant bit *up to and including the first '1'*, thereafter complementing (or reversing) all subsequent more significant bits. Alternatively, reverse each bit and then add 1.

The 2's complement of 010001 (i.e. 17_{10}) is thus 101111, and the binary form of the decimal sum $25 - 17$ can be worked by complementation as follows:

$$\begin{array}{l} 0\ 1\ 1\ 0\ 0\ 1\ (25_{10}) \\ +\ 1\ 0\ 1\ 1\ 1\ 1\ (\text{2's complement of } 17_{10}) \\ \hline 1\ 0\ 0\ 1\ 0\ 0\ 0\ (8_{10}). \end{array}$$

In the above sum, a non-significant zero is added in front of the upper number to make it the same length as the lower number; the spill-over 1 is discarded, leaving the total 1000 (equivalent to decimal 8).

The signs $+$ and $-$ cannot be represented as such in electronic terms, therefore the most significant bit is used to indicate the sign, where '0' represents positive and '1' represents negative; the upper bit in such cases is known as the *sign bit*. In 2's complement, the sign bit actually has numerical significance. For example, if 8-bit words are taken, and the above sum is repeated, the following is obtained, where the most significant bit is the sign bit:

Spill-over	128	64	32	16	8	4	2	1	(decimal weighting)
deleted	0	0	0	1	1	0	0	1	(decimal 25)
	1	1	1	0	1	1	1	1	(2's complement of 17)
1	0	0	0	0	1	0	0	0	(decimal +8)

Sign bits ————— | Binary numbers

The numerical significance of the 2's complement number can be observed above, for the decimal representation is: -128 (sign bit) $+111 = -17$. Those readers familiar with logarithms will see a certain familiarity of form.

If a negative sign bit results, the answer needs to be complemented to give it in a normal binary form, which should be preceded by a minus sign. The following simple example uses five numeric bits plus a sign bit:

Decimal		Binary	
10		0 | 0 1 0 1 0	
-18		1 | 0 1 1 1 0	(2's complement of 10010)
-8		1 | 1 1 0 0 0	(answer)
	Sign bits___↑	⌐0 1 0 0 0	(2's complement of answer)

Binary multiplication is simple, as the following example shows. The multiplicand is written down for each 1 in the multiplier, placing it in the same significance. This is a simple matter for arithmetic devices, employing the shift register principle.

multiplicand	1 0 1 1 0	(22_{10})
multiplier	×1 0 1	(5_{10})
line 1	1 0 1 1 0	(multiplicand – zero shift)
line 2	1 0 1 1 0 ←	(multiplicand – shifted 2 places)
answer	1 1 0 1 1 1 0	(110_{10})

Binary division is equally simple, as the following long division shows. This example divides the result of the previous example (decimal equivalent 110) by the previous multiplier (decimal equivalent 5), to obtain the original multiplicand (decimal equivalent 22). As each digit of the dividend is brought down, the quotient is entered with a 0 if the divisor cannot be subtracted, or with a 1 if it can be subtracted – far simpler than decimal long division!

```
                  0 0 1 0 1 1 0   quotient
  divisor   1 0 1) 1 1 0 1 1 1 0   dividend
                  1 0 1
                      1 1 1
                      1 0 1
                          1 0 1
                          1 0 1
                              0 0
```

Once again, the calculation makes use of a shift function, this time with the divisor. Thus all binary arithmetic can be performed by the processes of adding, shifting and subtracting, and subtracting itself can be converted to a process of complementing and adding. How such calculations are achieved is of little more than academic interest in practice, because all such calculations are performed by special arithmetic devices, or directly by a microprocessor or computer.

It is only practical to undertake fairly simple or repetitive calculations without a microprocessor, bearing in mind modern prices. Arithmetic devices are available when required, and these are the subject of the following chapter.

9
Arithmetic devices

A range of devices is available for performing binary arithmetic functions*. Their usefulness and cost-effectiveness is thrown into some doubt these days due to the low cost and availability of the microprocessor. They will always have a place where the arithmetic requirement is very simple or basic, or where a simple arithmetic procedure is a small part of a much more complex function best performed by discrete hardware. Complicated arithmetic calls for complicated circuits, and it is in these circumstances that the designer should really consider whether a microprocessor might be the better solution. For these reasons, and because of the fact that only a really experienced designer should tackle a design using arithmetic devices, this chapter takes only a brief look at the kind of devices available for the sake of completeness.

Full adders

The full adder was introduced in the previous chapter, but this considered only one bit, mentioning that there may be adjoining bits of lower and higher significance to consider in a practical case. The 7482 device is a 2-bit binary full adder, as shown in Figure 9.1. Examination of the function table shows how this device performs binary addition on two bits, where A1 and B1 are the least significant, and A2 and B2 are the most significant. For example, the second and third lines of the table show that with zeros in the second bit, a logic 1 (H) at either A1 or B1 produces a logic 1 at the sum output from this stage ($\Sigma1$); the fourth line of the table shows that a logic 1 at both A1 and B1 produces a carry, which becomes a logic 1 in the second stage, etc.

One of the problems when dealing with the addition of large binary numbers is that a carry may have to propagate through a lot

* Or 'number-crunching' in engineers' parlance.

Function table

Inputs				Outputs					
				When CO=1			When CO =H		
A1	B1	A2	B2	Σ1	Σ2	C2	Σ1	Σ2	C2
L	L	L	L	L	L	L	H	L	L
H	L	L	L	H	L	L	L	H	L
L	H	L	L	H	L	L	L	H	L
H	H	L	L	L	H	L	H	H	L
L	L	H	L	L	H	L	H	H	L
H	L	H	L	H	H	L	L	L	H
L	H	H	L	H	H	L	L	L	H
H	H	H	L	L	L	H	H	L	H
L	L	L	H	L	H	L	H	H	L
H	L	L	H	H	H	L	L	L	H
L	H	L	H	H	H	L	L	L	H
H	H	L	H	L	L	H	H	L	H
L	L	H	H	L	L	H	H	L	H
H	L	H	H	H	L	H	L	H	H
L	H	H	H	H	L	H	L	H	H
H	H	H	H	L	H	H	H	H	H

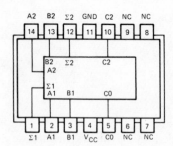

Figure 9.1. The 7482 2-bit binary full adder

of bits in the calculation, and this may cause considerable delay. For example, consider the following addition:

$$
\begin{array}{r}
1\,0\,1\,0\,1\,0\,1\,0\,1 \\
+\,0\,1\,0\,1\,0\,1\,0\,1\,1 \\
\hline
1\,1\,1\,1\,1\,1\,1\,1\,1 \\
1 \\
1\,0\,0\,0\,0\,0\,0\,0\,0\,0
\end{array}
$$

immediate sum
carry from immediate sum
final answer after carry propagation.

A method of minimising propagation delay in parallel addition utilises a technique known as *look-ahead carry*. This involves forming the carry from each bit position independently of the addition process. A carry-up is generated from each adder stage if one of three conditions is satisfied:

a. $An.Bn$ – both inputs of stage 'n' are 1's.
b. $An.Co$ – the A input and the carry-down are 1's.
c. $Bn.Co$ – the B input and the carry-down are 1's.

Low speed requirements or low bit-count numbers can often utilise simple full adder circuits without look-ahead carry, because propagation does not take long over a short word. Longer words usually utilise look-ahead carry, and this feature is normally built into 4-bit or greater capacity adder chips.

The 74283 is a 4-bit binary full adder with full look-ahead carry, generating the carry term in a mere 10 nanoseconds (10^{-8} s). Similar

78

devices are available for other single function arithmetic requirements (e.g. the 74285 4-bit × 4-bit multiplier), but where there is the requirement for more flexibility, the *accumulator* or *arithmetic logic unit* (ALU) is more versatile.

Arithmetic logic units

Figure 9.2 shows the 74S281 parallel binary accumulator. As may be seen, this incorporates a small ALU and a shift matrix. With the mode control (M) input low, this device performs one of eight arithmetic functions, as definea by an ALU function select code (ASO, AS1, AS2); with the mode control high, the device performs one from eight logic functions (e.g. AND, OR, XOR type functions). The shift register can be shifted in either direction and is of great value in arithmetic or logic operations. The $\overline{P}$ and $\overline{G}$ outputs are used where the look-ahead carry facility is required.

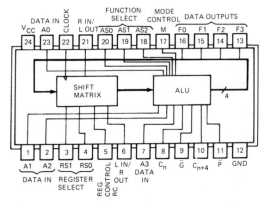

Figure 9.2. The 74S281 parallel binary accumulator

A more versatile ALU is the 74S181 arithmetic logic unit/function generator. This device performs 16 binary arithmetic operations on two 4-bit words as specified by four function select lines. Its many capabilities include addition, subtraction, decrement, and straight transfer as arithmetic functions, and AND, NAND, OR, NOR, XOR, and invert either input as logic functions.

Comparators

Comparators are arithmetic devices which are more generally useful, and can find useful applications in circuits which are not really concerned with binary arithmetic. Figure 9.3 depicts the 7485 4-bit magnitude comparator. This device compares two 4-bit words (A and B), and provides outputs indicating A > B, A < B and A = B with respect to the comparison of the binary values. Thus if A is

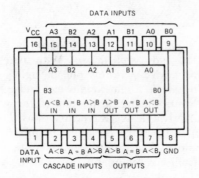

Figure 9.3. The 7485 4-bit magnitude comparator

1010, and B is 1000, the A>B output is high, and the other two outputs are low, since A (equivalent to decimal 10) is greater than B (equivalent to decimal 8). (See also App. H1.)

The modern alternative – the microprocessor

The microprocessor offers all these functions, plus the ability to perform involved calculations in binary arithmetic. The only disadvantage is that a microprocessor must be accompanied by memory devices for temporary data storage and program storage, and the user must devise appropriate software and load the memory with these instructions. The right choice depends both upon the application and the designer's familiarity with microprocessors; obtaining familiarity can be quite time consuming, but once attained, great versatility is opened up to him. More will be said in Part 3 of this book.

To conclude, it should be understood that arithmetic circuits are not the best proving ground for inexperienced designers, hence the lack of detail in this chapter.

10

Counters

Logic elements with two stable states are known as *bistables*. They are also often referred to as *flip-flops*, for one clock pulse causes them firstly to 'flip' to one state, and a subsequent clock pulse causes them to 'flop' back again. Chapter 7 discussed how a string of flip-flops can be connected to form a shift register. This chapter discusses connecting a string of flip-flops to form a *counter* or *divider*.

Asynchronous counters

Any kind of flip-flops can be used to produce counters/dividers, but D-types are best avoided because they require additional gating in order to make them toggle in the requisite manner. The J-K flip-flop is ideal, because it can be made to toggle or not upon receipt of clock pulses by simply controlling the J-K inputs; with the J-K inputs high, the flip-flop toggles, but with them low, it remains unchanged.

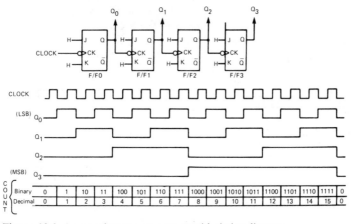

Figure 10.1. An asynchronous up-counter with timing diagram

Figure 10.1 shows a four-stage counter circuit employing four J-K bistables. The outputs along the chain are labelled Q_0, Q_1, Q_2 and Q_3, and these outputs produce a binary count, where Q_0 is the least significant bit (LSB), and Q_3 is the most significant bit (MSB). Master-slave J-K flip-flops may always be assumed throughout this book*, therefore clocking occurs on the *trailing* (or *negative*) edge of the clock pulse. All the J-K inputs are taken to a logic 1, represented by 'H' in the figure, i.e. they are taken high.

For simplicity, assume that all the flip-flops start in their reset state, i.e. $Q = _0$. The trailing edge of the first clock pulse clocks F/F0 to a logic 1. The trailing edge of the second clock pulse clocks F/F0 back to logic 0, and the action of Q_0 going from a high to a low clocks F/F1 to a logic 1. The trailing edge of the third clock pulse toggles F/F0 back to a 1, and the fourth clock pulse toggles F/F0 back to 0, Q_0 again toggling F/F1, this time back to a 0. The timing diagram depicts this quite clearly. If the waveforms are inspected, remembering that a low represents logic 0, and a high represents logic 1, the binary count can be determined as shown.

The more stages added, the greater the capacity of the counter. Clearly this goes up in multiples of two with respect to the number of stages. One flip-flop has two stable states, two flip-flops linked as a counter have four stable permutations, three flip-flops produce eight permutations, and the figure depicts a four-stage counter, thereby offering 16 different permutations. The timing diagram shows a complete cycle; it may be noted that after the count of binary 1111 (decimal 15), the counter reverts to zero. Because this counter counts *up*, it is known as an *up-counter*.

A counter is *also* a divider. The figure shows that two clock pulses are required to produce one pulse from the first stage (Q_0), four clock pulses to produce one pulse from the second stage (Q_1), eight clock pulses to produce one pulse from the third stage (Q_3), and 16 clock pulses to produce one pulse from the fourth stage (Q_4). Thus a

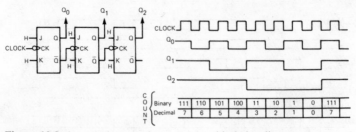

Figure 10.2. An asynchronous down-counter with timing diagram

* *Unless otherwise stated.*

chain of flip-flops connected in this manner can be used as a frequency divider; each stage divides the input clock frequency by two.

Figure 10.2 shows how a *down-counter* can be produced by clocking subsequent stages with the $\overline{Q}$ output instead of the Q output. In this case we consider the situation starting at maximum count (111 for a three-stage counter, or decimal 7). Since the inverted flip-flop outputs are used to do the clocking, these *fall* when their associated true (Q) output *rises*: hence Q_1 is seen to toggle in synchronism with the rising edge of Q_0, and similarly, Q_2 toggles when Q_1 is rising (remember that the Q and $\overline{Q}$ outputs of a flip-flop are *always* complementary). Once the limit of the counter has been reached – which is zero on count-down – the count repeats. In the example, the counter reverts to binary 111.

The maximum count of a binary counter is $2^n - 1$, where n represents the number of stages; the number of stable states is 2^n, since this includes the zero condition. A four-stage counter therefore has a maximum count of $2^4 - 1$, which equals 15. If a counter is required with a maximum count between the numbers offered by a binary progression, additional circuitry is required. This can be used to gate the J-K inputs, or more simply, to reset the counter. An up-counter needs to be *cleared*, whilst a down-counter needs to be *preset* to start the count.

Figure 10.3 shows how a decade counter can be produced by simple gating. A decade (or BCD) counter is required to have ten stable states; it therefore counts from 0000 to 1001 (i.e. 0 to 9 in

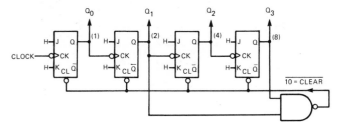

Figure 10.3. Resetting a counter at a particular count (e.g. a decade counter)

decimal equivalents). The NAND gate shown in the figure *decodes* the count of 1010 (decimal 10), and the output goes low to clear the counter back to zero. Such a counter counts up normally to 1001, momentarily reaches 1010, but immediately resets to 0000. Remember that the MSB of a counter is at the stage farthest away from the clock input.

The counters/dividers considered so far are said to be *asynchronous*, because the binary count does not change in synchronism with the input clock pulse. This is more easily seen if we expand the timing diagram for such a counter, as shown in Figure 10.4. This figure also includes a decoding gate at the count of 2_{10}, in order to show another phenomenon sometimes known as *glitch*.

The propagation delay of the 7476 J-K bistable, for example, can be as great as 40 ns between the trailing edge of the clock pulse and the change of outputs; this is represented by t_{p0} for F/F0 in Figure 10.4. It may be seen that F/F1 does not see a trailing clocking edge from Q_0 until the propagation delay t_{p0} has expired after the trailing edge of the input clock. Worse still, the similar propagation delay of F/F1, represented by t_{p1}, means that F/F1 does not reach its proper

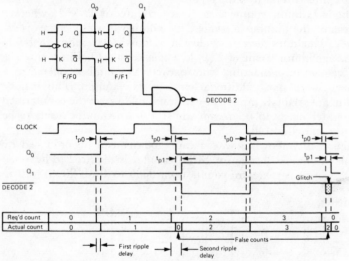

Figure 10.4. The ripple effect in an asynchronous counter, and decoding 'glitch'

binary value until a further delay has taken place. This is known as the *ripple effect*.

An asynchronous binary counter is rather like a stack of falling dominoes; a given domino cannot fall until all the preceding dominoes have fallen. This is so with an asynchronous counter. Beneath the timing diagram is shown the required (equivalent decimal) count and the actual count; it can be seen that propagation delays introduce false counts during the transitional period. The more stages there are in the counter, the longer this uncertain

84

transitional period becomes. It is for this reason that such counters are also known as *ripple counters*.

Whilst only talking about a mere 20ns delay for each stage, the effects can be unfortunate if the circuitry depends upon *decoding* the binary counter. A $\overline{\text{DECODE 2}}$ output in Figure 10.4 demonstrates this, for apart from decoding correctly, it sees a false 2 after the count of 3, during transition. This is sometimes referred to as *glitch* or *skew*. If this output was required to clock another bistable, for example, it would produce false clocking due to glitch.

One way of getting over the problem is to ensure that any following logic only takes notice of the ripple counter after it has had time to settle. The number of stages tells us the maximum settling time required for a given counter, and subsequent logic must therefore be *strobed* by a pulse generated *after* this settling time has expired. It is then known that no false count can be seen. The disadvantages of this are twofold: firstly it introduces what might be a significant time delay into the proceedings, and secondly, it is necessary to introduce circuitry to produce the required *strobe pulse*. All this can be avoided by the use of *synchronous counters*.

Asynchronous operation is not likely to concern the designer where only a frequency divider is required, and some applications may not be sensitive to decoding glitch. Asynchronous counters are usually simpler and cheaper than synchronous counters, therefore they do have their place in cost-effective design.

Synchronous counters

Returning briefly to the domino analogy, if we were able to strike all the dominoes simultaneously with a sideways blow by a ruler edge, all would topple in *synchronism*. The synchronous counter does

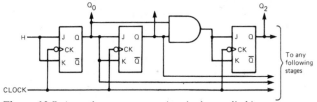

Figure 10.5. A synchronous counter (no ripple; no glitch)

likewise – by 'hitting' all the bistables simultaneously *with the same clock pulse*. Figure 10.5 depicts this, and comparison with Figure 7.2* shows that this is the same technique as that used with shift

* *See page 59.*

85

registers. It was explained in Chapter 7 that propagation delays can be nullified by synchronous clocking, and that a given bistable can be made to take on a condition set by another bistable also being synchronously clocked. This is the secret of the synchronous counter.

By connecting the J and K inputs of each bistable to the Q output of the preceding bistable, they are alternately allowed to toggle or remain unchanged, in sympathy with the common clock pulse. There is therefore no ripple effect, and hence no glitch with such a system. Decoders can be safely connected to the output from such counters without the fear of spurious decoding spikes.

Binary rate multiplier

The situation can arise where it is necessary to accurately divide a frequency down by something other than a power of two. It was shown how a counter can be reset at a given count by a decoder in Figure 10.3, but a more elegant way of achieving this is with a *binary rate multiplier*. Crystals are often used as frequency standards in digital equipment; by feeding the input of a crystal oscillator into a binary rate multiplier, it is possible to derive any desired lower frequency. Figure 10.6 shows a synchronous 6-bit binary rate multiplier (7497).

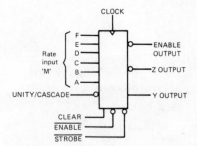

Figure 10.6. A synchronous 6-bit binary rate multiplier (7497)

This device is a 6-stage counter with special decoding logic on the outputs, which is gated with what is termed the *binary rate input*, or 'M' input. The input frequency is fed in as the CLOCK, and with the device enabled (CLEAR, STROBE and ENABLE inputs low), the output frequency at the Z OUTPUT is as follows:

$$F_{out} = \frac{M \cdot f_{in}}{64}$$

Six stages give the $\div 64$ factor, and the M input is a binary number input on lines A to F, where A is the least significant bit.

Another way of looking at it, is to say that for every 64 input pulses, the output produces the number of pulses programmed on the rate input. For example, if the rate input is binary 000101 (i.e. decimal 5), 64 CLOCK pulses produce 5 output pulses. The Y OUTPUT is simply a NAND of the Z OUTPUT and the UNITY/CASCADE input. Stages are cascaded by linking the ENABLE OUTPUT to the $\overline{\text{STROBE}}$ and $\overline{\text{ENABLE}}$ inputs of the following stage; the sub-multiple frequency outputs are then taken from the Y OUT-PUTs.

Other counter/dividers

There is a wide range of commercial devices for counting/dividing applications. Three useful counters are included on pages 276 and 277 of Appendix A.

The 74196 and 74197 are versatile four-stage ripple counters with three stages internally coupled and a fourth stage independently accessible; internal gating is included for reduced counts, and these devices allow for BCD counting or ÷ 2 and ÷ 5 (74196), and binary counting or ÷ 2 and ÷ 8 (74197); see also App. E1.

The 74163 is a synchronous 4-bit binary counter. It incorporates carry look-ahead circuitry enabling cascading, and a ripple carry output true during the count of 15. It features parallel load facilities for counting from a given start point, but can only operate as an up-counter. Preset and clear inputs are also provided, but their action is synchronous, and does not take place until the clocking edge; this device is clocked on the *rising* edge of the clock pulse due to an inverting buffer on the clock input line. The 74161 is a similar device, but has asynchronous clear, i.e. it is cleared immediately the clear input is activated. Partners to the above counters are the 74162 synchronous decade counter with synchronous clear, and the 74160 synchronous decade counter with asynchronous clear. See App. E2 for further details.

More versatile is the 74191 up/down synchronous counter, the count direction being controlled by a DOWN/$\overline{\text{UP}}$ input. This counter is fully programmable to any desired count via an asynchronous LOAD input. Like the previously mentioned counters, inverter buffering on the clock input means that transition occurs on the rising edge of the clock pulse. The 74190 is a companion device for decade counting. See App. E3 for further details.

Counters have many applications, as will be seen in Part 2 of this book. They are frequently used in conjunction with visual displays, hence the need for intermediate *display drivers*. These are dealt with in the following chapter.

11
Displays and display drivers

The majority of logic circuits require some form of visual display in order to indicate certain conditions. The *light emitting diode*, or LED, is probably the most convenient, because of its particular compatibility with logic devices. LEDs are available in a wide variety of forms from single lamps to alphanumeric displays. This chapter discusses how such devices may be interfaced, the types available, and the alternatives of tungsten bulbs, gas discharge tubes, and *liquid crystal displays* (LCD). Finally the technique of *multiplexing* is introduced as a method of conserving power, and minimising circuitry.

Light emitting diodes

Light emitting diodes – normally known simply as 'LEDs' – are manufactured from semiconducting material such as gallium phosphide. They are specially constructed diodes designed to give efficient recombination of carriers, which gives rise to the emission of visible light. They are available in red, high efficiency red, green, and yellow. Red is the easiest to manufacture and the most efficient, therefore red devices are more common and the least expensive.

Light emitting diodes are operated in their forward biased condition at currents normally lying in the range 1 mA to 40 mA; most produce a bright light at about 20 mA, with usable light levels down to the lower end of the range; the specific operational conditions must be considered, for operation in high ambient light levels calls for higher operating currents, and hence a greater visible output.

Figure 11.1 shows an LED in series with a current limiting resistor R_L. This resistor must be chosen to give a suitable diode bias current when connected to a given supply voltage. The potential difference across the forward-biased diode is in the range 1.5 V to 2.0 V. Figure 11.2 shows how a TTL gate may be used to drive an LED directly. An ordinary TTL gate can sink 16 mA, which is

88

Figure 11.1. LED with current limiting resistor

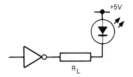

Figure 11.2. LED driven from a TTL output at a low level

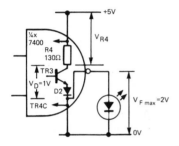

Figure 11.3. LED driven directly from a TTL output at high level (7400 shown – suitability depends upon type)

adequate for many LEDs, but a device such as the 7407 buffer is capable of sinking up to 40 mA where higher drives are required. It is necessary to consider the maximum possible LED current, obtained with V_F at a minimum, in order to determine whether any fanout can be achieved from a particular driver; as a general rule of thumb, unless LEDs are operated at under 10 mA, it is probably safest to reserve each driver gate for a single LED.

One method used for driving LEDs is illustrated in Figure 11.3. This makes use of the internal circuitry of a TTL gate such as the 7400, which includes a 130 Ω resistor as the collector load for the upper transistor of the totem-pole output stage*. Taking the maximum voltage drop across the LED (V_{Fmax}) as 2 V, and allowing for a further 1 V dropped across the TTL series diode (D2) and bottomed transistor (TR3), this leaves 3 V to be dropped across the 130 Ω resistor, thereby defining a current of around 15 mA. Even in the case where the V_F is only 1.5 V, this still only gives a maximum current of about 19 mA. Thus the LED drive range *can* be obtained in this manner without the need for any external components.

Whilst the above method is frequently used, *it cannot be recommended as good design practice,* as a simple calculation and reference back to Chapter 2 will show. A TTL output is designed to have a maximum high level output current (I_{OH}) of *only* 400 µA, far below the LED

* *Compare with Figure 2.3.*

drive current. At the maximum drive current of 19 mA, with 3.5 V dropped by the series components within the gate, nearly 70 mW are dissipated within the device, nearly 50 mW of which are dissipated within the resistor R4. When it is considered that the entire package does not usually dissipate more than 80 mW under the most adverse conditions, with this spread across four similar gates, this should be enough to make the designer cringe: certainly the manufacturer would! Clearly the limiting resistor is not designed to withstand continued dissipation of this order. It is therefore advised to completely avoid this method of driving LEDs, for any design which causes components to work outside their intended operating range is simply bad design practice.

One possible circumstance where this method of driving might be considered reasonably acceptable is where the LED is simply used as a fault or test indicator. The TTL-LED compatibility makes this an ideal method of indicating predictable fault conditions, and provides a service engineer with an easy guide to fault finding. On the assumption that such conditions do not normally exist, this is not placing any undue stress upon components, and does save a resistor.

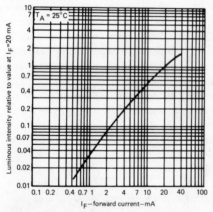

Figure 11.4. Relative luminous intensity of TIL209 LED vs I_F (courtesy of Texas Instruments)

The graph given in Figure 11.4 shows how luminous intensity varies with diode forward current, relative to the ideal drive of 20 mA. This curve is for the Texas Instruments TIL209 red LED, but is fairly representative of most similar devices. It may be seen that luminous intensity drops to lower than 1/10 of its value at 20 mA when the bias current is reduced to 2 mA.

90

Driving tungsten lamps

If there is a requirement to drive tungsten lamps, or other high current devices, it is necessary to buffer the TTL output such that the output current is within normal ratings.

An NPN transistor provides an ideal way to achieve this buffering. There are two possible methods of driving the base: either from the gate at a high level output, or via a base resistor. The former method is limited by the factor previously discussed, i.e. the preferred limit of 0.4 mA. Since bottomed transistors have relatively low current gain – say 20 – this only gives a drive capability at the transistor collector of say 8 mA, unless the gate is overdriven. The best solution is to bias the transistor base via a resistor, as shown in Figure 11.5, and to drive the base with an open-collector TTL gate. With this circuit, the lamp is driven on when the gate output is 'high', i.e. when the gate presents an open-circuit; when the gate output is low, all the current flowing through bias resistor R_B is

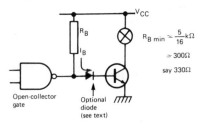

$$R_{B\,min} \simeq \frac{5}{16} k\Omega$$

$$\simeq 300\,\Omega$$

say 330 Ω

Figure 11.5. Driving a lamp (or other load) from TTL with a transistor driver

diverted to the TTL gate, cutting the transistor driver off. Since a normal gate can sink 16 mA, this allows R_B to be as low as 330 Ω. Thus R_B can drive the transistor base with nearly 16 mA of base current, and allowing for a bottomed current gain of only 10, this allows for loads of up to 160 mA. If lower drive currents are required, the resistor should be increased accordingly, thereby reducing the drive requirements of the TTL gate. R_B should be chosen as somewhat lower than that needed to ensure adequate base current for the drive requirement, whilst bearing in mind the lower limit of 330 Ω.

This circuit assumes a bulb, but the interface is equally suitable for any other load (e.g. a relay). It should be noted that the voltage at the TTL open-collector output never goes to a high level in this circuit: it is at about +0.7 V when the driver is on, or about +0.3 V when the driver is off. Thus fanout is not possible, as a logic 1 condition is never achieved. If it is required to ensure that the transistor is completely cut off when the gate output is low, a diode may be inserted in series with the transistor base; this ensures that the low output from the TTL gate is far below the voltage necessary to turn on the transistor.

Note also that this type of interface is ideal where a change in supply voltages is required. Whilst the base bias resistor must be connected to +5V for TTL compatibility, the transistor collector can be taken via its load to any positive potential within the transistor's rating.

Seven-segment displays

The seven-segment display is a common sight these days because of their widespread use in pocket calculators. Figure 11.6 shows such a display, with optional places for a decimal point. Each of the seven bar segments is actually a light emitting diode, therefore in order to display the shape of numerals, it is necessary to convert a BCD input into the appropriate seven drive lines. Such devices can be manufactured with common anodes or common cathodes, but they are generally more convenient to drive if they have common anodes – this allows low TTL outputs to drive individual segments, via a load resistor. Figure 11.7 shows a BCD to seven-segment decoder/driver chip which provides the necessary interface.

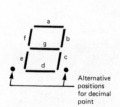

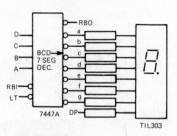

Figure 11.6. A seven-segment display (TIL302 has LH DP; TIL303 has RH DP) (courtesy of Texas Instruments)

Figure 11.7. A BCD to seven-segment display driver driving a display

Usual features of BCD to seven-segment decoders are *ripple-blanking* and *lamp test*. Ripple-blanking allows the designer to supp-ress leading zeros in a number, without affecting significant zeros. Thus a four digit display of the number '0040' can be converted to ' 40' by the use of ripple-blanking. Taking the ripple-blanking

92

input (RBI) low on the 7447A suppresses a zero display; a zero display at a given digit causes the ripple-blanking output (RBO) to go low. A multi-digit display simply requires linking of the RBO output from one digit to the RBI input of the next lower significant digit in order to suppress non-significant zeros – the RBI input of the most significant digit is taken to 0 V to suppress the first digit. If the RBI inputs are taken to a high level, no suppression occurs.

The lamp test input is taken low on the 7447A to test all the segments, i.e. all should be illuminated when LT is grounded. It is important to provide a lamp test feature on measuring equipment utilising seven-segment displays, for a segment failure could cause false readings.

Figure 11.8. Possible seven-segment displays using a display driver (7447A) (0–9 displays obtained from BCD input to driver; other symbols are optional)

Figure 11.8 shows the various displays available with the circuit shown in Figure 11.7. A straight BCD input provides appropriate numerals to be displayed, but the spare codes available can be used to display other unique symbols, as shown for codes 10–15 in the figure below. These might be of use for test purposes. Not all decoders provide these symbols for the spare codes, and variations occur between different manufacturers.

One of the limitations is that seven-segment displays do not lend themselves to the display of alphabetic characters, although surprisingly, ingenious use of the segments, with individual driving, can achieve all but eight of the alphabetics, if a mixture of upper and lower case is accepted, and perfect horizontal alignment is sacrificed. The following list illustrates the characters that can be displayed in this fashion, shown in either upper or lower case as appropriate; characters shown in upper case and enclosed by brackets cannot be adequately represented (except by means of a unique code): A b c d e F (G) h i j (K) L (M) n o P (Q) r S t u (V) (W) (X) y (Z). This might not be obvious at first, but a couple of examples might help. Illuminate segments b, g, e, d and c for the letter 'd'; illuminate segments f, e and g for the letter 't'. The letter 'y' appears in a raised position by illuminating segments f, g, b and c. (Refer to Figure 11.6 for segment letter coding.)

Seven-segment displays are not suitable for ordinary use where alphabetic characters are required, because of the lack of legibility, and the fact that the full range cannot be displayed. There are

93

applications where the amateur might find them of use, however, particularly in conjunction with microprocessors, which make it a relatively easy matter to drive segments individually from software bits, and provide a very cheap form of readout. With a little ingenuity, words with G, K, M, Q, V, W, X and Z can be avoided!

Dot-matrix displays

The dot-matrix display comprises a rectangular array of LED pinheads. By selecting which diodes in this matrix to illuminate, any desired symbol or alphabetic character can be represented. It is possible to obtain 4 × 7 displays, but more common – and more versatile and legible – is the 5 × 7 matrix. Figure 11.9 shows such a display with the letter 'S' illuminated. Note that the matrix format even allows curves to be simulated. (A display is much more legible than the illustration can represent.)

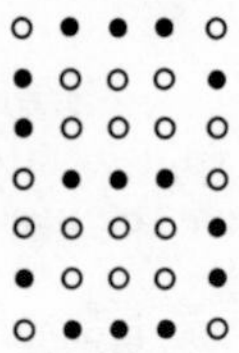

```
o  •  •  •  o
•  o  o  o  •
•  o  o  o  o
o  •  •  •  o
o  o  o  o  •
•  o  o  o  •
o  •  •  •  o
```

Figure 11.9. A 5 × 7 dot-matrix display, displaying the letter 'S'

Because there are 35 individual diodes to drive, decoding becomes much more complex than with the seven-segment displays. It is common practice for such devices to include an integral decoder and driver. The Hewlett Packard 5082-7391 is such a device designed for displaying hexadecimal characters (i.e. 0–9 and A–F) from a hex input.

In order to keep the number of pin connections down to a respectable level with such devices, alternative forms of input are used where a full character set is required. The HDSP-2000 device, for example, is a 4-character device in a DIL encapsulation, yet it has only 12 pins. This pin economy is achieved by incorporating integral 7-bit shift registers associated with each character row (7 rows), and common column strobes (5 columns). The individual shift registers are serially connected to form an effective 28-bit shift register. Data is clocked in via a serial input, and 28 clock pulses are required to enter the full data complement specifying the states of all the diodes in one row, of all the characters. Thus only one row in each character is actually illuminated at once, but fast switching – or *multiplexing* – means that this is not observed by the viewer. This process is repeated for each of the five columns, thus a complete refresh cycle constitutes 28 × 5 = 140 clock pulses; note that this is identical to the number of individual light emitting diodes (35 × 4).

Starburst displays

The *starburst* display is an excellent compromise between the limitations of the seven-segment display and the relative complexity of the dot-matrix. Figure 11.10 shows this arrangement. These devices add diagonal bars and a central vertical bar to the seven-segment arrangement, thereby making possible the construction of alphabetic characters including slanting lines; the illustration shows how the letter 'M' is displayed. The only limitation with this format is that certain characters are rather 'over-square'. The advantage is that decoding is not such a problem.

Figure 11.10. A 'starburst' display, displaying the letter 'M' (e.g. ¼ × DL–1416 memory/decoder/driver/LED or ¼ × 3970 LCD display)

The Litronix DL-1416 4-character display has a 16-segment fount and accepts a standard 7-bit input code known as ASCII* (American Standard Code for Information Interchange). This code is universally accepted and contains a full alphanumeric character set, plus symbols. Two address bits are used to select one from four characters, and a *write* pulse is then used to staticise the desired ASCII code for the selected character in an internal register. Internal decoding and driving then takes care of the rest: the desired character is displayed at the selected position. Because it is internally staticised, this character remains displayed when other characters are being written. Because a character remains for as long as required without *refreshing*, this is said to be a *static* display. (The 5 × 7 dot-matrix device described previously is said to be *dynamic* because it requires constant refreshing of input data.)

Such devices are not cheap when compared with seven-segment displays, but they do provide a reasonably cost-effective solution to a versatile form of readout for use with microprocessors.

* *See also Appendix D.*

Liquid crystal displays

Liquid crystal displays are dynamic devices which consume far less power than light emitting diode displays. Electrically they appear as series resistance and capacitance, as shown in the equivalent circuit of Figure 11.11(a). Because the actual display element is capacitive, there is no option but to drive these devices dynamically. Part (b) of the figure shows that each segment comprises a thin film of an organic liquid contained in a cell made by bonding together a pair of glass plates. The internal faces of the plates contain a transparent electrode which is etched to the required segment shape. The series resistances shown in the equivalent circuit represent lead-in resistance, and the parallel resistance and capacitance represents the fluid leakage resistance and the self-capacitance between opposing electrodes.

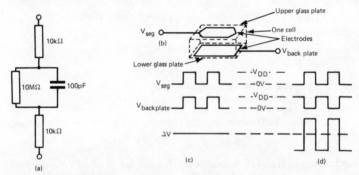

Figure 11.11. An LCD display: (a) equivalent circuit; (b) drive terminals; (c) segment off conditions; (d) segment on condition

The electrical field set up by an applied potential to the plates causes a rotation of the plane of polarisation of light passing through the cell; this is made visible by the use of polarisers, and the relative orientation of these films gives either a transparent image on an opaque background, or vice-versa. Constant d.c. applied to a cell can cause degradation, therefore only a.c. should be applied. Devices normally employ a common backplate with individual segment connections. Figure 11.11(c) shows that if identical square-waves are applied to both plates of a cell, no potential difference is obtained across it (ΔV). If the two plates are driven anti-phase, however, as shown in (d), a potential difference occurs. The segment is in the off condition with no potential difference, or the on condition when a potential difference exists. Logic levels are sufficient to drive these devices, and drive current is negligible because of their high impedance.

The simplest way of driving an LCD segment is with an exclusive-OR gate, as shown in Figure 11.12. The DRIVE input is a constant clocking waveform, and the SELECT input is placed high to switch the segment on. When SELECT is high, it causes the XOR gate to act as an inverter to the DRIVE waveform, thereby ensuring that the plates are always driven in anti-phase. When SELECT is low, the XOR gate does not invert, thereby ensuring that the same waveform is applied to both plates. CMOS integrated circuits are ideal for driving LCD displays.* The 4055A CMOS LCD display driver provides a seven-segment output suitable for driving an LCD character, provided an externally generated square-wave is applied to its DF input.

Figure 11.12. Exclusive-OR method of driving an LCD segment

LCD displays are available in seven-segment and starburst forms. This type of device can also be custom-made for the bulk user.

Gas discharge tubes

Low voltage fluorescent tubes are another means of reducing the current required by displays. Such displays are miniature cathode-ray indicators, and electrons from the hot filament are accelerated to impinge on the fluorescent anode, shaped according to the pattern required (e.g. seven-segments). Such displays require a supply of around +18 V minimum, and a low voltage heater supply (e.g. 1.6 V). These devices can be conveniently switched with open-collector TTL devices, and are available in both common anode and common cathode varieties. The fluorescent anode usually glows green in colour when switched on. Open-collector TTL devices are available with 30 V output transistors, allowing a good brilliance level to be obtained with a 30 V supply.

Multiplexing

Multiplexing is a technique whereby an apparently static condition is actually implemented by dynamic means (e.g. the HDSP-2000 dot-matrix display previously described). Multiplexing allows circuitry to *time-share* certain common lines or components, thereby greatly reducing component count and cost.

---

* *Application notes are available from most manufacturers of such devices, e.g. Hamlin Electronics Europe Ltd., Diss, Norfolk IP22 3AY, England.*

Figure 11.13 shows how multiplexing might be applied to four 7-segment displays. By so doing, a single latch/7-segment decoder/driver is used instead of one per digit. The CD4511B accepts a BCD input which is internally latched by means of a latch enable (LE) input. This is internally decoded to 7-segment form, and NPN bipolar transistors on the output stage provide *high* level emitter-follower drives to the 'on' segments. Limiting resistors are chosen to define the current *for a single display diode*, for multiplexing means that only one diode will be on at one time.

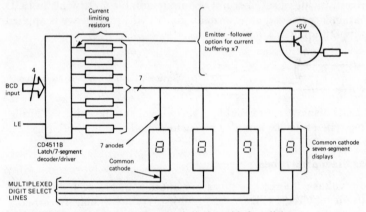

Figure 11.13. Multiplexing a 7-segment display with four digits

A common cathode display is suitable for this application, thereby allowing common resistance at the anode side; it is then only necessary to ground each of the MULTIPLEXED DIGIT SELECT LINES in turn, where the digit selected corresponds to the appropriate code *output* by the latch/decoder/driver. A suitable display is the Hewlett Packard HDSP-3533 high efficiency red display. This device requires an average current of 20 mA per segment, but if it is to be multiplexed, each segment is only on for a short interval. With four digits to be multiplexed, any given digit is only on for one-quarter of the time.

When it comes to any visual displays, a frequency of at least 100 Hz must be used in order to give a flicker-free appearance. Whilst multiplexing at a sufficiently high frequency can give the appearance of all four digits being constantly displayed, you cannot get something for nothing, therefore if you cut down the display time of each digit by 75%, you also cut down its apparent *brilliance*. This must be counteracted by stepping up the peak current per segment if the same brilliance is to be attained. If it is decided that 20 mA per

98

segment is required for a static (i.e. d.c. driven) display, then 80 mA per segment is required for four multiplexed digits to give the same brilliance (i.e. 20 mA × 4). This is better appreciated if the supply requirement is considered, bearing in mind that this must be the same for a given brilliance, no matter what technique is used. Four static digits require 20 × 4 = 80 mA for a particular segment in each digit. The multiplexed system supplies four consecutive pulses, which equates to a constant current; that constant current must be 80 mA.

A problem immediately faces us with the circuit shown above. The CD4511B can only source a maximum of 25 mA, therefore if it is to be used, there will be only two options: dropping the peak current, and hence the display brilliance, or providing current buffers. The CA3083 NPN transistor array chip is useful for such purposes since this contains five separate transistors each capable of handling 100 mA peak; transistors in this array could be used as emitter-followers to the CD4511B outputs, thereby allowing 80 mA peak drive; alternatively, discrete NPN transistors with suitable ratings could be used.

Similar transistors are required to sink the common cathodes of the MULTIPLEXED DIGIT SELECT LINES, but these must be capable of sinking a maximum of 80 mA peak × 7, i.e. 560 mA. The CA3724G is a suitable NPN transistor array for this purpose, containing four transistors, each with a 1 A rating. The circuit as shown is only capable of multiplexing the displays with the reduced brilliance equivalent to a static display with 6 mA per segment, but bear in mind that if a separate CD4511B is used for each digit in a static display, the device is quite capable of sourcing the more desirable 20 mA per segment. A static display has a peak current of 20 mA × 7, i.e. 140 mA.

This example shows how apparent savings in one direction (e.g. a common latch/7-segment decoder/driver) can bring about unexpected complications in another (e.g. driving capability). There is a lot to be said for the simplicity of static displays.

Finally, a general point about drawing techniques, which is illustrated in Figure 11.13. The drawing shows how parallel lines can be combined to save space and improve clarity. The optional slashed line across the BCD broad arrow input is marked with '4' to signify that this represents four separate lines. Similarly, the single line drawn from the limiting resistors is slashed with '7' to indicate that this represents seven individual lines. Special care must be taken in circuit diagrams to ensure that the same order of lines is maintained at either end, if these branch out to numbered pins.

12

Decoders and data selectors

Control circuitry frequently requires that a binary input be converted to a single line output, i.e. a separate output line for each unique binary number. Such a function is performed by a *decoder* (known also as a *demultiplexer*). Data processing sometimes requires that the reverse operation be performed, i.e. a number of input lines are routed to a single output line. The latter function is performed by *data selectors* (also known as *multiplexers*). This chapter considers both kinds of device.

Decoders

We have already seen simple examples of decoding, e.g. the decoding gate in Figure 10.4*. Figure 12.1 shows the circuitry

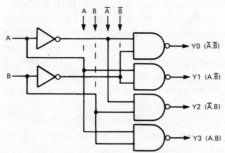

Figure 12.1. A decoder circuit for two-line to four-line conversion

required to decode two input lines, A and B. Because there are four permutations of two input lines, a full decoder requires there to be four outputs: one for each unique binary input. The figure shows that this is readily performed by NAND gates. Each gate requires the appropriate selection of true or false inputs from the two input terms; inverters are used to make the complementary conditions ($\overline{A}$ and $\overline{B}$) high when true.

* *See page 84.*

A decode of two input lines can readily be performed by a 7400 quad 2 i/p NAND gate, especially if true and complementary inputs are already available for the inputs, thereby obviating the need for the inverters. If the output is from bistables, this is often the case. Decoding more than two input lines would require more than one IC, and it is then more efficient to use a decoder chip. For more input lines the same principle applies, but each NAND gate decode has to select true or false inputs relating to *each* of the input lines; thus a decoder with three input lines requires 3 i/p gates, etc.

The following devices are worth noting:

(a) 74155 dual 2-line to 4-line decoder (or 74LS139 – App. F1).
(b) 74156 dual 2-line to 4-line decoder with open-collector output.
(c) 74LS138 3-line to 8-line decoder (App. F1).
(d) 74154 4-line to 16-line decoder (App. F2).
(e) 7445 BCD-decimal decoder/driver with open-collector outputs.

To consider one example, the 74LS138 produces only one output low at a time, and the number of that output is the decimal equivalent of the binary input; this may be seen by studying the function table presented for the device in the appendix (App. F1). It will be seen that in addition to the A, B and C select inputs, three enable inputs are provided; this facility is often convenient for combining other gating functions with the decode; if this facility is not required, it is simply necessary to tie the enables permanently in their enabled state, i.e. G1 high and G2A and G2B low.

Space considerations can often be of great importance in practical designs, therefore it might be very advantageous to use a device such as this even if it is under-utilised; it does not matter if all the outputs are not required.

Data selectors

Data selectors are rather like electronic switches, as indicated by the equivalent circuits shown inside the outline of the dual 4-line to 1-line data selector shown in Figure 12.2. If the device is made to continually scan all the input lines, it performs a *multiplexing* function; in this way it can convert parallel data to serial data.

The dual 4-line to 1-line data selector shown (74153) has common A and B select lines; the inputs are labelled in the format 'dCn', where 'd' is either a '1' or '2' to indicate the data selector number, and 'n' is '0–3', representing the decimal equivalent of the binary select input. Thus if A=1 and B=0, the 1C1 input is routed to

OUTPUT 1Y, and the 2C1 input is routed to OUTPUT 2Y; note that both are also dependent upon the related strobe input also being low. ('A' is the LSB; see App. G2 for further details.)

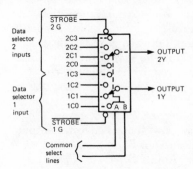

Figure 12.2. A dual four-line to one-line data selector (74153)

Such devices are particularly useful for sampling, where a number of different input lines are to be sampled in turn. For example, if it is required to compare a number of different inputs against a set value, as an alternative to using separate comparators for each comparison, a single comparator could be used, with one input the set value, and the other input fed from a data selector; each input can then be compared against the set value in turn, simply by selecting different binary inputs to the data selector. In practice, it may be necessary to operate a number of such devices in parallel if it is required to select data words comprising several bits. The 74153 is a dual 4-line to 1-line data selector, therefore it would require two such devices operating with common select lines, in order to select one from four 4-bit words.

Other devices worth noting are as follows:

(a) 74157 quad 2-line to 1-line data selector (App. G1).
(b) 74251 8-line to 1-line data selector.
(c) 74150 16-line to 1-line data selector (App. G3).

Examples of how both data selectors and decoders may be used in practice are given in Part 2.

13

Data transmission and parity

Parallel data is handled more efficiently and faster than serial data, therefore there is a general preference for parallel data handling. The only limitation with parallel data comes when it is required to route it for an appreciable distance. The physical bulk of a large number of parallel lines makes serial data transmission more attractive over longer path lengths. This physical limitation tends to tie in with the electrical limitation of driving longer lines.

As a general rule, it is possible to transmit digital data for up to about 30 cm without any special considerations.* This allows circuits on different printed circuit boards (PCBs) to be interlinked without any real problems. Data can even be transmitted over longer distances than this by the simple expedience of buffering at regular intervals, such that each section is under 30 cm. For such distances it is generally worthwhile to retain data in a parallel form.

For distances of up to about 15 metres, it is possible to transmit digital data at fairly high speeds by using various techniques of line driving and receiving, but because of the distance and added complication of line drivers and receivers, it then becomes a more attractive proposition to convert to serial data. A particular data transmission link can then be reduced to a single line.

For distances greater than 15 metres, the choices become fewer, and serial data is unquestionably the only possibility. For small multiples of 15 metres, line buffering can be considered, in much the same manner as previously described. For long distances, say from building to building, or from one part of the country to another, telephone lines must be used, and this requires the use of special interfacing circuitry for modulation and demodulation; the digital signals must be converted to voice grade channels, with a bandwidth limitation of 300 Hz to 3 kHz in most instances. The fast rise and fall times of digital signals can no longer be retained, and telephone line specifications must be considered. The logic 1 and logic 0 levels must now be converted to two different frequencies,

---

* *This is a recommendation – longer distances are frequently used in practice.*

known as *mark* and *space* respectively. *Mod*ulator/*dem*odulator devices for this purpose are known by the acronym of *modems*.

Figure 13.1 is used to illustrate these various forms of data transmission. Equipment A comprises four main functional areas labelled F1 to F4, and this equipment has both internal data highways and external data highways. A simple data highway is shown between F4 and a serial/parallel (S/P) converter; the latter may be considered to represent conversion in both directions, therefore it interfaces between the parallel data highway to F4, and a serial data highway to a line driver/receiver (Tx/Rx) which communicates across a short line with Equipment B. A similar serial/parallel conversion occurs in Equipment B, therefore parallel data may be relayed between the two equipments in either direction by means of a *serial data link*.

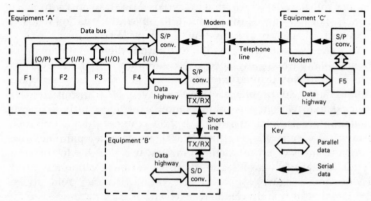

Figure 13.1. Types of data transmission (parallel/serial) and the use of modems

Intercommunication between the function F1 to F4 of equipment A is by means of a common *parallel data bus*. The broad arrows signify parallel data, and the use of arrow-heads or broadside connection illustrates the following:

(a) F1 simply outputs onto the bus (therefore no incoming arrow).
(b) F2 simply receives data from the bus (therefore no arrow towards the main bus line).
(c) F3 and F4 both receive (input) and transmit (output) data from/to the bus, therefore arrow-heads are used in both directions.

Some documentation utilises an incoming arrow (as for F2) to represent both incoming and outgoing data, which can become a misleading standard: there is no way of clearly showing where data is only incoming. Other documentation goes to the opposite extreme of even breaking bus lines with mating arrow-heads. Mixed standards deserve care when interpreting such diagrams.

The figure also shows a telephone link with Equipment C. Each end of this link requires a modem, and since both equipments utilise parallel data at the earliest opportunity, serial/parallel converters are employed adjacent to the modem in each case.

The amateur is not likely to be concerned with designs which require the transmission of data across appreciable distances, although he should be aware of the limitations and requirements for this. The novice should not attempt designs which require such techniques. This information is included in this chapter for the sake of completeness, and in order to introduce the idea of parallel and serial highways; the latter is of fundamental importance when considering microprocessors, as will be shown in Part 3.

Data transmission across short distances

Digital data can generally be transmitted for a few centimetres (e.g. between nearby PCBs) via single lines, provided high speed operation is not required. It is better still to use twisted pairs or a coaxial line, as shown in Figure 13.2(a). The transmitting and receiving

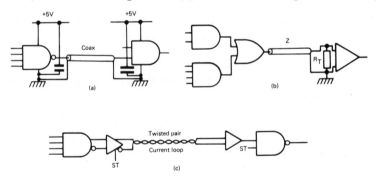

Figure 13.2. Line driving/receiving: (a) short distances; (b) using driver/receiver operating on voltage levels; (c) using driver/receiver with current loop

devices should be decoupled across the power supply close to the device ($0.1\,\mu F$ ceramic). Schottky clamped devices (with an 'S' in the type number, e.g. 74S00) are particularly good at reducing spikes. Normal precautions against creating earth loops, etc., should be taken.

105

Figure 13.2(b) shows how data transmission across short distances can be improved by the use of line drivers/receivers. The simplest of these simply drive a voltage level into the line, and utilise a line matching resistance (R_T) equal to the characteristic impedance of the line (Z). Figure 13.2(c) shows a more sophisticated arrangement utilising what is known as a *current loop*. Such devices drive a current in one direction to represent a logic 1, and in the opposite direction to represent a logic 0. The complementary currents produce cancelling electromagnetic fields and help minimise *crosstalk* between adjacent lines. Because a high current (usually 20 mA) is used to represent either logic state, this method minimises the problem of interference picked up from extraneous sources. The 20 mA current loop is a standard method of interfacing equipment, and many commercial devices are available. As shown in the figure, many of these incorporate strobe and logic gating into the basic device. Strobe inputs facilitate the connection of line drivers and receivers at the same point for bidirectional operation*.

Communications terms

There are different forms of data transmission, as follows:

a. *Simplex* transmission along a line is in one direction only, and requires only *two wires*.
b. *Duplex* transmission allows data to be transmitted in both directions simultaneously, and is usually implemented using *four wires*.
c. *Half-duplex* transmission is a *two-wire* compromise; data can be transmitted in either direction down the same wires, but only in one direction at a time.

It will be clear that some form of code must be employed when transmitting serial data, for the receiver must be able to distinguish the start and stop of the data words, or *characters*, as they are termed. Two methods are employed, as follows:

a. *Synchronous* data transmission utilises a separate channel on which a synchronising signal is transmitted. By this means it is possible to attain high transmission rates, and the start and finish of the characters is clearly identified. The drawback is the need for an extra channel or line.

* *During different time-slots.*

b. *Asynchronous* data transmission uses only one channel, but in addition to the data bits, employs a *start bit* and one or more *stop bits*. The usual method is to make the stop bit/s longer than a start or data bit, thereby providing a readily identifiable point between each character. Usually they are also opposite logic states.

Data transmission rates are described in terms of *bits per second* (bps). Alternatively, the rate may be specified in terms of *baud*. The *baud rate* describes the number of discrete events which occur each second, thus a Teletype® that transmits 10 characters per second, and represents a character by 11 bits (a start bit, 8 data bits, and 2 stop bits), has a baud rate of $10 \times 11 = 110$ baud (or 110 bps). Because three out of every eleven bits are required for synchronisation purposes, the actual data rate is only 8 bits/character $\times$ 10 characters/second $= 80$ bps.

Modems

Modems are used to convert signals from one type of equipment to a form suitable for use by another type of equipment. In the case of telephone links, it is necessary to generate *mark* and *space* frequencies suitably located in the audio band. The International Telegraph and Telephone Consultative Committee (CCITT – letters transposed due to translation from the original French) recommendations are widely used for such purposes; a logic 1 is represented by a *mark* frequency, and a logic 0 by a *space* frequency. The frequencies used vary. The CCITT recommendations for 50 baud and 200 baud working define different mark and space frequencies in accordance with particular channel numbers, as shown by a few examples below:

Baud rate	Channel	Mark freq.	Space freq.
50	001	390 Hz	450 Hz
50	002	510 Hz	570 Hz
.			
.			
50	024	3150 Hz	3210 Hz
200	401	480 Hz	720 Hz
.			
200	406	2880 Hz	3120 Hz

A microprocessor compatible modem is the Motorola MC6860, which has the following frequency standards:

	Originating modem	Answering modem
Mark freq.	1270 Hz	2225 Hz
Space freq.	1070 Hz	2025 Hz

This method of tone modulation is known as *Frequency Shift Keying* (FSK), or *FSK modulation*. Telephone links can be implemented directly, or via an *acoustic coupler*; the latter is a device into which an ordinary telephone handset is placed, and the link between the two equipments is purely acoustic.

Because of the low cost of microprocessors, and the sophistication possible where a number of microprocessors operate together and 'talk' to each other, the modem is a particularly useful tool in these applications; it provides an ideal means by which remote microprocessing systems may communicate with each other.

Parity

When data is transmitted between two distant points there is always the chance that the odd bit will 'drop out', i.e. occasionally a bit will be misread. In some applications this could be critical. A simple technique has been devised which allows each character to be checked; whilst the system is not foolproof, it can be relied upon to weed out the greater majority of errors. This system employs what is known as *parity*.

By adding a *parity bit* to every data word, it is possible to check that no *single* bit has been read incorrectly. This technique may be applied no matter how many data bits are contained within a word. The example below uses the more common 8-bit word.

Given a particular combination of logic 1's and 0's in a word, the total number of 1's is clearly always either odd or even. A parity bit is added to make the total block (including the parity bit itself) either odd or even; it is added to make the word odd for *odd parity*, or even for *even parity*. The example below shows two data words with both odd and even parity bits added.

Py		Py	
↓11001010	data word	↓01111010	
011001010	even parity	101111010	
111001010	odd parity	001111010	

The left-hand data word has four 1's; even parity is maintained by adding a logic 0 as the parity bit, or odd parity by the addition of a logic 1. The right-hand example has five 1's; even parity is created by adding a logic 1 as the parity bit, or odd parity is obtained by adding a logic 0. It can be seen that if a single data bit is incorrectly complemented, the parity is ruined; a parity checker at the receiver can detect this and provide a warning of characters in error. The system is not foolproof, since two (or an even number) of errors in the data word would go undetected; such a high error rate should be obvious in any case, and in normal systems, it is a rare occurrence to drop a single bit.

Figure 13.3 shows the format of a typical 8-bit data word as it is transmitted serially. It begins with a start bit, is followed by eight

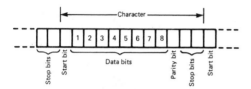

Figure 13.3. Format of a character in a serial data transmission

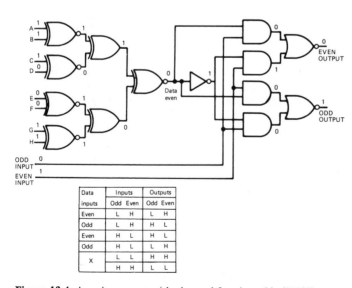

Figure 13.4. A parity generator/checker and function table (74180)

109

data bits, a parity bit, and is terminated by two stop bits. Typically the start bit is a logic 0, the data bits are set according to data requirements, the parity bit is set according to parity requirements, and the stop bits are always logic 1.

Devices are available to either check or generate parity. The equivalent circuit of the 74180 parity generator/checker is shown in Figure 13.4. This makes use of the fact that an XOR gate will determine whether a pair of bits is odd or even, and subsequent checks of pairs provides a final evaluation of the odd/even state of the data lines. Logic 1's and 0's have been added to show one particular condition with five logic 1's in the data, which produces a logic 0 at the output of the final *inverting* XOR gate; note that the first column and final XOR gates have inverting outputs, whereas the centre column does not.

The ODD/EVEN I/P control lines make it possible to use the device in several different ways; the examples given in Figure 13.5 represent just one option. Part (a) of the figure shows the device

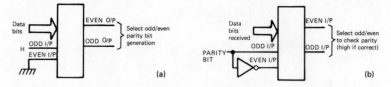

Figure 13.5. One method of using the parity generator/checker: (a) as a parity bit generator; (b) as a parity checker

used for parity bit generation; the eight data bits generate a 1 at the EVEN O/P if the data bits are odd, or a 1 at the ODD O/P if the data bits are even, such that the EVEN O/P may be used as the parity bit for even parity, or the ODD O/P for odd parity. In part (b) of the figure, it may be seen that if the ODD I/P is used for receiving the parity bit of a data word with parity, and the EVEN I/P receives its complement, then the EVEN O/P goes to logic 1 for even parity, or the ODD O/P to logic 1 for odd parity. This may be checked by reference to the function table given in Figure 13.4. In either case the user uses only one of the outputs according to his odd/even parity requirement.

The UART

This chapter has shown the importance of being able to easily convert data between serial and parallel forms. The Universal Asynchronous Receiver Transmitter – or UART – is a device intended for just this purpose. Figure 13.6 shows a block diagram of a typical device (COM2017). The upper portion represents the transmitter, the central section a common control area, and the lower section the receiver. The transmitter takes an 8-bit parallel data word and allows it to be shifted out as serial data. The receiver receives serial data in 8-bit data words and converts it to parallel form.

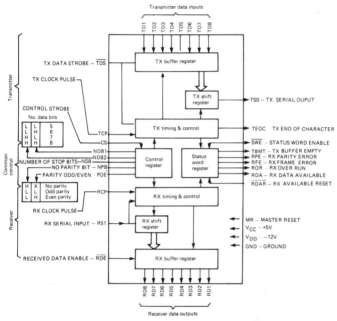

Figure 13.6. Block diagram of a universal asychronous receiver transmitter (UART)

This particular device is programmable for data word length (by means of inputs NBD1 and NBD2), the number of stop bits (by NSB), and the parity requirement (by NPB and POE). This allows for 5 to 8 data bits, 1 or 2 stop bits, and no parity, or odd/even parity. Before transfers take place for a given word format, a control word must be strobed into the control register by the control strobe (CS). Most applications do not change their format requirement, in which case the CS input may be hard-wired high.

The transmitter operation is as follows. A parallel data word present at inputs TD1–TD8 is strobed into the TX buffer register by a low TX DATA STROBE (TDS) pulse; data should only be loaded when the TBMT output is high (TX buffer empty). Note that TBMT,

111

and the other status word register bits, are only enabled when the STATUS WORD ENABLE ($\overline{\text{SWE}}$) is low. Once the TX buffer is full, TBMT goes low. The TRANSMITTER CLOCK PULSE (TCP) is then used to clock out the serial data output TSO (TCP is ×16 the required baud rate). The device automatically transmits a low start bit prior to the data bits, and inserts parity and then stop bit/s after the data bits in accordance with the programmed requirement; the stop bits are high bits. Once all bits have been transmitted (i.e. after the last stop bit), TBMT goes high again, signalling that fresh data may be strobed into the TX buffer register. The output TRANSMITTER END OF CHARACTER (TEOC) goes high after completion of transmission of a full character, and stays high until the transmission begins for the subsequent character.

The receiver operation is as follows. The serial data input (RSI) is clocked into the RX buffer register by the RECEIVER CLOCK PULSE (RCP); (RCP is ×16 the baud rate). The RECEIVER DATA AVAILABLE (RDA) output goes high midway into the first stop bit, indicating that the RX buffer register is full. The received data word is output as an 8-bit parallel word on RD1–RD8 by the RECEIVED DATA ENABLE input ($\overline{\text{RDE}}$) being taken low.

The status word register contains additional bits to indicate receiver faults: RECEIVER PARITY ERROR (RPE); RECEIVER FRAME ERROR (RFE) (no valid stop bit); RECEIVER OVER RUN (ROR) (i.e. previously written character not read). The RECEIVER DATA AVAILABLE output (RDA) is reset by external circuitry when a data word is read by the RECEIVER DATA ENABLE RESET ($\overline{\text{RDAR}}$) input.

The UART therefore provides an ideal interface between a parallel data highway and a modem, i.e. the S/P conversion requirements shown in Figure 13.1*. They are also ideal for use in conjunction with microprocessors, where communication is required with remote processors.

ASCII code

Whilst it is possible to design a data link employing any desired code, it is obviously preferable to use a universally recognised code. Such a code is the American Standard Code for Information Interchange: the 'ASCII code'. This code is widely used in digital and computer engineering. Further details are provided in Appendix D.

* *Appropriate input/output three-state buffering is also needed between the UART line and commoned lines.*

112

14

Logic families

There are quite a number of different logic families in current use, as this chapter shows, but the amateur – and indeed the average designer – will only be concerned with two major types: TTL and CMOS. The amateur, in particular, should only design with devices which are easily obtainable, therefore it is a wise practice to have a copy of a recent enthusiasts' electronics journal to hand, open at a suitable page listing device types and prices. This book concentrates on popular device types, for practical reasons.

The main purpose of this chapter is to complete this part of the book on basic logic by familiarising the reader with the different logic families available, and to briefly show how the families with which he will become familiar differ from other kinds available.

Figure 14.1 is a family tree of the most common logic families and their derivatives, complete with circuit details, showing how they differ. Bipolar devices are junction devices in which the majority current flow is across the junctions: as with diodes and transistors. MOS – metal oxide silicon – devices operate in a different way, dependent upon the *field effect*, and the majority current flow stays within the different semiconductor types, apart from minute leakage currents. Of the two major logic types, TTL is more widely used because it is much more tolerant towards the handler; special precautions must be taken when handling MOS devices to prevent damaging them by stray electrostatic fields. The particular advantage of the latter type is its low power consumption, and wide supply voltage tolerance.

Each family type and derivative shown on the family tree is now separately discussed.

DTL – diode transistor logic

DTL was the first development in custom-made logic devices; for most purposes it has been superseded by TTL. A NAND gate is shown. If both A and B inputs are high, current flows through R1 to switch the transistor on, giving a low output. If one or both of the

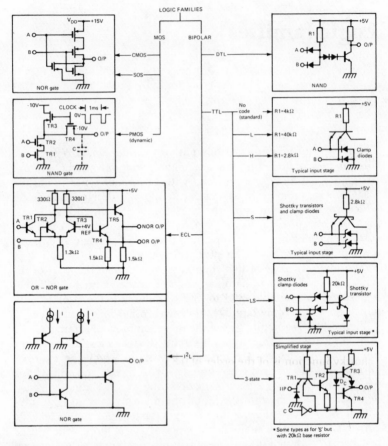

Figure 14.1. Logic family tree and primary circuit differences

inputs is low, this pulls the common anode point down to approximately +0.7 V, thereby ensuring that the transistor is cut off, giving a high output.

DTL is discussed in Chapter 2.

TTL – transistor transistor logic

TTL is probably the most common form of logic in use, and is certainly the most economic, and the easiest to handle. It is available in 6 major types, offering different power-speed combinations. These are discussed separately.

114

Standard, L and H types

Standard devices (Texas: no code) have a 4 kΩ base resistor at the input stage, and can operate up to 35 MHz. Lower power versions (Texas: L) have a 40 kΩ base resistor, and have either emitter inputs as shown in the figure, or diode inputs (in a similar manner to that illustrated for Schottky LS types). The emitter inputs halve the low level input current from the standard 1.6 mA to 0.8 mA, whereas the diode inputs (to a transistor base) improve this to 0.18 mA. The maximum frequency of 'L' types is 3 MHz. A higher speed/power compromise is available (Texas: H) utilising a 2.8 kΩ base resistor, a low level input current of 2 mA, and a maximum frequency of 50 MHz.

Clamp diodes are used on the inputs to prevent any input being taken more than about −0.7 V into reverse bias; in normal operation these diodes are reverse-biased and have no effect.

S type

Schottky transistors are used in conjunction with Schottky clamping diodes in a high-speed version of TTL (Texas: S). Switching delays are cut by a factor of two or three to one, and the forward bias of a Schottky junction is of the order of 0.3 V, instead of the usual 0.7 V. The disadvantages of Schottky are higher power requirements, and the possibility of producing ringing from the faster rise time in the output transistors; the latter can be particularly troublesome in printed circuit boards with connections longer than about 13 cm.

The Schottky diode uses a metal* junction with the silicon, producing a surface barrier which has a rectifying characteristic similar to a p-n junction. These diodes are principally majority carrier devices, and these majority carriers easily cross the junction between the silicon and metal, reducing the storage charge, and hence the potential difference. The Schottky transistor is really a conventional transistor with a Schottky diode between base and collector; the anode is connected to the transistor base, therefore the cathode clamps the transistor when approaching bottoming, so preventing its normal saturation, and significantly improving its switching characteristics. Schottky TTL can attain frequencies of 125 MHz. Schottky diode clamps further restrict negative-going spikes on gate inputs, limiting excursions to about −0.3 V.

---

* *Usually aluminium.*

Schottky transistors and diodes are used in a configuration to give a compromise between speed and low power in another version of TTL (Texas: LS). Diode connections to a $20\,k\Omega$ base resistor give the desired compromise, and a typical gate dissipation of only $2\,mW$ (as opposed to the standard $10\,mW$), combined with a maximum frequency of $45\,MHz$ (against the standard $35\,MHz$).

3-state outputs

The 3-state output is a means by which other logic types can be forced into a high impedance output state; this allows outputs to be commoned, providing that control circuitry ensures that only one such gate is enabled at once. A simplified circuit of an inverter is shown with a control (C) input; the control is taken high to disable the output. When C is high, the control inverter (shown by an inverter symbol) output is low. An additional diode D_c pulls the base of TR3 low, cutting it off; at the same time, one of the input transistor's emitters (TR1) is pulled low, which cuts off TR2 and hence TR4. Since both output transistors are cut-off, the output goes into high impedance. When the control input is low, the gate operates normally, and the output is either a high level or a low level, depending upon the input.

ECL – emitter coupled logic

Emitter coupled logic is available where high speed applications are called for, although voltage levels are very different to DTL and TTL. Linear designers will recognise the differential amplier which forms the standard input. An OR-NOR gate is shown; note that a reference supply of $+4\,V$ is required. The A or B inputs are taken to about $+3.3\,V$ for a low, and $+4.3\,V$ for a high.

With a low level input on both A and B, TR1 and TR2 are cut-off, therefore TR3 takes all the current through the $1.3\,k\Omega$ common-emitter resistor ($2.8\,mA$), dropping about $1\,V$ across the collector load of 330Ω; note that the transistor does not bottom. Emitter-follower TR4 shifts the voltage level of the OR output to around $+3.3\,V$, for a low level output. Since TR1 and TR2 are cut-off, TR5 is switched hard on, and the emitter is at about $+4.3\,V$, for a high level output.

If either inputs A or B are taken high, all the current through the common emitter resistor is diverted away from TR3, and the opposite condition is attained by the gate; this gives a high on the OR output, and a low on the NOR output.

Transistors are always slow in switching when they are in the bottomed region, i.e. collector-base forward-biased; this is because it has to change polarity, and a high current flow must firstly be stemmed. We have seen that Schottky clamping prevents transistors from entering this region; ECL logic prevents bottoming by careful biasing which maintains the transistors in their linear region.

I^2L – integrated injection logic

Integrated injection logic is an interesting alternative offering low power dissipation and small size. This is achieved by avoiding the need for integrated resistors – which take up considerable space and waste power – and utilising complementary transistors and an injected constant-current, shown as I in the figure. A NOR gate is shown.

With either or both the A and B inputs high (or open-circuit), at least one (or both) of the NPN transistors is switched hard on by current I, thereby causing the output to go low. If both inputs are low, each sinks the appropriate injected current I, thereby diverting it from the NPN transistor bases; both NPN transistors are cut-off, giving a high impedance output. Thus a high impedance represents logic 1, and a low level represents logic 0 (in positive logic).

Considering the outputs as inputs to similar gates, it may be seen that they are suited to sinking the outflowing injected current from an input.

CMOS and SOS

Metal oxide semiconductors may be n-channel or p-channel; CMOS logic employs both in complementary pairs, giving CMOS. The NOR gate shown in the figure employs PMOS transistors (inward pointing arrows) and NMOS transistors (outward pointing arrows); PMOS is switched off by a high level voltage, whereas NMOS is switched on. These devices may be regarded as solid-state switches which are either low impedance (on), or high impedance (off).

If either inputs A or B are high (or if both are high), the associated lower NMOS transistor switches on, taking the output low; both upper PMOS transistors are off. If both the A and B inputs are low, both PMOS transistors are on, and both NMOS transistors are off. Since the PMOS transistors are in series, both must be on in order to take the output high.

SOS – silicon on sapphire – is an alternative method of fabricating MOS devices using a sapphire substrate. The method of fabrication allows a higher packing density for a given chip area. These devices are highly reliable, but more expensive. Electrically they are similar to CMOS.

PMOS dynamic

A way of further reducing power dissipation in devices is to operate them in a *dynamic mode*; all the logic previously discussed is termed *static*.

Devices in the dynamic mode require a constant clock pulse. The illustration shows a single-phase clock, but two-phase clocks are also used. *Note the use of a negative supply rail.*

It may be seen that if both inputs A and B are taken negative, the two PMOS devices connected to the inputs switch on. When the clock goes negative, this switches on TR3 and TR4; this links the parasitic capacitance of the device – shown dotted as C – to TR2 output. If A and B are both on, this grounds C; if either TR1 or TR2 is off, the capacitor is charged to $-10\,V$ via TR3. When the clock pulse returns to $0\,V$, the self-capacitance C stores the charge until the next clock pulse occurs. A refresh clock frequency of about $1\,kHz$ is generally satisfactory, giving a $1\,ms$ clock period.

The 54/74 TTL family

The most common TTL family types are the complementary 54 and 74 series. Electrically they are similar, but ceramic (54) and plastic (74) encapsulations offer two different operating temperature ranges. The 54 series can operate from -55 to $+125\,°C$, and are therefore suitable for military requirements, or stringent commercial use. The cheaper 74 series operates from 0 to $+70\,°C$, which is adequate for most purposes, and is the only type the amateur will usually consider.

A great many manufacturers offer compatible devices in these families, as shown by Figure 14.2. One of the largest manufacturers is Texas Instruments, therefore the example type number chosen in the figure is by Texas. The type number or 'function code' part of the identity is common to all manufacturers, in that any devices

118

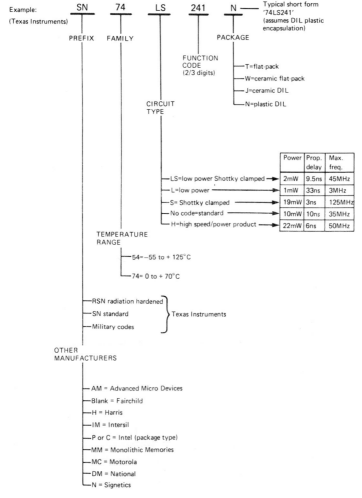

Figure 14.2. An example of the 54/74 TTL series numbering

similarly numbered should be compatible. This does not mean that certain manufacturers might not produce an equivalent with a totally different number.

The flat-pack and dual in line (DIL) encapsulations are illustrated in Figure 14.3. Clearly the size of the device varies in accordance with the number of pins, but the *pitch* – the distance between pins/leads – does not. Most users – and all amateurs – prefer the DIL, with its standard 0.1″ pitch. This is complemented

119

by 0.1" pitch Veroboard® and other PCB products for mounting the devices.

Short-form numbers, as used by most mail-order companies, utilise only the family, circuit type and function code part of the

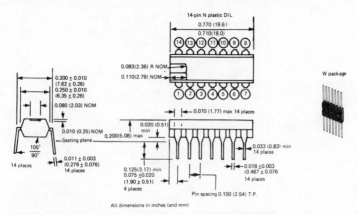

Figure 14.3. 14-pin DIL plastic encapsulation, and a view of a 14-pin flat-pack

device number, e.g. 74LS241, or 74241. This allows them to supply any manufacturer's version according to stock; such advertisements assume the reader appreciates that they are DIL plastic encapsulations, unless otherwise specified.

4000 series CMOS

The 4000 series CMOS is the most popular complementary MOS logic family available, and Figure 14.4 provides an example of typical numbering for these devices; RCA is the manufacturer taken in this example. Other manufacturers offer compatible devices with totally different numbers, but sufficient manufacturers do use the same 4000 numbering scheme for there to be little confusion with these type numbers. These devices are similar to those shown as CMOS in Figure 14.1.

Electrical characteristics and pin-outs

Appendices are provided at the rear of this book to get the reader started right away on TTL designs. Appendix A provides connection diagrams of the most common 74 series devices which have been

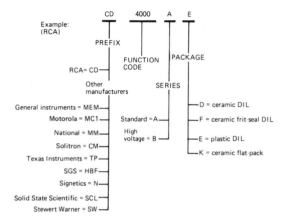

Figure 14.4. An example of CMOS series numbering

mentioned so far in the book; Appendix B lists more devices, but presents pin-out information in a more condensed tabular form. Appendix C contains basic information on the electrical characteristics of this family of devices. For more information, and for serious design, the reader should purchase: 'The TTL Data Book for Design Engineers', by Texas Instruments, or its equivalent.

Space does not permit similar coverage of the less common 4000 series devices, although Appendix C does contain electrical characteristics for the purpose of comparison. For further details, the reader should obtain a manufacturer's data book, such as: 'RCA Integrated Circuits', by RCA.

Part 2 – design practice

To think is to see.

Honoré de Balzac (1799–1850).

Always design a thing by considering it
in its next larger context – a chair
in a room, a room in a house, a house
in an environment, an environment
in a city plan.

Elial Saarinen, 'Time', 2 July 1956.

15
Basic principles

If Part 1 of this book may be considered as the *hors d'oeuvres*, then this part may be considered as the main course. Design can only be taught to a limited degree, after which the aspiring designer must participate himself. This part of the book firstly discusses basic principles, and then shows the application of these principles and the use of digital components by example.

Switch inputs

It is usually necessary to interface a logic circuit with switch inputs, and this does present a minor problem due to switch bounce. When a switch is either opened or closed, the switch contacts bounce on parting and meeting, respectively. This can introduce a series of pulses into the logic instead of the required single switching edge, and does not meet with the fast rise and fall times required for digital circuitry.

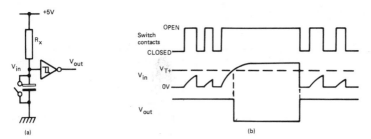

Figure 15.1. Switch de-bounce circuit using CR delay: (a) circuit; (b) waveforms

Figure 15.1 shows one method of overcoming switch bounce by means of a capacitor-resistor (CR) delay. Resistor R_X is chosen to be the maximum value suitable for the logic being used, e.g. $3.9\,\text{k}\Omega$ for standard 74 Series TTL ($4\,\text{k}\Omega$ is quoted as the maximum pull-up

125

resistance in Appendix C of this book). Bounce can last for anything up to about 50 or 60 ms, therefore this *filter* should have a time-constant at least as long as this. The 0.7 CR approximation is accurate enough for such calculations, thus with a $3.9\,\text{k}\Omega$ pull-up resistor, a capacitance of around $22\,\mu\text{F}$ is required to give a 60 ms time-constant. Only tantalum capacitors should be used in this circuit in order to ensure low leakage current.

Operation of the circuit is as follows. Consider the switch initially closed. The voltage at the input to the Schmitt gate is initially at 0 V. When the switch is opened, the voltage begins to rise as C_X begins to charge towards $+5\,\text{V}$ through R_X; initial switch bounce short-circuits the capacitor, each time setting it back to 0 V. After the final bounce, the capacitor charges freely, and once the gate input voltage exceeds the positive threshold V_{T+}, the gate output goes low. Because the voltage remained below the upper threshold during the period of contact bounce, the gate output is not affected. When the switch is closed again, the capacitor is immediately short-circuited by the low impedance path presented by the switch, and subsequent bounce of the contacts, as before, does not allow the voltage to rise to the positive threshold.

A method of increasing the time-constant even further is to incorporate a transistor buffer into the circuit: the base resistor is therefore the timing resistor and may be considerably higher; the collector resistor is connected to the Schmitt trigger input. The worst possible bounce can be eliminated in this way.

Another method of removing the effects of contact bounce with switches is to interface the switch with a latch circuit, as shown in Figure 15.2; the figure shows two variations, (a) for a switch employing three contacts, and (b), for a switch employing only two switch contacts. In the first case, one of the latch inputs is always held low by the switch when it is in one of the two set positions. When the switch is operated, both contacts are suddenly open-circuited*, but this does not affect the latch condition, because it requires the definite action of being taken to 0 V on the opposite latch input to cause it to switch. When the switch closes in the opposite condition, the latch immediately changes state; if the contacts bounce open, this has no effect, since they will not bounce right back to the opposite condition. This circuit does not even require Schmitt trigger gates. The circuit shown in part (b) of the figure utilises an inverter to provide the opposite condition to one side of the latch, but apart from this, works in the same way. The logic states shown are for the circuit with the switch as indicated;

---

* *If rotary switches are used, a 'break-before-make' action is required.*

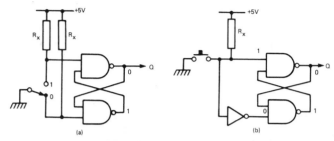

Figure 15.2. Switch de-bounce using a latch: (a) using three switch contacts; (b) using only two switch contacts

these conditions reverse when the switch is placed in the opposite condition.

Delay circuits

It is sometimes required to create a small time delay in a digital circuit, and the simple CR delay shown in Figure 15.3 is generally adequate. The only limitations with this kind of circuit are concerned with the maximum resistance value which may be used without degrading the noise immunity of the following gate too greatly, and the need to keep capacitor leakage current to a minimum; the latter is best ensured by only using <u>non-electrolytic</u> <u>types,</u> or where larger values are needed, by only using tantalum types.

Figure 15.3. A delay circuit

In order to keep the voltage drop across the series resistor to a minimum, the type of gate must be considered, <u>and the low level</u> <u>input current (I_{IL}) taken into consideration</u>; this resistor should not drop more than 100 mV to 200 mV, therefore if I_{IL} is 1.6 mA (as for most 74 Series devices), this value should be a maximum of about 120 Ω. Wherever possible, this value should be lower, such that it drops less than 100 mV.

The 0.7 CR approximation is good enough to give us an accurate enough indication of delay, therefore a 120 Ω resistor and a 1 μF capacitor would give a delay of about 84 μs. Tantalum capacitors of the order of 68 μF to as high as 100 μF are available as small bead types, and are well suited to this application, offering delays of up to around 10 ms with standard 74 Series devices; lower current gates allow longer times to be achieved more easily.

Edge-detection

It is often required to develop a complete pulse from a single changing edge; this is known as *edge-detection*. The differentiator is an obvious way of achieving this, as shown in Figure 15.4, but it is not a way to be recommended. The principle will be shown, but readers are strongly advised to use alternative solutions, for reasons to be given shortly.

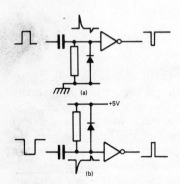

Figure 15.4. Differentiator circuits used for edge-detection (not recommended): (a) positive-edge; (b) negative-edge

Part (a) of the figure shows the detection of a positive-going edge, and part (b) the detection of a negative-going edge. In the case of part (a), the inverter input is normally held low by the resistor, but a positive-going edge applied to the capacitor produces a different-iated spike at the gate input, which is translated into a negative-going pulse at the output; part (b) shows the complete reverse. The diode is employed in each case to limit the excursion of the capacitively-coupled input voltage on the opposite swing.

This type of circuit is particularly sensitive to noise, as are any differentiator circuits, since they readily respond to any spurious input spike. In a digital circuit they represent an a.c. coupling in what is otherwise a directly coupled circuit. The low impedance output of the driving gate is an open invitation for any line spikes to spuriously register as input pulses.

The delay circuit shown in Figure 15.3, on the other hand, is thoroughly reliable, since this acts like a filter to any spurious voltages, and only responds to a pulse *longer* than the delay of its

128

time-constant. The delay circuit can be used to good effect in pulse edge-detection, as shown in Figure 15.5 and 15.6, and these are the types of circuit to be recommended. An inverter is shown in each case, since the inverse of the input signal is required as well as its original form, but logic circuits frequently have available true and complementary forms (e.g. from latches or flip-flops), therefore the inverter need not always be a special component.

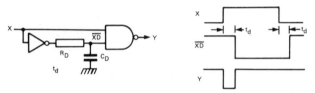

Figure 15.5. Positive-edge detector using a delay circuit

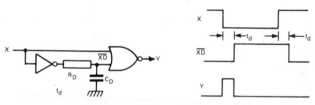

Figure 15.6. Negative-edge detector using a delay circuit

Any type of two-input gate is suitable for this purpose, although the most common NAND and NOR gates are shown in the figures; the gate can be selected with the required output in mind. To best understand the circuit, note that when the input changes, the delayed gate input does not change *immediately*. Thus with X low in Figure 15.5, the delayed gate input ($\overline{\text{XD}}$) is initially high; if X is taken high, both gate inputs are momentarily high, giving a low output at Y. After the delay time t_d (set by time-constant 0.7 $C_D R_D$), $\overline{\text{XD}}$ goes low, forcing the output high again. The timing diagram shows that this results in a pulse developed from the positive edge of the input waveform. Where the NAND gate produces a negative pulse, as shown, an AND gate would produce a positive-pulse, but again synchronised to the positive-edge of the input waveform.

As an instructive exercise, the reader is invited to draw another option with this type of circuit, this time placing the inverter between the X input and one of the NAND gate inputs, the other input being delayed but not inverted (i.e. the inverter produces $\overline{\text{X}}$

rather than the delayed $\overline{XD}$). The timing diagram should then be drawn for X, $\overline{X}$, XD and Y.

Figure 15.6 is similar to the previous figure, except that a NOR gate replaces the NAND gate. As the timing diagram shows, this gives us a negative-edge detector, which is just what the suggested exercise above produced; the only difference is that the exercise produces a negative pulse at the output, whereas the circuit of Figure 15.6 produces a positive pulse. To extend the same exercise suggested above, redraw the output Y assuming an AND gate instead of a NAND gate; it will then be seen that this is equivalent to the NOR gate circuit of Figure 15.6.

In a similar manner it is possible to use an OR gate, or move the delay to the opposite input of the circuit shown in Figure 15.6, producing a negative-edge detector with a negative pulse output, or a positive-edge detector with a positive pulse output, respectively. (Try drawing the alternatives!)

Thus a single gate, plus complementary signal inputs and a single delay, is all that is required to produce any kind of edge-detection pulse, without the need to resort to a.c. coupling.

Interfacing circuitry

Care should be taken when interfacing logic circuitry to other circuitry, perhaps with different supply voltages. Figure 15.7 shows an input interface to TTL from other circuitry, and employs two normally reverse-biased diodes in order to prevent damage to the TTL gate caused by positive swing above the +5 V rail (limited by D1), or negative swing below earth (limited by D2); the diodes clamp the input voltage to within the diode V_F (say 0.7 V). The series resistor R_S is used to limit the current drawn from the driving source under limiting conditions, but should be chosen with the usual care, in order to ensure that it only drops around 100 mV for a logic 0 input.

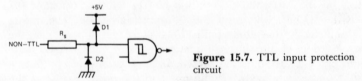

Figure 15.7. TTL input protection circuit

If there is no danger of overswing from the driving source because of direct coupling to a positive supply, the circuit shown in Figure 15.8 provides a simple method of reducing the input voltage to TTL compatibility. In this case, R_L is chosen to drop the required voltage for a logic 1 input. With a logic 1 input, transistor TR1 is switched

130

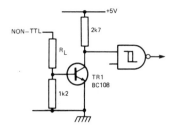

Figure 15.8. TTL input interface
circuit utilising a transistor

hard on, producing a low at the TTL gate input; with a logic 0 at the
input, TR1 is biased off, and the $2.7\,k\Omega$ collector load resistor pulls
the TTL gate input high.

In both the above cases a Schmitt trigger gate is used to ensure
that any slow edges fed into the system are converted to the fast
edges required by normal TTL gates. Note that a circuit using a
bottoming transistor is limited in switching speed and is only useful
for relatively low speed operation (as determined by the individual
transistor used).

Output interfacing has previously been considered in Chapter 11,
but is taken a little farther here. Figure 15.9 shows a direct coupling
to an NPN transistor, but the limitation here is in the fairly low base
drive current which can be achieved. The diode is optional, but is a
wise addition to ensure that the transistor is cut-off for a logic 0
output from the gate. Capacitor C_s is an optional small speed-up
capacitor for high speed applications, although the latter is limited
in any case by transistor switching speed. Since the transistor
bottoms in this circuit, high speed is not possible, nor is high gain;
this circuit can only provide a fairly modest current drive.

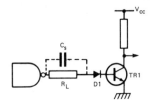

Figure 15.9. TTL output circuit
for low current drives

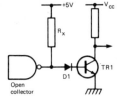

Figure 15.10. TTL output circuit
for medium current drives

The circuit of Figure 15.10 uses an open-collector gate and a
pull-up resistor R_x; again a diode (D1) is used to ensure that TR1
switches off in the logic 0 condition from the gate. Because an
external resistor biases the transistor, higher base and hence collect-
or current is possible.

131

Higher current drive is readily achieved by replacing the single transistor of Figure 15.10 by a Darlington-pair, as shown in Figure 15.11; this provides large current gain (equal to the product of the individual transistor gains), and means that the series diode is no longer required to guarantee an off condition for logic 0 output from the gate, since the diode V_F is replaced by the V_{BE} of TR1.

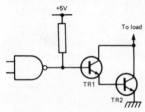

Figure 15.11. TTL output circuit for higher current drive utilising a Darlington-pair

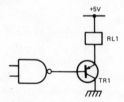

Figure 15.12. TTL output circuit to a relay (or indicator) utilising an emitter-follower

The emitter-follower is not often seen as a TTL output interface, but it should not be overlooked in applications where it is not important to ensure complete cut-off in the logic 1 condition. Figure 15.12 shows this method used to drive a relay coil, and it is also suitable for driving indicators (e.g. high current LEDs*). A transistor such as the BCY71 with a maximum collector current of 200 mA can be driven to its maximum with this circuit. Since the transistor never bottoms (the base potential is always slightly higher than the collector potential), it retains its normal gain characteristics. With h_{FE}min of 100, this means that the base drive will be a maximum of 2 mA, and a 74 series TTL gate can drive up to 16 mA; the power dissipation is thus a maximum of approximately 200 mW, bearing in mind that the collector-emitter voltage is always less than 1 V (the BCY71 is rated at 350 mW).

The emitter-follower also offers one other advantage: speed. Because it does not enter saturation, switching speed does not suffer. If the driving gate is an open-collector type, and a base pull-up resistor is used to ensure cut-off of the transistor in the logic 1 condition, a faster transistor interface can be achieved than with NPN types in the circuit configurations shown in Figures 15.9 to 15.11.

Power-on reset

An important consideration for the designer to take into account in any circuit containing latches, flip-flops, counters or registers, is

* *Do not overlook the series load resistor.*

whether they need to be preset or cleared from the 'power-on' condition. Such devices otherwise settle in a random condition, and this may place them in an incorrect state for satisfactory operation of the circuit.

Figure 15.13 shows a simple *power-on reset* (POR) circuit (sometimes also known as an *initial reset* (IR). Such a circuit may be used to initialise devices as required. If a design utilises a rapid cyclic form of control logic that automatically initialises such devices, it may not be important if they are in invalid states for a short time after power-on. Clearly it is impossible to generalise, but it can be said that if a design includes latches, flip-flops, counters or registers, the designer should always consider whether each and every one requires a particular POR condition applying. The figure shows complementary forms of the signal in its simplest form, but only one of these may be required in many circuits.

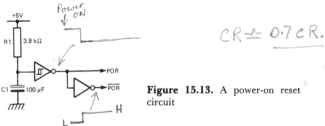

$$CR \doteq 0.7\,CR.$$

Figure 15.13. A power-on reset circuit

The capacitor and resistor form a time-constant; this should be made as long as conveniently possible. If 74 series TTL is being used, $4\,k\Omega$ is the maximum pull-up resistance, therefore $3.9\,k\Omega$ is used; $100\,\mu F$ is the highest tantalum bead capacitor, this type being chosen to ensure low leakage current. Only use tantalum capacitors for long time-constants, for other types can have high leakage currents which prevent correct operation; a high leakage current in this circuit would prevent the voltage from rising at the input to the first gate. The circuit shown has a time-constant of approximately 270 ms.

After switch-on of the equipment, the power supply gradually rises up to $+5\,V$, but the voltage across the capacitor C1 rises more slowly, since it must charge through R1. The capacitor voltage does not exceed the Schmitt trigger positive threshold until some time after the logic circuitry is operational, therefore POR is asserted from soon after power-on until the threshold has been exceeded; from this point the POR signal is negated. It can be seen that this circuit only produces a short initialising pulse on power-on, and thereafter remains inactive so long as power is maintained. The $\overline{\text{POR}}$ signal is suitable for clearing or presetting standard flip-flops

133

and NAND-type latch circuits, or POR may be used for setting or resetting NOR-type latch circuits.

Power supplies

The design of +5V power supplies for logic circuitry is greatly simplified by the availability of single integrated circuits which provide automatic regulation of +5V without the need for external components; such devices include internal thermal overload protection and internal short-circuit current limiting, making them virtually immune to damage by overloading. Figure 15.14 shows the μA7805C regulator in a simple circuit capable of providing in excess of 1 A current drive to logic circuitry, when suitably mounted on a heatsink, or in direct thermal contact with a cabinet case.

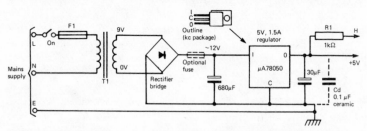

Figure 15.14. A +5 V power supply using a 5 V regulator integrated circuit

The rectifier bridge is also a single device, since these are usually *cheaper* than four individual diodes. A 50 V PIV* is suitable, and the current rating should bear in mind the requirement; a 1 A type may be sufficient, if the circuit requirement is less than this, otherwise a 1.5 A or 2 A type is required. Such regulators require a minimum of around 3 V between input (I) and output (O) terminals, therefore the input voltage must never fall below about +8 V, and can go as high as +20 V, although it should be kept as low as possible to minimise power dissipation.

Resistor R1 is shown in this circuit, with an output H; this is to provide a logic 1 (or *high*) rail for tying device inputs to a fixed level, where required. A single 1 kΩ resistor may be used to tie up to 25 standard inputs. Note that it is permitted to tie 54LS/74LS series inputs directly to the +5 V rail, if desired. *All unused device inputs should be tied to ground or to a high level.* The only alternative, as already discussed, is to tie unused gate inputs in parallel with used inputs *on the same gate.*

* *PIV = peak inverse voltage.*

134

Power supply rails should be arranged to avoid loops, and 0.1 µF *ceramic* decoupling capacitors should be evenly distributed along power supply spurs, with at least one to each spur. Individual spurs feeding back to a larger on-board decoupling capacitor at the point where the supply enters the board represents a good arrangement, if ceramic capacitors terminate each spur, and one is placed directly in parallel with the larger decoupling capacitor at the supply entry point. The normal practice of avoiding small (and hence resistive) power supply wires should be observed.

For less demanding applications, where the current requirement is well under 1 A, it is possible to utilise low current regulator devices and/or avoid the need for heat-sinking. For large systems requiring a number of printed circuit boards, each one of which requires a significant supply current, it can be an economic and practical solution to provide each board with its own discrete 5 V regulator fed from an unregulated (but smoothed) supply. This has obvious advantages in minimising earth loops.

An input fuse should be used to protect the supply (in addition to a low current fuse in the secondary circuit, if desired). Remember that the transformer transfers input power from the primary (i.e. volt-amps) to the secondary, and the volt-amp (VA) product is of the same order on both sides of the transformer. When calculating the fuse requirement, the higher input voltage leads to a lower current input than that drawn on the secondary side. Thus a transformer operating at 10 VA from a 240 V mains supply may only deliver an average of around 40 mA at the primary; allowance for surges must be taken into account on top of this. It is the need for low input fuses which prompts designers to sometimes incorporate fuses in the secondary supply, where their rating relates to the actual current drawn by the circuitry; the primary fuse is then regarded as fall-back protection, and standard 2 A/3 A values may be used. Anti-surge fuses are useful in allowing a lower current rating to be used, without the fuse blowing during switch-on surges.

16
Control logic

The previous chapter discussed logic input and output circuits. This chapter covers that part of the circuit in-between: the control logic itself. It is a 'hot chestnut' which is generally avoided.

Figure 16.1 represents a logic circuit in a simplified block diagram form. The functional gating logic comprises all the special-to-purpose gating required to logically combine input and output signal lines. If a logic circuit is so simple that the outputs can always be represented by the state of the inputs, and are therefore expressable in the form of a truth table (no matter how complex), then no control logic is necessary. If the outputs are a function of both the inputs and of *time*, then control logic is necessary.

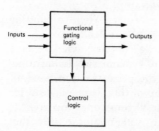

Figure 16.1. Simplified block diagram of a logic circuit

The kind of circuits that we have discussed in detail so far (e.g. Figures 3.9 and 5.1*) have been simple functional gating circuits, and no control logic was necessary. As soon as the circuit has to perform some kind of *apparently intelligent* operation with respect to time, we have the need for control logic. Control logic samples input conditions, and possibly also output conditions, and *controls* the outputs in accordance with some form of *timing logic*.

Control logic is invariably the most complicated area of any logic circuit, and there is no universally recognised standard approach. In consequence, every designer 'does his own thing', and just what he is about is likely to be a puzzle to anyone else who picks up the circuit and tries to understand it. It is also the most difficult problem to discuss, simply because control circuitry tends to grow in random

* See pages 25 and 36 respectively.

conceptual directions during the various stages of a design. The end result can be a frightening conglomeration of gating and flip-flops which even the designer has a job to understand after a lapse of a week or so! Figure 16.2 is a block diagram of this form of control logic, which I have termed *conditional control logic*. This phrase has been chosen, because it generally results in a number of flip-flops which represent various *modes*, i.e. control flip-flops, and input and output gating logic which controls the condition of these flip-flops, generally with a lot of interlinking.

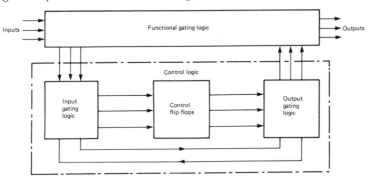

Figure 16.2. Conditional control logic – the end result of random development

A complicated design requires extremely complicated control logic if this approach is taken, and this is the kind of design approach most likely to lead to 'bugs' which prove difficult to irradicate. If a given flip-flop has to be set by given input conditions, this is easy to cope with, but the problems generally arise when the designer considers how to cancel that particular staticised condition; convenient signals are often just not available, and he has to create them, or to 'poach' a logically unrelated signal which just happens to give him the switching edge he needs for a particular timing requirement. At best, this leads to a lot of apparently meaningless gating, and at worse, it misleads others into assuming a logical connection between certain signals, when their relationship is perhaps purely coincidental. The 'make it up as you go along' approach to control logic design is not to be recommended!

The right approach

The right approach is to think hard about what you are trying to achieve right at the start. A very simple circuit perhaps justifies the conditional control logic approach, but anything at all complex

137

should be based upon a sensible form of timing logic. The designer then has two options: synchronous or asynchronous operation. If he chooses synchronous operation, the control logic is rather like a clock which is *constantly* providing timing outputs, and these are used to provide timing strobes within the functional gating logic. For this to succeed, the input/output relationship with respect to time cannot always be instantaneous: the timing of outputs in relation to inputs, in complex relationships, may have to take into account the timing rate chosen. An asynchronous approach is generally one which uses a form of timing, but one that is not free-running: rather it is influenced by input/output conditions.

This should become clearer shortly. What should be appreciated at this point, however, is that conditional gating can be greatly simplified if the inputs and outputs of the circuit are related to discrete time-slots. This is where prior thought comes in. Without time-slots, a particular output may require countless conditional inputs related to both circuit inputs and other outputs. With time-slots, a given output can only occur during a discrete time interval, and possible complications, introduced by irrelevant conditions, are removed when areas of logic are simply not enabled because they are not used during the relevant time-slot.

The microprocessor is an example of synchronous operation, for cycle timing is based upon a fixed-rate crystal-controlled oscillator, and inputs and outputs are considered during time-slots dictated by this oscillator. If the cycle rate is sufficiently fast, there need be no apparent delay between the sampling of an input and the switching of an output, at least in human terms!

Given a particular problem, the first step is to see if it can be translated into a timed sequence of events: rather like a computer program, which must take everything one step at a time. By using timing techniques, the most complex tasks may be performed with relative ease, where conditional control logic would lead to a nightmare of control logic, and probably many frustrating (and perhaps *costly*) hours wasted finding out design errors the hard way.

A simple example might help clarify this. Let us suppose that the task is to control an electric typewriter by means of an electro-mechanical interface with the keys. Whilst ASCII code may have different codes for upper-case and lower-case characters, the machine in question requires that the shift be operated prior to the alphanumeric code. Let us suppose that this is achieved by two separately timed commands: *change shift*, followed by *print* of the required character. Timed logic can go through a given sequence of possible typewriter opeations, and control bits can specify which are required for a particular operation. In the case mentioned, the cycle would need to consider the shift state *before* the character to be printed, which dictates a certain time relationship between shift and print; they are given different time-slots, where shift always precedes print. By considering the mechanical requirements of the typewriter, it is possible to derive an acceptable sequence of events related to time-slots which enables any desired typewriter action to be initiated by selection of particular commands during their related time-slots. In order to achieve the required time relationship by means of conditional control logic, not only would complex conditional logic be required, but various timing monostables would probably also be needed.

Now whilst monostables may well be required in a particular circuit (e.g. to generate a print strobe pulse for the typewriter in the previous example), a circuit full of them is generally representative of bad design. Monostables represent 'open-loop' control, in that they have indeterminate pulse lengths: they may be determined by a known CR relationship, but the tolerance of the timing components introduces an element of uncertainty. Elements of uncertainty are to be avoided in logic circuits. More than one monostable timing-out simultaneously can obviously lead to a race condition, and once again, this is something to be avoided like the plague.

If the application depends upon timing, then the right approach is invariably to use a single timing source, and to relate everything to this. If the application depends upon complex control, then the introduction of timing can simplify the circuit. If the application requires several similar logic networks, it is possible that one such network can perform the task by multiplexing it into the various signal lines under timed control, although this is not the right approach if the end result is more complicated than the simple duplication of networks!

There are always many, many ways of designing a logic circuit. That is why the designer should think hard before he settles for a given approach. Given one idea, he should first spend a little time thinking about possible alternatives. There might always be a better way.

Synchronous control logic

Synchronous control logic is dependent upon control timing logic which constantly outputs timing signals to the control gating logic. The control gating logic is responsible for introducing the time element into the functional gating logic. This is shown in block diagram form in Figure 16.3.

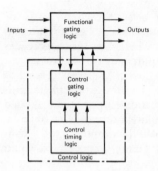

Figure 16.3. Synchronous control logic

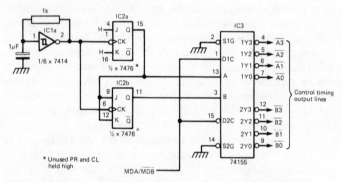

Figure 16.4. An example of control timing logic for synchronous operation

An example of control timing logic for synchronous operation is given in Figure 16.4. IC1a is a Schmitt trigger gate used in an oscillator circuit to form a *clock generator* running at a frequency of around 700 Hz, the time-constant for a *half-period* being approximately $0.7 \times 1 \times 10^{-6} \times 1 \times 10^3 = 0.7$ ms. The two J-K flip-flops of IC2 are used as a *synchronous 2-bit binary counter*, which outputs a binary count to the A and B inputs of the 2-to-4 line decoder of IC3.

The particular line decoder shown happens to be a dual device which has two independent sets of outputs, although both are related to the same A and B binary input for addressing purposes. In its simplest form, consider pin 1 to be high (the notation 'pin 3-1' is commonly used in such circumstances, quoting the IC number followed by the pin number); only one of the 'A' output lines is low at any given binary count, e.g. $\overline{A1}$ is low for the binary input of O1 (the A input being the least significant binary digit).

In this example, the MDA/$\overline{\text{MDB}}$ input line is used as a control input which can change the *mode* of the timing logic; when it is high

140

(MDA true), the 'A' output lines are active, and when it is low ($\overline{\text{MDB}}$ asserted), the 'B' lines are active. This is achieved because the data inputs of the two separate decoders are complementary. Note that the G enable inputs related to each decoder are tied permanently low; they are not required for gating purposes, but they must be low in order for the decoders to work.* This particular trick might save gating elsewhere, for it is obtained *gratis* at IC3. Always take heed of any unused portions of devices: they could be handy in surprising ways!

The control timing output lines then form inputs to gates within the control gating logic (refer back to Figure 16.3). Since only one timing line can be active at any one time, it is possible to restrict the areas of active logic, and indirectly disable other areas of logic.

Figure 16.5 provides a simple example of control gating logic; the G1, G2, H1, H2, H3 and $\overline{\text{K1}}$ inputs are from the functional gating logic, and the Y output is to the functional gating logic. The circuit shows $\overline{\text{A0}}$, $\overline{\text{A1}}$ and $\overline{\text{A2}}$ as control timing lines from the control timing logic; remember that only one of the latter can be low at once.

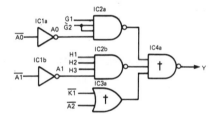

Figure 16.5. Control gating logic

When $\overline{\text{A0}}$ is active, NAND gate IC2a is *enabled*, providing a high output at Y if G1.G2 is true. When $\overline{\text{A1}}$ is active, NAND gate IC2b is enabled, this time providing an output at Y if the condition H1.H2.H3 is met. When $\overline{\text{A2}}$ is active, an output is obtained at Y when $\overline{\text{K1}}$ is active (i.e. low in this case). Thus IC4a is acting as an inverted-input OR gate, and the † symbol has been used to indicate that the gate is not being used for the expected NAND function. The OR gate of IC3a is being used as an inverted-input NAND gate (i.e. if both inputs are low, the output is low).

Note that whilst one area of the logic is enabled, the other areas are inhibited. For example, when $\overline{\text{A1}}$ is low to enable gate IC2b, $\overline{\text{A0}}$ and $\overline{\text{A2}}$ are high, thereby disabling gates IC2a and IC3a respectively; thus whatever the states of G1 and G2, or $\overline{\text{K1}}$, only the input lines H1, H2 and H3 can have any effect on the output at Y.

* *It is important to always ensure that all device enables are held in their active state if they are not required for gating purposes.*

141

Asynchronous control logic

Asynchronous control logic responds directly to external inputs, and thereby avoids any delay which might occur when waiting for synchronism with control timing logic. For example, computers generally 'talk' to their peripherals by means of a sequence of asynchronous exchanges. The computer might tell a peripheral to 'get ready', and the peripheral might respond 'ready'; the computer might then say 'data present' and the peripheral might reply 'data received'. Such an exchange is referred to as a *handshake-sequence*, and this form of control avoids delays: that is why computers use it, for they have no time to 'hang around'.

A complex logic circuit can greatly benefit from control timing, and it would be useful to be able to combine the advantages of a timed sequence with an asynchronous operation. This adds greater versatility, for it allows the individual time-slots to be of variable length. Reference to Figure 16.4 clearly shows that each time-slot in a synchronous system is of the same length. The way to achieve this is to employ the same kind of sequential logic, but to replace the clock input by some form of asynchronous control.

The state encoder

The author developed a *state encoder* (or sequencer) as a general means of obtaining asynchronous sequential control logic. Not only does this simplify control logic, but it does suggest a standard approach towards control logic, and this was the primary design aim. Indeed, it is perfectly possible for design groups to standardise on this approach, and they could then reap the benefits of readily understandable control circuitry. Going one step further, if state encoder chips were produced*, it could lead to a much simpler method of asynchronous control.

The state encoder can be based upon either a binary counter or a shift register. The counter needs a companion decoder to provide the state outputs, where the shift register provides these directly, but the counter/decoder option does have the advantage that it is *impossible* for more than one state output to be active at one time. Spurious switching or a fault could lead to more than one state being active at once with the shift register, but the latter does provide outputs directly from one chip. If the reader chooses to design a circuit employing a state encoder, he is advised to use the counter/decoder option, for this is also simpler. This book provides examples of both forms.

* *Patent applied for.*

Figure 16.6 shows a logic circuit employing a state encoder in block diagram form. The state encoder responds directly to external inputs and can directly control circuit outputs, hence it minimises the need for control gating logic. Figure 16.7 depicts a counter/decoder state encoder capable of providing up to a maximum of eight different states; obviously it may be simplified for four or less states by using a 4-bit decoder, and less following gating.

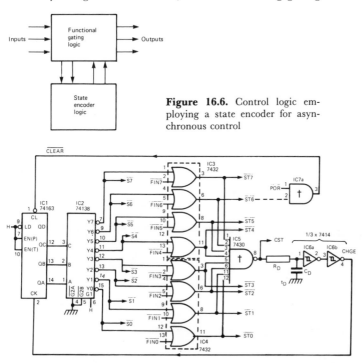

Figure 16.6. Control logic employing a state encoder for asynchronous control

Figure 16.7. A counter-based state encoder with up to eight state outputs

The state encoder effectively replaces the need for various state or mode flip-flops. At any given instant the counter (IC1) is set to a unique binary code, and the decoder (IC2) therefore outputs only one *state line* ($\overline{S0}$–$\overline{S7}$) as active low. For example, if the counter is set to 101 (equivalent to decimal 5), only the $\overline{S5}$ output is asserted (i.e. low). Given such a condition, the state encoder requires an input $\overline{FIN5}$ to be taken low before that state may be terminated; thus each state has a unique finish input line to terminate that state.

To continue with the example given above, by asserting $\overline{FIN5}$ during state $\overline{S5}$, the unique strobe output $\overline{ST5}$ goes low; apart from being a useful strobe for external use, this strobe is ORed by an inverted-input OR gate IC5a, producing a common strobe CST. The output CST is also extremely useful for control purposes, since it occurs prior to each change of state, but it is used to change the state encoder itself after a time delay t_D, which is set by R_D and C_D. The two (Schmitt) inverter gates following provide a delayed version of CST which is labelled CHGE. The counter (74163) is clocked by a rising edge on the clock input, therefore the state encoder changes state as soon as CHGE goes high. Once it has changed state – in this case to $\overline{S6}$ – the strobe $\overline{ST5}$ is terminated, hence also terminating CST, and after the delay t_D, the CHGE line is returned to its low state. The timing diagram given as Figure 16.8 should help to make this clear.

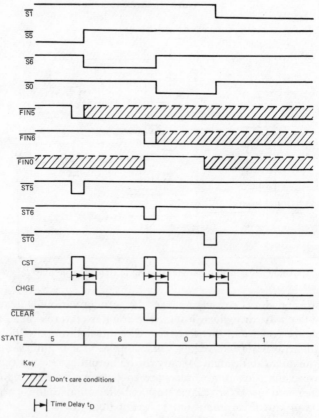

Figure 16.8. Timing diagram of the counter-based state encoder shown in Figure 16.7

144

Examination of the timing diagram shows that t_D sets the length of both the unique strobe pulses ($\overline{ST0}$–$\overline{ST7}$) and the common strobe (CST) and CHGE pulses. Once a $\overline{FIN}$ input has been used to terminate a particular state, it *need not* be removed until just before the same state is re-entered, which gives such flexibility to the terminating pulses that control is made much simpler.

The state encoder may be terminated at any count simply by using the state strobe line to clear the counter. In the example, $\overline{ST6}$ is used, thereby preventing the counter from ever entering the $\overline{S7}$ state. Because the counter has a synchronous clear input, clearing does not occur until the CHGE pulse goes high, thereby maintaining $\overline{ST6}$ at the normal length t_D. If it is desired to shorten the control cycle during normal operation, it is only necessary to OR a different state strobe to the clear line.

Note that the selected state strobe for the clear operation is effectively ORed with a $\overline{POR}$* input, to ensure that the counter starts at zero on power-on. Failure to do this leads to an indeterminate state after power-on, and the entire circuit might then be 'stuck', with no $\overline{FIN}$ pulses to get it started. This is actually achieved by using an AND gate IC7a as an inverted input NOR gate, taking $\overline{CLEAR}$ low if either input goes low.

The state encoder therefore steps from one state to the next when tripped by a state terminating input which is unique for each state. It provides both unique state strobes and common state strobes for general timing requirements, and it also incorporates the input gating logic necessary to control its own operation. As such, it incorporates virtually all the gating requirements for complete control of associated functional gating logic.

An example of the shift register form of state encoder is given later in Chapter 19, which considers its use in a design example. For either form of state encoder, selection of the delay t_D is open to the designer, and may be set to anything from nanoseconds to milliseconds. In certain applications it may be advantageous to AND the CHGE input to the sequential element with a clocking input; Figure 19.3 shows an example of this. This technique can be useful in order to delay the change of state, perhaps thereby prolonging a particular state output. Alternatively, this technique is a simple method of generating a complete strobe pulse for the sequential element (i.e. counter or shift register).

It is hoped that this chapter has shown the many different ways the designer may go about the task of designing control logic, and that the reader may now appreciate the importance of giving this

---

* $\overline{POR}$ = *power-on reset. See page 132.*

particular aspect of the design his most careful attention before even starting. The control logic is the heart of a logic circuit, and nothing will 'tick' unless this is right. Choose the right method, and you will ensure the most reliable operation. Even more important, you will then minimise heartache with the prototype!

17
Design, construction and testing

Any form of design is a creative pursuit, and whilst it is first necessary to learn a certain amont of theory, it soon becomes necessary to get actively involved in the actual process of design. The foregoing chapters of this book provide the basic knowledge required by an aspiring digital designer, and the point has now been reached where this must be applied to actual design practice. The best way to learn, in such circumstances, is by example, and the following two chapters comprise a simple and then a more complex exercise in design.

This chapter provides a lead-in to the process of design, covering also the equally important stages which must follow: the construction of a prototype and test procedures. A code of practice is suggested, and this is applied in the two examples to follow. Hopefully the reader should then be ready to go ahead with his own simple design, which he is recommended to build: *do not attempt anything using more than about ten integrated circuits until you have gained some practical experience accompanied by success!*

Suggested code of practice

The following code of practice is suggested. If it is followed, it should ensure that the design and construction of a project follow a sensible planned route. The code of practice is given in abbreviated form first, and is useful for subsequent reference; it is discussed later.

1. Define the requirement.
2. Analyse the requirement.
3. Design the man-machine-interface (MMI). (Draw panels, controls, inputs and outputs in best ergonomic fashion.)
4. Write a specification for the equipment.
5. Decide on control logic approach and logic type.
6. Design circuit. (Attempt to use all separate gates/functions in each IC within each functional area, but do not under-utilise ICs at this stage. Forget pin details. Make full use of sensible signal names. Check critical timing with timing diagrams.)

147

7. Pin-out. (Use an 'IC Usage' table to optimise usage and highlight 'spares'.)
8. Calculate power supply current. (Use 'IC Technical Detail' table.)
9. Design power supply.
10. Build prototype. (Use 'functional build and test' technique where possible. Label ICs. Mark pin 8. Mark non-standard power supply connections.)
11. Test. (Modify if necessary.)
12. Ensure that circuit diagram incorporates any modifications, and add a power supply table.

If a final (or production) model is to follow the prototype, continue with the following steps.

13. Revise pin-out and device usage for optimum.
14. Design prototype printed circuit board (PCB).
15. Prepare PCB/s.
16. Build.
17. Test. (Modify PCB if necessary due to errors.)
18. Draw final circuit diagram. (Show all 'spares'.)
19. Document design in sufficient detail to explain your approach. (This might be for others, or for *you* in times to come. The reasons for a given approach can soon be forgotten. Include any important timing diagrams.)

Now to amplify the suggested code of practice. Before attempting to design anything, it is important to clearly define the requirement and to analyse how it may be tackled in conceptual terms. Consider the MMI at this point, for by drawing all controls, input and output sockets, indicators, etc., you ensure that nothing important is overlooked. Write a specification for an equipment if it is sufficiently complicated to warrant this (e.g. interface voltage levels, timing, etc.). The last task before embarking on the actual design is to choose the most appropriate logic type and to decide upon the form of control logic you wish to use. These latter factors should be easier to resolve if the previous steps have been carried out.

Never rush into a design without this planning, for it may lead to some unfortunate oversights, and the steps taken to counteract these may lead to a far from optimum solution.

Design the circuit, bearing in mind the form of control logic to be used. Break it down into separate functional areas, and so far as possible, try to use all gates/functions within the ICs used; in so doing, do not under-utilise gates (e.g. multi-input gates for inverters – this kind of decision comes later on). When the design is complete,

148

draw timing diagrams on squared paper, thereby making sure that no timing errors have been made; modify if necessary.

'Pinning-out' is the process of writing in IC numbers and pin numbers. The following two chapters provide examples of how this may be most efficiently undertaken using what I have termed an 'IC Usage' table. This ensures that all devices are used most efficiently, and assists in the final exercise in device optimisation; it is at this stage that inverters may be replaced by spare multi-input inverting gates. The power supply current is then calculated, using what I have termed an 'IC Technical Detail' table; the latter also serves as an IC components list, power supply table, and cost analysis. After this, the power supply may be designed.

Careful thought must be given before building the prototype, and further information regarding this follows later in this chapter. Where it is possible to divide the circuit into separate functional areas which may be tested independently, a 'functional build and test' approach is best: this involves the construction and testing of functional blocks in stages, rather than building the whole equipment and testing it afterwards. It is worth thinking how functional test and build might be achieved, for it can be the easiest method of getting a prototype to work: it is less daunting to test a small area of logic at once, and wiring errors are more easily spotted. Do not overlook the necessity to update the circuit diagram to incorporate any modifications, or great confusion can subsequently ensue!

If a final (or production) model is to be made, the pin-out should be revised if any modifications have taken place: there may be a slightly different optimum solution. When making modifications, always make use of previously under-utilised gates wherever possible. The last steps are to design the PCB layout, obtain (or make) the PCB, check out a complete board, correcting any errors, and to finally make sure that the circuit diagram is up to date. It is wise procedure to write a few notes on the circuit whilst it is fresh in your mind, and to include any timing diagrams that you have produced.

Choice of logic type

Chapter 14 covered the different logic families, but for practical purposes, and most situations, these may be narrowed down to two types: CMOS and TTL; this is certainly the case if cost and availability are taken into account. These two types are readily available, and devices may be obtained at extremely competitive prices from the mail order specialists who advertise in the monthly electronics DIY magazines. The 4000 series is the best CMOS choice, and either the 74 or 74LS series for TTL; the 74 series is the cheapest, but the 74LS can be worthwhile if the design is at all complex, for it significantly reduces the power supply current requirement. Figure 17.1 is provided as a general guide to the choice of logic type. To use this figure, look down the central column noting

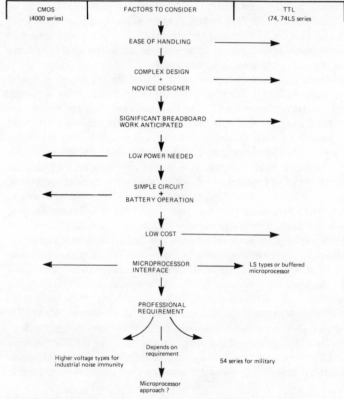

Figure 17.1. Factors to consider when selecting logic type

the important factors relevant to your requirement; the arrows indicate which way to turn. The various factors are listed in what amounts to their approximate order of significance. Clearly you may have to take into account several of the factors listed, but it should be possible to decide which way they tend to point; remember that higher factors on the list are more significant.

Construction

Logic circuitry requires complex wiring, therefore it is essential to build prototypes on some form of circuit board, based upon the 0.1″ hole pitch required by logic ICs. Scan the mail order advertisements for suitable boards. Vero manufacture a range of suitable boards, including what is known as DIP board: this comprises rows of pads for IC pins, plus power supply tracks routed conveniently around the board. A 156 mm × 114 mm DIP board can hold up to 20 14-pin devices, or 16 16-pin devices.

Standard 0.1″ pitch Veroboard® can also be used, although there is the added trouble of using a spot-face cutter to remove a lot of copper track; it can be worth the effort if dense packing or economy are considerations. The 3.75″ wide boards contain 36 parallel tracks, which may be arranged as follows, considering the tracks to be labelled 1–36: 1–8 = device pins; 9 = 0 V; 10 = +5 V; 11–18 = device pins; 19–26 = device pins; 27 = 0 V; 28 = +5 V; 29–36 = device pins. This comprises four ICs in depth across the board, any of which may be 14 or 16 pins. There are two power supply tracks across the board, which are always adjacent to one edge of every IC. An IC bridges four holes in width, and two further holes must be allowed for wire connections on each side (i.e. each IC pin has two wiring holes next to it); allowing for a further row of holes to be wasted where the tracks are broken between horizontally adjacent ICs, each line of four ICs requires 9 holes in breadth. The densest packing possible is therefore one line of four ICs per inch along the board.

Whilst it is common practice to draw a paper layout of intended wiring for linear circuits, digital circuits are too complex for this; the end result would prove impossible to follow, and it is just not needed. Providing that the pin-out exercise has been done sensibly to keep functionally associated ICs in the same region, a reasonable layout should result if the ICs are placed in numerical sequence. If the layout is split between several boards, make sure that sensible breaks are made in order to minimise interconnections between the boards. If a number of different IC pins are connected together, it is simply a matter of linking from one pin to the next.

Because of the complexity of the wiring, it is necessary to strictly follow a wiring plan. Obtain a photocopy of the circuit diagram before beginning wiring, and have a coloured pencil at the ready. As each wire is added to the board, the appropriate line should be coloured over on the circuit diagram. This keeps a constant record of the wiring that has been done, and ensures that none are forgotten: *this is an essential practice.*

The usual soldering precautions should be taken: each pin should be soldered quickly; heat should never be applied for more than a few seconds to each pin. The best practice is to first connect all the power supply lines on the board, to ensure that none are forgotten, and then to begin with the signal lines. It is easy to misjudge the number of pins on a device if there is a mixture of 14 and 16 pin devices. A good plan is to mark a dot by pin 8 on each IC, which clearly distinguishes between the two types. It is also wise to number each IC. The typist's correction fluid (such as *Snopake*®) is useful for marking purposes; use the solution to provide a white background on which you may write with pencil or ballpoint pen. *Ensure the type number still shows!*

Because each IC has so many pins (at least 14, and sometimes many more), it is a very difficult task to remove an IC once it has been soldered into a circuit. Should this be necessary, it is impossible to attempt to remove it by heating up all the pins simultaneously. There are three options:

a. Cut the leads, discard the IC, and then remove each severed leg individually.
b. Use a 'desoldering wick'.
c. Use a desoldering tool.

The 'butchering' method is always available as a last resort. Desoldering wick is useful if you seldom need to undertake any desoldering, and is a reasonably economic method; a special wick is held against the solder as it is heated up, and it attracts the solder. The wick is cut off and discarded as it is used up. The best method is to use a desoldering tool. It is used against molten solder like the wick, but it is a mechanical device which sucks the solder into a container; a mechanical plunger is depressed against a spring, and a release button initiates the sucking action.

An alternative method of construction to obviate the need for desoldering is to use IC sockets; low profile types take up no more room than the IC base itself. The only drawback is cost: they can cost more than some simple ICs themselves. A sensible compromise is to use IC sockets for the more expensive ICs. This is a cost-effective solution, for rather than fit an expensive socket for a cheap device, it pays to run the risk of throwing a defective cheap device away.

The only case where it is strongly advised to use IC sockets for all ICs is when you are dealing with CMOS devices. This is justified in the section to follow.

Handling precautions

No special precautions need be taken when handling TTL devices, except to keep them in their carriers until use, in order to prevent any pins becoming bent. CMOS require the utmost care when handling, and the novice is advised to avoid this logic type until he has gained some experience. The reader is strongly advised to use IC sockets when using CMOS devices, in order to prevent them being damaged by static electricity.

The high resistance of the gate terminals means that CMOS devices are very easily damaged by stray voltages. Electrostatic voltage on insulators, PCBs, and particularly human hands, can mean doom for the IC. It is true that such devices contain protective circuitry, but this does not become effective until the device is connected into circuit and the circuit properly earthed. The following procedure is advised:

1. Complete all other wiring first, including IC holders for all ICs.
2. Make sure that the power supply rails are connected to all the ICs, and earth the 0 V line.
3. Remove the CMOS devices from their protective shorting holder/material without touching the pins.
4. Carefully insert in the IC sockets.

Under no circumstances should a CMOS device be removed from its protective holder or the common conductive plastic foam until it is desired to insert it into the circuit.

Extra precautions are necessary if CMOS devices are to be soldered directly into a board. Although not advised, these are given for completeness. As before, wire all other components first, then fit each IC, soldering the power supply leads first (earth followed by the power connection). Make sure the 0 V line is earthed during all handling of the board. Only when all devices have been connected to earth should the other pins be soldered.

The pins on new ICs tend to be slightly splayed out, and generally need to be gently bent in before they fit the 0.4" pitch between DIL rows. This is easily achieved by laying all the pins of one side of the device onto a flat hard surface and applying slight pressure to all pins at once; this need only be done to one side.

Testing and trouble-shooting

When all the wiring has been completed, make a visual check of the PCB to ensure that:

a. All pins are soldered.
b. No solder is shorting between tracks.
c. No dry joints exist.
d. Any necessary breaks in the copper track have been made.

The next step is to test the power supply without the rest of the circuitry connected. Load the regulator with a resistor in order to make it drive into a load. Check that the voltage is within prescribed limits for the logic type.

The next step is to connect the circuitry, and to recheck the power supply voltage. After this comes the testing proper. It is not necessary to have any highly sophisticated test apparatus, and little more than a logic level indicator is necessary, combined with intelligent use, and a little trickery!

If things in the circuit are happening too fast to see them with such simple test apparatus, slow the circuit down! This is generally only a matter of changing a capacitor on a clock generator, or arranging it to 'one-shot' when a button is pressed.

If the apparatus to be tested incorporates an LED, this may be used as a level tester simply by connecting it to the output of a spare gate through a suitable load resistor. The gate input is then connected to a probe, with a point small enough to ensure that it cannot inadvertently short-circuit adjacent pins on an IC.

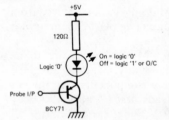

Figure 17.2. A simple level indicator

Figure 17.2 depicts a very simple level indicator which uses no more than the indicator LED and its load resistor, plus a driving transistor. The probe is connected to the transistor base. When touched to earth or a logic 0 level, the transistor is biased on, and the LED is illuminated. When the probe is either open-circuit, or connected to a logic 1, the voltage level is too high to cause the LED to be illuminated; V_{OH} is always greater than $+2.4\,V$, meaning that the emitter is greater than $+3.1\,V$; the LED drops nearly $2\,V$, therefore current flow is minimal, and should not be visible under nomal conditions; should a particular LED have a low V_F, causing the LED to glow dimly when it should be off, simply insert a forward biased diode in series with the LED.

Figure 17.3 depicts a slightly more sophisticated logic tester, with the added feature of a pulse detector. A quad 2-input exclusive-OR gate is used to provide inverters or non-inverters, as required. IC1a is always a non-inverter (i.e. a buffer), and IC1b and IC1d are always inverters; IC1c is controlled to be non-inverting with the switch in the position shown, or inverting with the switch in the opposite condition. The 'LOGIC 1' LED is illuminated when the probe input is open circuit or at logic 1, or extinguished when at logic 0.

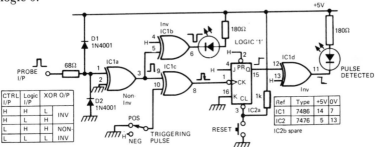

Figure 17.3. A simple logic analyser with level and pulse detection facilitates

The J-K flip-flop is 'RESET' by means of a press-button *after* connection of the probe to a circuit point to be monitored; the 'PULSE DETECTED' LED is illuminated if it subsequently detects a complete pulse (or pulse train).

The switch allows the XOR gate at IC1c to be inverting or non-inverting as desired. Since the J-K flip-flop is clocked on the falling (or negative) edge of the clock pulse applied to it, this facility allows the rear edge of either a positive or a negative pulse to trigger it, as indicated. These two indicators provide a wealth of information, as the following table shows.

Note that this figure illustrates how a table appended to a circuit diagram is an efficient way of indicating power supply pins.

Switch setting	LOGIC 1	PULSE DETECTED	Meaning
POS/NEG	ON	OFF	Steady logic 1 level
POS/NEG	OFF	OFF	Steady logic 0 level
POS	ON	ON	⎍
POS	OFF	ON	⎍
NEG	ON	ON	⎍
NEG	OFF	ON	⎍

155

The reader should study Figure 17.3 in detail and should be able to follow its complete operation without further information. The only point to particularly note, is that the pulse detector cannot discriminate one pulse from a pulse train, although if a pulse train is present, the level indicating LED will probably be dimmer than its normal level with a steady logic 1 applied at the input. A functional table for the XOR gate is included in the figure for convenience.

Power for either of the above logic level analysers should be obtained from the *host* circuit, via short twisted leads. Note that IC1a in Figure 17.3 provides a standard gate load to the circuit being monitored.

18

A CMOS design example – audible process timer

This is the first of two design examples. The reader should study these examples until he is fully familiar with every aspect of them. If he can reach the point where he understands the need for every component – for each and every gate – then he is ready to embark upon his own designs! These two examples follow the suggested code of practice given in the preceding chapter.

Defining the requirement

An industrial process requires an operator to perform a task for a minimum of 10 seconds; personal judgement is involved to decide when the task is completed, and it may take up to 20 seconds, or just over. It is most important that proper timing is maintained, therefore operators presently count to themselves – which is greatly fatiguing. A *simple but reliable* mains operated equipment is required which will produce an audible tone after 10 seconds, with repeated tones at ten second intervals; an intermediate tone of different pitch is required at the intermediate 5 second intervals, but this should not sound until after the first ten seconds has expired. The start and finish of the process may be detected by means of a photocell.

Analysing the requirement

Input: a photocell indicates when the process starts and stops.
Output: audible tones at the following time intervals from START to STOP:

    After 10 seconds: TONE 1
    After 15 seconds: TONE 2
    After 20 seconds: TONE 1
    After 25 seconds: TONE 2
    etc. until STOP.

One solution would be to use 555 timers, but this would involve quite a lot of associated logic. Such a scheme would also be at the mercy of component drift, since the 555 timer is CR based, and capacitors age; the apparatus *must* stay accurate. Crystal oscillators stay accurate, but are of high frequency, and require a lot of dividing down to reach the time intervals required in this case. Since the equipment is to be mains operated, what better than to make use of the mains input frequency?

Although the mains frequency is relatively low – 50 Hz in the desired area of operation – the apparatus will still require a fair number of divider stages. It is known that single CMOS devices are available which provide many dividing stages, therefore CMOS is an attractive logic type, especially since its wide supply voltage tolerance ($+3$ V to $+12$ V or $+18$ V – see Appendix C) means that a smoothed but unregulated power supply should be adequate for a simple design.

It is now easy to step through stages 3–5 of the suggested code of practice, as follows:

3. *Design the man-machine-interface.* Apart from an ON/OFF switch, there is nothing to consider except a loudspeaker. Nothing need be drawn.
4. *Write a specification for the equipment.* The only relevant figures are the input timing frequency of 50 Hz, and the output timing of tones, as defined above.
5. *Decide on the control logic approach and logic type.* The outputs are directly related to the timing input (i.e. 50 Hz), therefore no special approach is needed; because it is anticipated that the design should be quite simple, involving very few ICs, the *conditional control logic* approach is justified. The logic type shall be CMOS.

Design

Space restrictions within this book make it impossible to include abridged data of the 4000 series of CMOS ICs other than the general characteristics given in Appendix C. The reader must look elsewhere for individual device data. RCA are a large manufacturer of such devices, and Appendix C provides various addresses relevant to this company, where readers may write for further information. Most technical colleges that have courses in electronics contain data books within their libraries, and this is another possible source of reference.

Figure 18.2 shows the resulting design, which will be discussed in detail. The figure appears at the end of this chapter for convenience.

Although the power supply is normally the last thing to design, it is necessary to establish what is needed in general, e.g. voltage output. In this case the supply current drawn by the logic is bound to be negligible because CMOS are low current devices; the main power dissipation will be associated with the audio output stage. A full-wave rectifier circuit using a centre-tapped 6-0-6 V supply is to be used, and this type of circuit produces a capacitively smoothed output voltage of $0.7 V_{ac}$*, where V_{ac} is the sum of the two phases, i.e. 12 V in this example; the circuit diagram shows a nominal voltage of $+9$V, but something just less than this can be expected. CMOS can readily take any variation in supply voltage due to mains variations. The output from this power supply is taken to be V_{DD}, and a further H output is taken via a resistor for tying-up inputs required to be at logic 1. A 555 timer IC is to be used as a simple means of providing an audio stage, for such a device can drive a high impedance loudspeaker directly. These devices have a maximum power dissipation of 600 mW, therefore this power supply is not likely to supply in excess of this power. Since this calls for under 1 VA from the transformer, the smallest of transformers should be suitable.

One phase of the mains frequency is taken off from the transformer via diode D3 to provide the waveform CK. The amplitude of this signal is 6 V less the diode V_F; this is sufficient amplitude to switch the CMOS gate. The series resistor R4, and the zener diode D5, are simply protection components, protecting the following IC in the event of a surge.

The counter chosen is a 4040 (IC1). Since this contains pulse-shaping circuitry on the clock input, no external measures need to be taken to convert the half-wave rectified waveform to a square-wave.

The 4040 (IC1) is a 12-stage counter divider with an output from each stage (Q1–Q12). In this application, with an input frequency of 50 Hz, the time for a complete period of CK is 1/50s, or 20 ms. If we regard IC1 as a counter counting pulses once every 20 ms, we need to calculate how many pulses it needs to count for 5 s and for 10 s, in order to achieve our timing requirement. The table below shows the binary weighting of each stage of the counter.

Q	Weighting	Q	Weighting
1	1	7	64
2	2	8	128
3	4	9	256
4	8	10	512
5	16	11	1024
6	32	12	2048

* Unlike full-wave rectification with a bridge rectifier, which is $1.4 V_{ac}$.

To discriminate a time interval of 5 s, the number of pulses to be detected is $5/0.02 = 250$. The Q9 output goes high after 256 pulses, which is only 6×20 ms longer than the required time, i.e. 0.12 s; it is decided that this is quite accurate enough for a manual process. Similarly, to discriminate an interval of 10 s, the number of pulses to be detected is $10/0.02 = 500$. The Q10 output goes high after 512 pulses, which is only 12×20 ms longer than the required time, i.e. 0.24 s longer, which is again quite accurate enough. Since we are only concerned with discrete time measurements, no cumulative error can result, and the error for each measurement is acceptable. This avoids the need for gating circuitry to detect the precise counts of 250 and 500. Had we decided to make the timer completely accurate, the 5 s discriminator would require the following outputs to be ANDed: Q8, Q7, Q6, Q5, Q4, Q2; the 10 s discriminator would similarly require the following outputs to be ANDed: Q9, Q8, Q7, Q6, Q5, and Q3. This is a case where practicality and cost-effectiveness overrule theory.

A general point of interest worth noting is that it is possible to design-in the error rate in this kind of circuit. By partially decoding a number of the more significant bits in a required count, the error can be reduced in relation to the number of bits decoded. For example, if five bits were decoded in the required 5 s interval for this timer, these would comprise Q8, Q7, Q6, Q5 and Q4, thereby discriminating a count of 248, reducing the error to 2×20 ms = 40 ms *short*. Note that by decoding only the top four bits (Q8 down to Q5), the count determined is only 240, and this produces a larger error in under-timing, than the chosen solution does with over-timing.

The counter is to be held disabled when it is not required for timing, and is only to be enabled when the photocell is illuminated. D4 is the reverse-biased silicon photodiode to be used, and TR1 is a current amplifier. The photodiode does not conduct when it is dark, therefore the output from TR1 collector is labelled OFF; a gate determined to be spare at a later stage of the design is used as an inverter (IC4d), thus the output at 4–10* is labelled ON, i.e. it is high when we want the counter to be enabled. The counter has a reset (R) input at 1–11, therefore the input to this pin must be low to enable a count, hence the name $\overline{\text{COUNT}}$. IC3b is a NAND gate providing the required inversion relative to ON, and also allowing the $\overline{\text{RESET}}$ input to be gated in: the latter input is used to reset the counter when it has counted the pulses required for the 10 s interval. If the counter is operating, ON is high, and $\overline{\text{RESET}}$ goes low after a

* *IC4 – pin 10.*

10 s period; this causes $\overline{\text{COUNT}}$ to go high, thereby resetting the counter. IC3c is used to NAND Q10 and Q1 together, thereby providing a $\overline{\text{RESET}}$ pulse one CK period *after* Q10 goes high; this ensures a clean output pulse from the Q10 output *before* the counter is reset, which naturally takes Q10 low again, along with all the other Q outputs.

A timing diagram of the circuit is provided as Figure 18.1. Because this is drawn to show the timing over some 30 s, it is not possible to show short pulse lengths clearly, except by slight exaggeration. This diagram shows the short Q10 pulse obtained before the timer is reset, occurring immediately after the trailing edge of the Q9 pulses. As soon as $\overline{\text{COUNT}}$ goes high, this resets the timer, and Q outputs all go low; this removes the $\overline{\text{RESET}}$ pulse, and timing resumes at once.

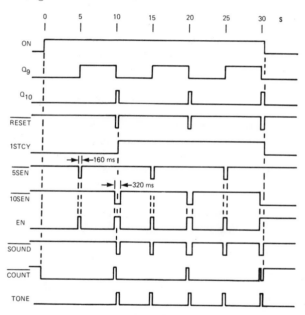

Figure 18.1. Timing diagram for the process timer

Because IC1 is a timer, it may be used for any other timing requirements of the circuit, such as determination of the length of the audible tones. In order to use it in this manner, it is necessary to set a latch or flip-flop at the time a tone is required to start, and to reset it when the tone is to finish. IC2b is a flip-flop which performs this function for the 5 s tone. When Q9 goes high it clocks the

161

flip-flop to the set condition, since a logic 1 is input to D (pin 2–9). Thus $\overline{5SEN}$ (5 s enable) goes low at this point. Q4 goes high after a further $8 \times 20\,\text{ms} = 160\,\text{ms}$, and this is used to reset the flip-flop via pin 2–10. This sets the length of the 5 s tone to 160 ms, i.e. just under two-tenths of a second.

Our design requirement is that the *first* 5 s interval shall not sound a tone, therefore this must be discriminated from subsequent 5 s intervals. The other flip-flop within IC2 is used to do this. IC2a is clocked into the set condition by the lagging (rising) edge of the $\overline{RESET}$ pulse, taking 1STCY (1st cycle) high after the first 10 s interval, as shown in the timing diagram; this output is subsequently gated with an enable waveform EN, thereby ensuring that no tone can cause $\overline{SOUND}$ to go low prior to the 10 s interval.

All that remains is to staticise the 10 s interval. This could be done with another flip-flop, but a more cost-effective solution is to use available NOR gates, and to use a latch. IC4a and IC4b form the latch circuit, which is set by taking pin 4–1 high, and reset by taking pin 4–6 high. Since the set input is taken from the Q10 output of the timer, the latch is set after the nominal 10 s period; it is reset by the Q5 output, which occurs after a subsequent $16 \times 20\,\text{ms} = 320\,\text{ms}$, as shown on the timing diagram. Note that both Q4 and Q5 are going high and low all the time during the time interval, but after each higher significance bit is first set on the counter, all the lower significant bits return to zero; these other high states of Q4 and Q5 are not significant so far as the timing flip-flop or latch is concerned, because they simply reconfirm their *reset* condition. The latch causes $\overline{10SEN}$ (10 s enable) to go low after the nominal 10 s period, and to return high after the further 320 ms.

IC3a is used as an inverted input OR-gate, producing EN high when either $\overline{5SEN}$ or $\overline{10SEN}$ goes low; once 1STCY is true (as from the first 10 s period, when $\overline{10SEN}$ first goes low), these two timing pulses cause $\overline{SOUND}$ to go low. IC4c is an inverted input AND gate, producing TONE high if both $\overline{SOUND}$ and $\overline{COUNT}$ are low. By gating $\overline{COUNT}$ with $\overline{SOUND}$, it is *ensured* that the audible tone is cut off immediately the OFF condition is reached, should this occur mid-tone. More practically, it is a good safety feature, ensuring that no tone can ever occur in the OFF condition, no matter what spurious conditions might occur in the rest of the logic. Such precautions are well worth taking.

The $\overline{COUNT}$ control of the audio also has one other effect. When the controlling input reverts to OFF, the OFF signal resets the 1STCY flip-flop and the counter; *what it does not do* is to reset the 5SEN flip-flop or the $\overline{10SEN}$ latch, for these must be reset by the timer itself; the timing diagram shows this, where the $\overline{10SEN}$ latch is left set because OFF occur mid-tone. Because 1STCY goes false, this prevents $\overline{\text{SOUND}}$ going low in the OFF condition in any case. Under circumstances where the OFF condition occurs mid-tone, the appropriate timing enable stays active until the timer restarts and the resetting time interval has timed-out. This has no effect on the audible output due to the fact that 1STCY is false for the first 10 s.

Note that there are no spare gates in the circuit. It would have been preferred practice to buffer all the logic from the analogue input (TR1) by a single gate (e.g. IC4d), but because of a gate shortage, it was deemed acceptable to provide the additional load of IC2a reset input. Had there been a spare gate, normal practice would have to generate OFF from ON, by means of an inverter. No de-bounce precautions are necessary, for the light switch has a clean switching edge, and even if there was a bounce effect, it could do no more than reset the timer a few times, which would have no effect on circuit operation.

The audio stage comprises a 555 timer connected as an astable circuit.* C2 is the timing capacitor, and R1 and R2 provide the charging path. A different tone is achieved in the two timing conditions by switching a lower resistance across R1 during the $\overline{\text{5SEN}}$ tone; this is achieved quite simply by TR2, which is biased on when $\overline{\text{5SEN}}$ is active. The base current of TR2 is minimal loading for IC2b $\overline{\text{Q}}$ output.

For the 10 second tone, R1, R2 and C2 are the timing components, giving $T_m = 0.7 (56\text{K} + 100\text{K}) 0.01\,\mu\text{F}$, giving a period of 1.092 ms; during discharge, $T_s = 0.7 \times 100\text{K} \times 0.01\,\mu\text{F}$, giving 0.7 ms. The total period of a complete cycle is therefore 1.792 ms, and the frequency is therefore 1/1.792 kHz, i.e. 558 Hz. The 'mark' time (T_m) for the 5 second tone is reduced, since R6 now appears in parallel with R1, reducing the effective resistance to 9.9 K, and hence T_m to 0.77 ms, and the total period to $(0.77 + 0.7)$ ms, i.e. 1.47 ms, thereby giving a frequency of 680 Hz.

The 555 timer output is driven directly into a 200 Ω potentiometer, which acts as a volume control. A 33 μF capacitor is used to couple a 64 Ω loudspeaker to the potentiometer, for this has an impedance of around 10 Ω at the lower frequency, providing minimal attenuation of the sound. The maximum power output of a square-wave, assuming a 1:1 mark-space ratio for simplicity, is half that which could be dissipated by connecting a 64 Ω load across the 9 V supply, i.e. about 0.6 W. Since this only occurs for a maximum of 320 ms every 10 seconds (or 160 ms every 5 s), this only occurs for 0.32/10 × 100%, i.e. 3.2% of the time, thereby reducing the average

---

* *Refer to Chapter 6 for details of the 555 timer, and also App. K1.*

loading of the audio stage to minimal proportions so far as the power supply is concerned (equivalent to about 20 mW).

Because the tones vary in length and pitch, they are readily distinguished. The end result is as follows:

10 second tone (TONE 1): 558 Hz for a duration of 320 ms.
5 second tone (TONE 2): 680 Hz for a duration of 160 ms.

This timing produces a low pitch long tone for 10 s intervals, and a higher pitched shorter tone for *intermediate* 5 s intervals. This results in a *sound pattern* with which the operator readily associates subconsciously. This sound pattern relates to a given time, and timing becomes a mere subconscious act. Now, instead of counting to themselves all day long, they can actually *talk* whilst they work. Productivity and efficiency have improved, not to mention morale!

Notes

It is no accident that there are no spare gates in the foregoing design; this is the result of careful optimisation. Earlier versions of the design used another quad NAND gate, and the result was spare NAND gates *and* spare NOR gates; careful optimisation, and use of a direct connection of pin 2–4 to the input, enabled the final solution to be reached.

The final stage in any design should be an exercise in optimisation. Given spare NAND *and* spare NOR gates, it is generally possible to find a solution which releases at least one of these ICs.

One useful tip worth bearing in mind, is that where spare gates exist in a design, the supply current drawn by such gates can be minimised by causing the output to be high; thus inverter gates must have their inputs tied to 0 V to achieve this situation.

One final point. Because of the small number of ICs used in this simple example, it did not warrant the use of an 'IC Usage' table or an 'IC Technical Detail' table, as mentioned in the suggested code of practice. Examples of such tables are to be found in the more complex example given in the following chapter.

The reader should now study this design example in depth. Every attempt should be made to fully understand the design, and this involves knowing why *every* component and gate is required. The earlier chapters and appendices provide all the cross references required to achieve this.

The following design example is considerably more complicated than this example, therefore there is little hope of fully understanding it if the present example cannot be fully understood. It is stressed

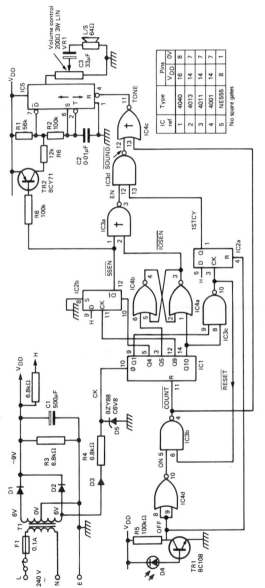

Figure 18.2. Circuit diagram of the audible process timer

165

that every effort should therefore be made to understand the present example. If this can be fully understood, the reader is well on the way to appreciating the requirements of good logic design, and is all set to tackle the much more difficult TTL example which follows. If both examples can be fully understood, then the reader really is set to begin his own designs!

19

A TTL design example – an automated 'NIM' machine – the 'AUTONIM'

This is the final complete design example to be presented, and it is an understatement to say that it is rather more complex than the preceding example. It is therefore necessary to emphasise yet again that unless the reader first works at completely understanding the audible process timer design, he has little hope of understanding the design which follows.

The good news is that it should be possible for *any* reader who has carefully read the preceding chapters to understand this design example if he is prepared to work at it, using the preceding chapters and the appendices where he has any doubt. No new knowledge is called for, and the design if fully explained. This particular example has been chosen because it uses just about every different type of TTL device. If the reader can understand this example, then he is ready to embark upon his own simple digital design projects using TTL logic.

Now is the time to draw in a deep breath – preferably take a short holiday beforehand – and then dive straight in at the deep end!

Defining the requirement

The aim is to produce a fully automated machine capable of playing the game of 'NIM'. For those readers not familiar with this game, it is covered in the following section. The machine should be capable of playing against a human player, or of allowing two human players to play each other. The machine should be given a 'personality' to add interest, and should incorporate several levels of skill when playing against a human opponent. The machine must make its own moves, and not call upon its opponent to do any of the work for it. The machine and the man should take equal turns at starting play, for fairness.

Analysing the requirement

The game of NIM

Before analysing the requirement, the game itself must be understood. It is usually played by two players with a number of matchsticks. These are arranged in several lines, as shown in Figure 19.1. The precise arrangement is not important, but the illustrated layout comprising four lines of 7, 5, 3 and 1 matches is common.

Figure 19.1. An arrangement of matches for NIM

This is the arrangement which will be considered, for it is about the minimum number of matches which produces an interesting game. To play the game, each player in turn removes *as many matches as he wishes* from *one* complete line; he can take a whole line out at one go, or simply one match, just as he pleases, but lines only comprise *horizontal* lines, *never* columns. The winner of the game is the player who takes the *last* match. (There is another version of the game where the winner is the player leaving the last match, but this introduces an additional complication, and is not therefore considered.)

The theory of NIM

If a machine is to be designed to play a game, first the game itself must be analysed. Fortunately there is a complete theory for the game of NIM, and rather appropriately, this involves binary arithmetic. Every position in the game of NIM may be described as either *safe* or *unsafe*: if a player leaves a safe position, he is bound to win if he makes no mistakes, for any subsequent move makes the position unsafe. It is always possible to make a move from an unsafe position which converts it into a safe position.

The way to determine if a position is safe or unsafe, is to consider the number of matches in each line as a series of binary numbers. Thus the starting position may be expressed as follows, where the lines have been given reference letters:

Line	Binary weight		
	4	2	1
D	1	1	1
C	1	0	1
B		1	1
A			1
Even/Odd	E	E	E

Each binary digit is separately added, and a note made of whether the resulting number is either *odd* (O) or *even* (E); if all rows are even, the position is *safe*, but if one or more are *odd*, the position is *unsafe*. Thus the starting position above is safe. Let us suppose that the first player removes 5 matches from line D. This leaves the position as follows:

Matches						Line	4	2	1
				I	I	D		1	0
I	I	I	I	I	I	C	1	0	1
			I	I	I	B		1	1
					I	A			1
							O	E	O

This position leaves an odd number of 4's, and an odd number of 1's. The next player must make the position safe, and can do so by removing 5 matches from line C, hence reaching the following position:

Matches				Line	4	2	1
		I	I	D		1	0
				C			0
I	I	I		B		1	1
		I		A			1
					E	E	E

Play the game with matches, and you will see that this system can never fail. This is the method which the machine must use to analyse the game position before making its reply against a human opponent!

Designing the man-machine-interface

Any electronic game should have the minimum number of controls. The panel layout given in Figure 19.2 is a sensible ergonomic layout with the minimum of lettering. The machine was christened 'AUTONIM' because it is an *auto*mated NIM game, and also because of its 'automaton'-like properties!

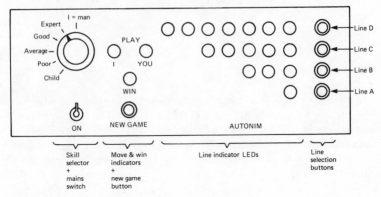

Figure 19.2. A panel layout for the AUTONIM

It may be seen from the figure that matchsticks have been replaced by indicator LEDs. A button adjacent to each line is depressed by the player to indicate his line selection. Since no provision is made for indicating the end of a player's move other than the release of one of these buttons, the chosen button must be depressed and held only once for each move. An internal clock must therefore slowly take off one LED at a time until the player releases the button. The two PLAY indicator LEDs marked I and YOU indicate the machine's move or the human player's move respectively; the only exception to this is when the left-hand rotary switch is set to the 'I = man' position, which indicates manual play, with a second person playing the 'I' rôle. The remaining settings on the rotary switch select varying degrees of machine skill from 'expert' down to 'child'. A NEW GAME button is used for calling up a new game. A toggle switch switches the equipment on by controlling the mains input. A power-on indicator is superfluous since there is always at least one of the LEDs on at any time: one of the PLAY indicators must always be on.

Equipment specification

The following specification indicates how the equipment is required to operate, and broadly specifies the general requirements.

170

Power input:	240 V a.c. mains (or as appropriate).
Game indicators:	Line D, 7 LEDs.
	Line C, 5 LEDs.
	Line B, 3 LEDs.
	Line A, 1 LED.
PLAY indicators:	I for machine's play (or man playing machine's rôle).
	YOU for man's play.
	WIN LED to flash at slow rate when man/machine wins, with the appropriate PLAY LED indicating which player has won.
Line selection push-buttons:	One for each indicator line. Button is depressed to start slow internal clock which extinguishes LEDs one by one in the selected row until the button is released. Cheat protection against depression of more than one button at once. Release of button causes PLAY indicators to be complemented. If machine is playing, machine replies when I LED is illuminated.
Machine's play:	Variable time of response required, to simulate human opponent; immediate reply to be prevented. Where several options lie open for the machine, its choice to be random, preventing two identical games being played in such a situation.
Machine skill:	The 'expert' setting specifies that the machine must play the perfect game. The other settings call for a reducing level of skill, achieved by forcing the machine to make errors at an increasing rate.
Audible output:	A tone to accompany the 'taking' of LEDs by man/machine; a different tone for man and machine.
	A third form of two-tone effect to signify a win, which is cut off after a number of times, to simply leave the WIN indicator flashing.
NEW GAME button:	Depression resets the machine for a new game by illuminating all the line indicators. The first player to alternate each game betwen I and YOU.

Control logic approach and logic type

Clearly the machine is going to be quite complicated, therefore the control logic is going to be complicated. There are no external signals to take into account, therefore the best choice is to use a state encoder. This choice means that operation can be based upon a planned sequence of events. Because of the complexity of the anticipated design, and the probable need for a wide variety of device types, TTL seems the best choice. Allowing for a one-off build, or taking into account possible debugging, TTL is again the best choice. In order to keep current levels down, bearing in mind that the equipment will use many ICs, the 74LS series is the best choice due to good availability, moderate cost, and lower operating currents.

Design

For ease of reference, the circuit diagram of the final design is located at the rear of this chapter as Figures 19.10 to 19.18. The design has been broken down into functional areas, and each of these figures has been given an 'F' reference number; this allows a relevant section of the circuit to be called up by the simple means of a reference such as 'F4'. Earlier figures in the chapter are used to aid the general explanation. The following text is also broken down into these functional areas, but clearly a good deal of cross-referencing is needed.

First thoughts on the method of control

Having decided to use a state encoder for the method of control, it is a good starting point to decide what states this will require; it may be found later on in the design that we may wish to add additional states, but by forming some idea of the requirements at the outset, we will have provided some foundation upon which to build.

When considering the various states required, it is useful to draw a 'state diagram' for the equipment. Such a diagram is shown in Figure 19.3, and the reasoning behind its development for the AUTONIM is as follows.

At the start of a new game, the machine firstly enters a state called BUTSCAN; in this state, the machine scans the line buttons, looking for one that is depressed. When it locates a depressed

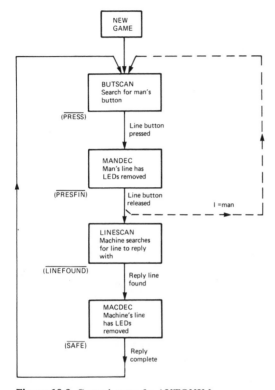

Figure 19.3. Control states for AUTONIM

button, it locks-on to that button, ignoring the other buttons, thereby providing cheat protection against more than one button being depressed at one time. The machine therefore leaves BUTS-CAN when a line button is pressed. It is known that 'finish' signals to the state encoder will be active low, therefore a signal $\overline{\text{PRESS}}$ shall end the BUTSCAN state.

The machine then enters the MANDEC (manual decrement) state, during which the selected line *counter* is decremented, thereby taking LEDs out at the machine clock rate; this continues until the pressed button is released, signified by a signal $\overline{\text{PRESFIN}}$, which ends the MANDEC state.

The machine then enters the LINESCAN state, during which it scans the various lines, searching for a suitable line in which to make a move. When the line is selected, a signal $\overline{\text{LINEFOUND}}$ ends the LINESCAN state.

173

The machine then enters the MACDEC (machine decrement) state, during which the selected line *counter* is decremented until a safe position is reached, signified by the $\overline{\text{SAFE}}$ signal. If the machine is required to make a mistake, or no safe position can be reached, the $\overline{\text{SAFE}}$ signal must be forced in an unsafe condition, in order to terminate the state. Once the state is terminated, the BUTSCAN state is re-entered, for it is now the man's turn to play again.

It can be seen from the diagram that if the machine is used in the manual mode (i.e. man plays man), this can be achieved by forcing a return to BUTSCAN from MANDEC, rather than entering LINESCAN.

Explanation of design description

The following description of the design procedure refers to the circuit diagrams provided at the end of the chapter by means of the 'F' reference which appears after the figure title. These diagrams contain the final IC and pin numbering details, which are useful for reference purposes in the following description, but it should be appreciated that the act of numbering the devices comes *after* the actual design. *Pin-out* is discussed in a later section of this chapter.

AUTONIM display logic (F1)   Figure 19.10

The circuit diagram of the display logic is given in diagram F1. This circuit evolved as follows.

It is required to display four lines of LEDs containing 7 diodes (line D), 5 diodes (line C), 3 diodes (line B) and one diode (line A). The 7445 (no LS version) BCD-to-decimal decoder/driver is a suitable device for driving the position display LEDs directly, for it has an 80 mA sink-current capability, and offers a separate discrete output for each discrete binary number; the problem is that one diode is not required to be illuminated for each count, but rather the *number* of diodes illuminated should *equal the count*. Rather than design separate encoding circuitry, it is easier to use the 'chain' principle, and connect the diodes for a given line in series; the appropriate decoder output is then used to sink the appropriate *number* of diodes in this chain. Since each diode can drop up to 2 V, this requires in excess of 14 V for the longest chain of seven diodes (line D).

Realising this, the designer would then put some thought in on the power supply (F9); clearly this must now supply not only +5 V for the logic, but *at least* +15 V for the LED supply.

Diagram F1 shows three 7445 devices (ICs 10–12); these are used for lines B, C and D. Since line A comprises only one LED, this does not warrant the use of a decoder/driver, and a simple buffer/driver gate (IC13a) is sufficient; this gate, like the decoder/driver outputs, is of the open-circuit variety, allowing a load connected to a higher value rail, since the output transistors have a 30 V breakdown characteristic.

Clearly each line must have an associated binary counter capable of counting *down* from an initial preset count equal to the game start position; the only exception is for line A, which can be a single flip-flop. The 74LS191 up/down synchronous counter is suitable for this purpose, for not only can it count down and be preset with any desired count, but it has outputs indicating when maximum/minimum counts are reached; it is necessary to detect when a count of zero has been reached, for further counting must then be inhibited. Without such an inhibit during manual operation, the counter would reset to its highest count and would then count down again, offering the player the cheat facility of *increasing* the number of LEDs left in a line! Thus ICs 4–6 are line counters D, C and B respectively, and the Q outputs directly drive the decoder/drivers (ICs 10–12); the Q outputs of the counters also provide the machine with an indication of the current count in each line, with these lines being labelled 'CTR', followed by the line reference letter, and the binary weighting of the line. There is no 'CTRB4' line since only two bits are required in line B to indicate the maximum count of three.

These counters are clocked on the positive-edge of the clock input CK, therefore a D-type flip-flop provides the same facility for line A (i.e. IC9a), which only has a single output bit: CTRA1. The counters are made to count down by holding the input on pin 5 high; pin 4 is an enable input G, which must be held low to enable the counters. The A, B, C and D inputs allow the counters to be loaded with a preset count value when the CK input is taken high during *load*; the counters must first be placed in the load mode by taking pin 14 low. The LD inputs to the counters are therefore controlled by a common input line $\overline{\text{LOAD}}$; this same line is connected to the preset input of line A flip-flop, thereby also setting this to a count of one. Examination of the counter inputs shows that these are wired to provide the counts of 7, 5 and 3 for ICs 4, 5 and 6 respectively.

When the 74LS191 counters are finally clocked to zero, the MX/MIN (i.e. max/min) output goes high; this output from pin 12 of each counter is used to set a latch associated with the counter; when the latch is set, this indicates a zero count in the related line. The latch outputs are therefore labelled ZEROD (for line D), through to ZEROB (for line B). The ZEROA signal is taken directly from the $\overline{Q}$ output of the line A flip-flop. Complementary outputs are also taken from the latches and the flip-flop (i.e. $\overline{ZEROD}$ through to $\overline{ZEROA}$).

All that is now required is to provide the logic necessary to control the clocking of the counters and flip-flop. IC3 provides four AND gates, which gate a common low frequency clock waveform LFCK with an enable associated with each line (e.g. ENCKD for *enable clock for line D*). The LFCK waveform is to be considered later (F5), but it is known that it will be sufficiently slow to take off LEDs from the selected row at a rate allowing the player to stop it at a required count (e.g. of the order of 1 Hz, or slower).

The enable signals can be derived from one of two sources: line button selection, or from the machine's control logic during MAC-DEC. The signals $\overline{SLD}$ through $\overline{SLA}$ are the *select line* signals activated by the machine during MACDEC; these are the signals used to make the machine's *reply*. IC2 is a quad Schmitt trigger NAND gate used as an inverted-input OR gate; the separate outputs are the clocking enables, which go true if either input is taken low. The reason a Schmitt gate is used, is that the button inputs are part of the button debounce circuitry, formed from identical resistors R_x and capacitors C_x; the $18\,\text{k}\Omega$ pull-up resistor is the maximum allowed for LS type devices (see Appendix C), and the chosen *tantalum* capacitors form a filter with a time-constant of around 60 ms, thereby removing the effects of contact bounce from the line buttons.

Normally buttons in this arrangement are connected on one side to $0\,\text{V}$; in this design, they have been connected to the output of OR gates (IC1). The reason is that this provides an economical way of scanning the buttons; a button can only be effective if the input terminal is taken low, since R_x pulls the output terminal high under all other conditions. The OR gate outputs can only be low if both of their inputs are also low, i.e. they are used as inverted-input NAND gates. Of the two inputs to each of these scanning gates, one is the related true ZEROn output from the zero latch, and the other input is a scanning selection line $\overline{SKn}$ from the control logic. Thus to consider line D as an example, in order to enable the button, $\overline{SKD}$ and ZEROD must be low; $\overline{SKD}$ is taken low regularly during the BUTSCAN state, but if line D reaches zero, ZEROD goes high and stays high, thereby inhibiting the selection of that button for the rest of the game.

It is necessary to determine when any one of the line select buttons has been depressed, in order to derive the $\overline{PRESS}$ signal needed to terminate the BUTSCAN state; the line enable outputs (ENCKD-ENCKA) are used elsewhere to derive $\overline{PRESS}$; the signal

176

$\overline{\text{PRESSFIN}}$, required to terminate the MANDEC state, is simply the complement of $\overline{\text{PRESS}}$ (i.e. $\overline{\text{PRESSFIN}} = \text{PRESS}$). (See F4 for derivation of $\overline{\text{PRESSFIN}}$ and for the effects of $\overline{\text{PRESSFIN}}$ and $\overline{\text{PRESS}}$ on the state encoder.)

> *Note.* The LFCK signal is a constantly running clock; it is tempting to think of controlling the binary counters by directly linking the enable clock input (e.g. ENCKD) to the G enable input of the related counter (e.g. IC4); this does not work in practice, for the correct relationship between the clock and the enable is not achieved, and spurious clocking will result. Hence the use of IC3 AND gates, to directly control the clocking input to each counter.

AUTONIM position analyser (F2)   Figure 19.11

The earlier section of this chapter entitled 'The theory of NIM' discussed *how* position analysis can be achieved. We must now convert this into electronic form.

It was shown that the binary weightings of the numbers associated with each line must be checked for even/odd content. The simplest problem will be considered first: *binary weight 4*. Binary weight 4 is simplest because only two lines can contain a 4, i.e. lines D and C. We shall derive a logical output named 4ODD for an odd count. Figure 19.4 shows a truth table for the requirement, where the two left-hand columns (CTRD4 and CTRC4) are the most significant bits from the line D and line C counters, as shown in F1. It can immediately be seen that 4ODD is a simple exclusive-OR function.

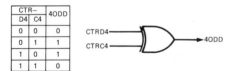

CTR—		4ODD
D4	C4	
0	0	0
0	1	1
1	0	1
1	1	0

Figure 19.4. Truth table and circuit for the 4ODD output

The situation is a little more complicated for producing a 2ODD output, i.e. an analysis of the binary weighted 2 bits. In this case there are three bits to consider, relating to lines D, C and B. A Karnaugh map for this situation is shown in Figure 19.5, and the Boolean algebra equivalent for the map is derived underneath,

177

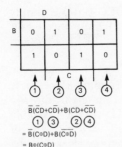

$$\overline{B}(C\overline{D}+\overline{C}D)+B(CD+\overline{C}\overline{D})$$

①③ ②④

$$= \overline{B}(C\oplus D)+B(\overline{C\oplus D})$$

$$= B\oplus(C\oplus D)$$

Figure 19.5. Karnaugh map for 2ODD (CTRB2, CTRC2, CTRD2)

where vertical lines on the Karnaugh map are associated with Boolean terms by the circled numbers, as indicated. The final simplification of $B \oplus (C \oplus D)$ is translated into circuit form by two XOR gates, as shown in Figure 19.6; the truth table given in the latter figure is drawn up from the circuit as proof of the fact that the required function is achieved. Note that 2ODD is only true when there are an odd number of 1's in the three CTR- columns. Thus a Karnaugh map solved the problem, and a truth table proved the solution effective under *all input conditions*.

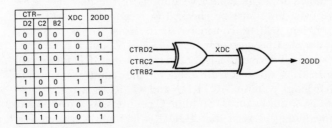

CTR-			XDC	2ODD
D2	C2	B2		
0	0	0	0	0
0	0	1	0	1
0	1	0	1	1
0	1	1	1	0
1	0	0	1	1
1	0	1	1	0
1	1	0	0	0
1	1	1	0	1

Figure 19.6. Truth table and circuit for the 2ODD output

The situation is the most complicated for producing the 1ODD output, for now we have four bits to contend with. Figure 19.7 shows a Karnaugh map for this situation, and it will be seen that the 1's are spaced out such that none can be readily grouped together. The circled numbered arrows indicate an approach which can be taken to analyse this map, and the Boolean expressions are once again to be seen to take the XOR form; the terms to the left of the vertical line are those first derived, and those to the right are derived by means of the Distributive laws (see Chapter 4); the only difference to be taken into account is the fact that exclusive-OR and exclusive-NOR terms are being dealt with. The final simplification utilises only XOR gates.

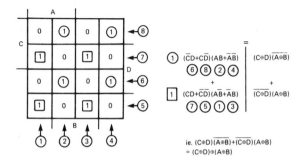

Figure 19.7. Karnaugh map for 1ODD (CTRA1, CTRB1, CTRC1, CTRD1)

It is interesting to note that this particular requirement is very similar to that of parity checking, previously discussed in Chapter 13 (see Figure 13.4). It is possible to use a parity checker IC to perform the required function, but this is not a cost-effective solution since such parity checkers are designed to check 8-bits, and our maximum requirement is only 4-bits, which does not need more than a single quad XOR chip in any case.

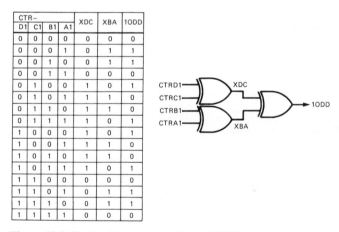

Figure 19.8. Truth table and circuit for the 1ODD output

Figure 19.8 shows the three-gate implementation of the Boolean expression: $(C \oplus D) \oplus (A \oplus B)$. The truth table also included in the figure provides the comforting proof that the solution is correct by considering every input condition. Note that XDC = CTRD1 $\oplus$

179

CTRC1, and XBA = CTRB1 ⊕ CTRA1; the final output is naturally: 1ODD = XDC ⊕ XBA.

Having designed a method of obtaining 4ODD, 2ODD and 1ODD, it now only remains necessary to establish *which* lines contain odd bits, since these are potential lines to select for the machine's move. The final circuit shown in F2 achieves this quite simply by ANDing the appropriate xODD output with each CTR-index, e.g. 2ODD.CTRC2 produces an output C2, which is only true if there is an odd number of binary weighted 2 bits AND one of these is in line C. The final circuit is seen to be elegant in its simplicity, and remarkably is the main requisite of the machine's 'intelligence'.

AUTONIM priority encoder and line multiplexer (F3)   Figure 19.12

The position analyser logic (F2) simply indicates which lines are odd, and which bits in those lines contribute to that odd status. In order to decide *which line* to move in, the theory of NIM will be thought about a little more deeply. A little thought will show that certain positions can produce the option of several solutions, viz.

Matches						Line	4	2	1
I	I	I	I	I		D	1	0	1
I	I	I	I	I		C	1	0	1
						B			0
				I		A			1

In the above example, 1ODD would be true since there are an odd number of 1's; 4ODD and 2ODD would be false, because these are both even. The following outputs would also be true: D1, C1 and A1. Thus taking one match (or LED) from line D, line C or line A is a satisfactory move, giving us three options. The machine must be allowed to make a *decision* where it is presented with options, otherwise it may have a 'brainstorm'!

Given a little thought, it may be established that it is always a satisfactory solution to select the line containing the most significant odd bit *under any circumstances*; where this still leaves an option, as in the example given above, the machine should make a *random* selection from the available lines. By making the selection random, it is ensured that the machine will not always play precisely the same game in a similar situation.

There are now two further requirements to be translated into electronic terms:

a. A priority selection of the line with the most significant odd bit.

b. A random selection of a line, given available options.

There is still one further complication to take into account: the spec. requirement for varying levels of *machine skill*. We have established how the machine should play as an *expert*, but it needs to make mistakes when it is not playing as an expert. Furthermore, we must decide what the machine is to do when forced to move from a safe position: it will not 'like' making the position unsafe!

The solution adopted is to create an ability to 'hedge' under such circumstances. If the machine is forced to make the position unsafe, its best tactic is to take only one LED, so making the game last out as long as possible, and thereby maximising the chances of the human opponent making a mistake and giving the machine an unsafe position to move from. If the machine is required to make a mistake due to a lowering of its level of skill, this can be similarly achieved by forcing it to 'hedge' rather than make the optimum move. *How* we get the machine to decide *when* to make a mistake is discussed elsewhere (F7).

The circuit given in F3 shows a *priority encoder* in the upper-half of the figure; this analyses the 4ODD, 2ODD and 1ODD inputs to produce priority selection lines PS4, PS2 and PS1. In addition, it produces a HEDGE output for a SAFE position OR when a MISTAKE is required (implemented by means of an inverted-input OR gate IC21a). Note that the signal $\overline{\text{SAFE}}$ is only active low when all three inputs are low (i.e. the *safe* situation). The priority encoder produces the outputs as follows:

$$PS4 = \overline{\text{HEDGE}}.4ODD$$
$$PS2 = \overline{\text{HEDGE}}.\overline{4ODD}.2ODD$$
$$PS1 = \overline{\text{HEDGE}}.\overline{4ODD}.\overline{2ODD}.1ODD$$

Thus if HEDGE is true, none of the normal priority encoder outputs may be true, and the machine is required to take one LED from any *available* line (i.e. lines still containing at least one LED illuminated).

The lower part of F3 shows a multiplexer designed to *scan* the various odd bit outputs from F2, utilising two 74LS153 4–line to 1–line multiplexers, each of which is a dual device. Thus output MPLX1 is a multiplexed version of the binary weighted 1 input lines D1, C1, B1 and A1. Similarly, MPLX2 is a multiplexed version of the binary weighted 2 input lines of D2, C2 and B2; note that the unused input is taken to 0 V. MPLX4 is similar for the binary

181

weighted 4 input lines of D4 and C4, with the two unused inputs again being tied to 0 V. By applying a moving counter to the A and B select inputs of both devices, on lines SCA and SCB, the multiplexer scans each line in turn, where the binary value of the input lines SCA and SCB establishes which line is sampled. It may be seen that the following applies:

Input count (equiv. decimal) 0 selects line A.
Input count (equiv. decimal) 1 selects line B.
Input count (equiv. decimal) 2 selects line C.
Input count (equiv. decimal) 3 selects line D.

It can be seen that for a given line selection made by the multiplexer, the NAND gates of IC20 apply the priority selection requirement to the selected line. For example, say PS2 is true; when the multiplexer selects a line which produces MPLX2 true, $\overline{PMX2}$ goes low, indicating that a suitable line has been found (i.e. 2 is the highest odd bit, and the line selected by the multiplexer contains an odd binary weighted 2-bit). Gate IC22a is used an an inverted input OR gate, which after inversion by IC23d produces a signal $\overline{LINE-FOUND}$ when a suitable line has been found*.

Since the HEDGE condition must overrule any other, this is given the highest priority. When HEDGE is true, the machine is simply looking for a line containing at least one illuminated LED, hence the $\overline{ZEROx}$ inputs to the multiplexer in order to produce the $\overline{MPLXZ}$ output. MPLXZ is combined with HEDGE to produce $\overline{PMXH}$ low when a suitable line has been found in the HEDGE condition; as with the other outputs from IC20, this results in $\overline{LINEFOUND}$ going low.

It may be seen that if several line options are available after a given move, the multiplexing system responds to the first acceptable line that it scans. In order to introduce the required random element into this selection, it is simply necessary to *start* the multiplexer at a random count. How this is achieved is discussed later (F7).

The multiplexer chips are enabled when $\overline{LINESCAN}$ goes low, thereby only allowing this circuitry to function during the LINE-SCAN state.

AUTONIM state encoder (F4)   Figure 19.13

State encoders were discussed in detail in Chapter 16, therefore this account will assume complete familiarity with the principle involved. It was mentioned that two forms of state encoder are

---

* *Refer back to Figure 19.3.*

182

possible: those using a counter/decoder, and those using a shift register. This design will employ a shift register in order to provide an example of this alternative technique.

The circuit shown in F4 employs a 74LS195 4-bit shift register. In order to prevent it entering an illegal condition at switch-on, it is necessary to clear the register on power-on. The start of a new game is similar to the power-on condition, therefore the circuitry for the two states is combined. At power-on, capacitor C_I is discharged, and charges slowly through R_I; the indicated values produce a time-constant of 380 ms, which is approximately the length of time that LOAD is asserted at switch-on. The NEW GAME button is used to short-circuit the capacitor, and causes LOAD to be asserted for as long as the button is depressed. The CR combination also acts as debounce circuitry for the NEW GAME button. When LOAD is true, $\overline{\text{SRLD}}$ goes low, to produce the input requirement for a load operation at the shift register; a subsequent rising edge at the CK input loads this *synchronous* shift register. LOAD true causes TRIP to be true (after a short delay to be explained later); TRIP is ANDed with a regular free-running clock pulse $\overline{\text{CK}}$. For the duration of the LOAD pulse, this repeatedly loads the shift register with the data set up at the parallel inputs (A, B, C and D).

For simplicity, at this stage assume that the A input is a logic 1, and that the other inputs are at logic 0. Thus QA goes to logic 1, resulting in $\overline{\text{BUTSCAN}}$ going low, i.e. the BUTSCAN state is entered. Inverted input OR gate IC43a is combined with input and output inverters (to use up spare gates), so forming what amounts to a four input NOR gate, with pin 45–4 going low if any button is pressed, i.e. if any ENCKx input goes high. MACDEC is low during the BUTSCAN mode, therefore $\overline{\text{PRESFIN}}$ can go high; during MACDEC, when an enable also goes high, the input on pin 44–6 inhibits $\overline{\text{PRESFIN}}$ from going high. (Note that $\overline{\text{PRESFIN}}$ is so named rather than PRESS, because its action *when going low* is used to trip the state encoder at *press-finish*.)

Thus $\overline{\text{PRESFIN}}$ is high when a line button is pressed, which causes $\overline{\text{PRESS}}$ to go go low at pin 26–10; as a result, pin 29–11 goes low, causing CHGSTATE to go true. TRIP goes true after the delay set up by the 470 Ω resistor and the 0.22 μF capacitor, giving a nominal 70 μs delay. STATECK goes high as soon as $\overline{\text{CK}}$ is high: if $\overline{\text{CK}}$ is already high when TRIP goes high, STATECK goes high at once. It is for this reason that the delay exists, for it guarantees a predetermined delay between a finish line going low (e.g. $\overline{\text{PRESS}}$), and a change of state at the state encoder, and thereby prevents spike outputs from the state strobes (see general discussion of state encoders in Chapter 16).

It will be explained later why TRIP is gated with $\overline{\text{CK}}$ (in the discussion on F8); similarly, the purpose of gates IC30b and IC26a will be discussed when appropriate (also during the F8 discussion). This illusrates an important point. Such subtleties are not obvious at this stage, but come out as a later requirement. It is not possible to design *all* the control circuitry until the major part of the design is known.

Thus there is a four-stage state encoder, which starts with QA true, and shifts a logic 1 one bit at a time for each change of state. This gives the required sequence of states: BUTSCAN, MANDEC, LINESCAN and MACDEC. When the MACDEC state is terminated by $\overline{\text{CSAFE}}$ going low, the state strobe $\overline{\text{MACFIN}}$ goes low; this is input at pin 30–13, causing $\overline{\text{SRLD}}$ to go low. When STATECK subsequently occurs, it causes a load, which sets up the initial condition again, thereby reverting to the BUTSCAN state.

It may be recalled that it is required that the machine can be played in a manual mode, i.e. man versus man. The selection of this mode (in F7), causes $\overline{\text{MAN}}$ to be low; this is combined with the state strobe $\overline{\text{MANFIN}}$ to generate $\overline{\text{SHORTEN}}$, and also a shift by means of taking $\overline{\text{SRLD}}$ low. Looking back at Figure 19.3 for a moment, this has the effect of returning control along the dotted line to BUTS-CAN, i.e. it prevents the states of LINESCAN and MACDEC being entered, and thereby prevents the machine from making a reply.

The NAND gate IC21c is used to generate a clear pulse to the shift register on the front edge of LOAD (compare with Figure 15.5*). This is simply a safety-measure which cancels any states prior to the initial setting-up of the BUTSCAN state; the setting-up for a new game has to wait for $\overline{\text{CK}}$ going high, and $\overline{\text{CK}}$ is a fairly slow running clock.

Autonim clock generators (F5)   Figure 19.14

The circuit shown in F5 produces two different clocking sources: a high frequency clock HFCK, and a low frequency clock LFCK. Both are formed from 555 timers, followed by a wave-shaping Schmitt trigger gate. The period of the HFCK generator is set by 0.7 $\times$ 3 MΩ $\times$ 2.2 nF, i.e. 4.6 ms. The period of the LFCK generator is set by 0.7 $\times$ 300 kΩ $\times$ 5 μF, i.e. 1 s.

There is the need to slow the HFCK down to a really slow rate during the LINESCAN state (discussed under F7), therefore $\overline{\text{LINESCAN}}$ is fed to a non-inverting open-collector buffer gate IC13b, to introduce a 2.2 μF capacitor in parallel with the 2.2 nF capacitor during LINESCAN. This increases the time-constant to 4.6 s.

* See page 129.

LFCK is used to clock the line counters in F1, but must only do this during MANDEC and MACDEC states; gate IC21b ensures this, since DEC is only true for one of these conditions, and DEC must be true to enable LFCK. The $\overline{\text{CK}}$ signal is used for other purposes and must therefore be separate to LFCK.

AUTONIM false-safe hedge logic (F6)   Figure 19.15

If F3 is referred back to for a moment, it will be seen that $\overline{\text{SAFE}}$ is low for a safe condition of the NIM game. The *controlled safe* output from F6 $\overline{\text{CSAFE}}$ is the signal which actually terminates the MAC-DEC state. The logic of F6 is designed to introduce a false-safe condition *for one move* when the machine is faced with the 'hedge' situation. In this condition it does not 'want' to move, since a move makes the position unsafe. The logic 'fools it' into thinking that the position is safe for one move, thereby causing one LED to be taken. It depends upon a latch formed by gates IC33a and IC33b.

If HEDGE is true during the LINESCAN state – as detected by IC21d – this gives warning that a false-safe condition is coming up; this condition is used to set the NAND-gate latch, causing SETFAL to go high. During normal play, with SETFAL low, $\overline{\text{TSAFE}}$ (true-safe) follows the $\overline{\text{SAFE}}$ input, but with SETFAL high, it is inhibited, forcing $\overline{\text{TSAFE}}$ high. When the MACDEC state is entered, the next LFCK pulse causes $\overline{\text{FSAFE}}$ (false-safe) to go low, but since the *presence* of LFCK high means that a line counter has been decremented (on the rising-edge of LFCK), it is now possible to assert $\overline{\text{CSAFE}}$ to end the MACDEC state. So long as the latch is reset before this condition can occur again, all is well. It is conveniently reset by the subsequent $\overline{\text{BUTSCAN}}$ signal.

AUTONIM line scanner and machine skill scanner (F7)   Figure 19.16

It will be remembered that it is required to introduce a random element into the line multiplexer (F3). This is achieved by the line scanner shown as the upper part of F7. The dual 2-to-4 line decoder (IC36), a 74LS155, is driven from the same binary counter that drives the line multiplexer, i.e. 4-bit synchronous counter IC35. The counter is clocked by HFCK at about 217 Hz *except* during the MACDEC state. This frequency is halved by the first stage of the counter, before clocking the two stages which provide the SCA and SCB outputs. This association with SCA/SCB provides synchronisation between line multiplexer and scanner.

The upper half of IC36 is used to generate the button enable lines $\overline{\text{SKA}}$ to $\overline{\text{SKD}}$, whilst the lower half is used to generate the machine enable lines $\overline{\text{SLA}}$ to $\overline{\text{SLD}}$. The combination of enable (G) inputs and data inputs to each decoder, allows it to be controlled directly from available signals, without additional gating. Control is arranged such that one line in the functioning half of the dual decoder goes low for a given binary input at the A and B terminals.

During BUTSCAN, $\overline{\text{LINESCAN}}$ is high and MACDEC is low, enabling the upper decoder. IC38 is a 4-bit bistable latch of the variety previously shown in Figure 6.3, i.e. it is *transparent* when the enable input is high. Since $\overline{\text{MANDEC}}$ is high during BUTSCAN, the latch is transparent, and the outputs follow the inputs; thus the lines $\overline{\text{SKA}}$ to $\overline{\text{SKD}}$ are enabled in turn according to the binary input (e.g. binary 2 in causes $\overline{\text{SKC}}$ to be active). When a line button is pressed the state changes to MANDEC, therefore $\overline{\text{MANDEC}}$ goes low and staticises the present condition of the quad latch. This locks the present button enable line to the pressed button, with two effects: firstly it means that if any other line button is depressed it will disregard it, and secondly, it allows the line scanner *to continue scanning*. The latter action introduces the required random aspect, for this scanning action continues for as long as a line button is depressed. Since the scanning frequency is much higher than human responses with respect to releasing buttons, it is purely random where the scanner might be when the line button is finally released.

When the LINESCAN state is entered, the upper decoder is disabled by $\overline{\text{LINESCAN}}$ going low. The machine then searches for a suitable line, starting its scan with a random line according to the present state of the scanner. When a suitable line has been found, the MACDEC state is entered. In this state, the upper decoder is disabled by the MACDEC input going high; at the same time $\overline{\text{MACDEC}}$ goes low to enable the lower decoder, and hence the appropriate machine line selection from $\overline{\text{SLA}}$ to $\overline{\text{SLD}}$.

It was previously mentioned that the HFCK frequency is drastically reduced during the LINESCAN state due to the effects of $\overline{\text{LINESCAN}}$ via IC13b (see F5). This is to simulate a variable 'thinking response' when it is the machine's move; there is nothing more frustrating than playing against a machine which gives apparently instant replies to your own well thought out moves. Since the line scanner starts at a random position during LINESCAN, it passes through a random number of scans before finding a suitable line (with a maximum of four). By making this scanning speed slow, a variable time of response is introduced.

Note that two flip-flops could be used in place of the counter as IC35, but this would still utilise one IC requiring more interconnections, therefore there is no particular advantage.

The lower half of F7 is the machine skill scanner. This also utilises the random effect created by the line scanner running during manual depression of a line button, but is provided with its own discrete binary counter, IC39. This time three bits are required, and the *decade* counter provides sufficient output states. This counter is driven by the high frequency HFCK signal, providing that the machine is not in the LINESCAN state; this condition is detected by gate IC34c. Once the machine enters LINESCAN the counter is frozen. The decoder used this time (IC40) is similar to that used above (IC36), except that it has open-circuit outputs. This allows the outputs to be wired together (wire-OR) to a common pull-up resistor, this multiple output then providing the $\overline{\text{MISTAKE}}$ signal. Thus if the decoder is stopped with a low output linked to pole A of the skill select switch, a mistake is called for, otherwise an optimum move is made by the machine ($\overline{\text{MISTAKE}}$ is an input to the priority encoder in F3).

The skill switch is wired to provide the following *average percentage errors* according to selection:

expert	–	none
good	–	10%
average	–	20%
poor	–	30%
child	–	40%

This is achieved by a rather novel method, using the decade counter/decoder combination, as the following table shows. Note that the decoder decodes two particular outputs *twice**; thus each output decoded once provides a 10% error rate (on average), whilst those decoded twice provide a 20% error rate. It is possible to conveniently talk directly in terms of *percent* because a *decade* counter is being used. Parallel linking of the required *number* of outputs provides the requisite error rate, e.g. 30% is achieved for the *poor* selection by linking three 10% error rate outputs together and taking them to contact 2 of the switch.

Because the *manual* condition obviates a machine skill setting, it is

Decoder output	Counts decoded	Error rate
2Y0	0 & 8	20%
2Y1	1 & 9	20%
2Y2	2	10%
2Y3	3	10%
1Y0	4	10%
1Y1	5	10%
1Y2	6	10%
1Y3	7	10%

* *Because QD on decade counter IC39 is not used.*

built into the same switch, and another pole provides the $\overline{\text{MAN}}$ output for this setting.

Remember this as a useful way of introducing a random element into a circuit, for wherever a manual input is used, if this is combined with a fast oscillator circuit, it can be used to generate genuine random selections.

AUTONIM move indicator logic and audio stage (F8)   Figure 19.17

The upper half of the circuit shown in F8 provides the front panel PLAY LED indicator drive for I/YOU, and the WIN indicator drive. It also *remembers* which player starts, and controls play such that the other player starts the following game. This introduces an element of fairness into a game which can be won on a purely theoretical basis. Flip-flop IC42b provides the indication of PLAY, and its complementary Q and $\overline{\text{Q}}$ outputs drive the I and YOU LEDs. During normal play, $\overline{\text{END}}$ is high, thus the two XOR gates IC14d and IC15d are normally inverting. A dual AND-OR-INVERT gate IC41 controls this flip-flop.

The upper AND-OR-INVERT controls the D input of the PLAY indicator flip-flop. During normal play – with $\overline{\text{LOAD}}$ high – the upper AND gate is enabled, thereby allowing the flip-flop Q output to be fed back to the D input after inversion; this causes the flip-flop to be complemented at each clock pulse, which occurs during the manual mode at a pulse MANTOG. As soon as a line button has been released during the MAN mode, $\overline{\text{MANDEC}}$ goes high, which via the lower AND gate, causes MANTOG to go high, thereby toggling the play flip-flop.

Flip-flop IC42a 'remembers' the last player to start a game, and is clocked by $\overline{\text{LOAD}}$, i.e. at the *end* of a load; this flip-flop is connected to toggle every time it is clocked. During load, the upper AND gate is disabled by $\overline{\text{LOAD}}$ going low, and the D input of the play flip-flop is then set by the Q output of the last starter flip-flop, due to LOAD going high at pin 41–11. Under these circumstances the play flip-flop is again clocked by MANTOG, but this time due to LOAD.STATECK; hence the previously mentioned delay during load.

When the machine is not operating in the manual mode, there must be a definite relationship between the PLAY indicator flip-flop and the state encoder. Further complication at the clocking input and D input is avoided, and the required synchronisation is *guaranteed* by using the preset and clear inputs in this mode. When the flip-flop is set (i.e. Q = 1), $\overline{\text{MACGO}}$ is high and $\overline{\text{MANGO}}$ is low, indicating *man's go*; thus only the YOU LED is illuminated

188

(remember that the XOR gates are acting as inverters). The flip-flop is set externally via the preset input, pin 42–10, i.e. $\overline{\text{STRTMAN}}$ goes low. Gate IC28d detects the right condition: $\overline{\text{BUTSCAN}}$ and MAN must both be low. Conversely, the flip-flop is cleared down to the $\overline{\text{MACGO}} = 0$ state by taking $\overline{\text{STRTMAC}}$ low; this is the case when both $\overline{\text{LINESCAN}}$ and MAN are low.

When the game is over, all the ZERO latches in F1 are set. IC43b detects this condition and outputs $\overline{\text{END}}$ low; this causes the XOR gates driving the PLAY LEDs to become non-inverting. After the final winning move, the PLAY flip-flop is complemented to indicate the next player: in this case the *loser*. By reversing the action of the XOR gates, the indicators now indicate the *winner*. END is NANDed with $\overline{\text{CK}}$ by IC33c, and the output is used to drive the WIN LED via an emitter follower; this LED is conveniently powered from the $+5\,\text{V}$ rail. This causes the WIN LED to flash on and off at the low frequency clocking rate until a new game is called for.

It will be remembered that there is a slight complication to the A and B parallel inputs of the state encoder (see F4). This is to 'nudge' the state encoder out of the BUTSCAN condition when it is the machine's turn to start a game. Thus LOAD.$\overline{\text{MAN}}$.NMAC is the condition used to preset the MANDEC state during a load (NMAC indicates *next-machine*, and is obtained from IC42a in F8). Since PRESFIN is low in this condition, the state encoder at once moves on to the LINESCAN state, and hence the machine is forced to make the first move. Under *all* other conditions the parallel inputs to the state encoder are A = 1 and B = 0, as previously assumed.

The audio portion of F8 is required to provide a tone as each LED is extinguished, and different tones for each player. It is also required to provide a distinctive indication when a win occurs, but this is to be limited in time to prevent it being annoying. These requirements are met by the lower portion of F8.

A counter, IC46, is held inoperative during normal play by END being low on the clear input; thus the QD output is low, giving INSD (inhibit sound) low. If $\overline{\text{CKSD}}$ (clock sound) is also low, GCKSD (gated clock sound) is high, thereby enabling the 555 timer IC47, connected as an oscillator. This circuit is similar to the audio stage described in the previous chapter, and further details of the principle are to be found there. $\overline{\text{MACGO}}$ is coupled through a non-inverting open-collector buffer gate IC13f to introduce a 2nF capacitor in parallel with the normal 10nF capacitor when it is the machine's go (or the player taking the machine's place during manual play). This changes the tone of the oscillator during the machine's go, hence providing two tones.

At the end of play, END is gated with the output from a flip-flop at IC33d; when the flip-flop Q output (pin 9–9) is high, a p-n-p transistor is driven on via a $100\,\text{k}\Omega$ base resistance, thereby linking a $10\,\text{k}\Omega$ resistor in parallel with the normal $47\,\text{k}\Omega$ resistor of the 555 timer circuit; this provides yet another change of tone for the win condition. The output $\overline{\text{WINCK}}$ from pin 33–8 is at the slow clocking rate, but only occurs after a win. This is used to toggle a win flip-flop (IC9b), which alternately switches the transistor on and off, thereby providing a two-tone effect for a win. Because END goes high, the counter (IC46) is released to count, and the count takes INSD high, this inhibits GCKSD, forcing it low, and thereby cutting off the audio as required after a set number of clock pulses. The QD output provides the longest win tones, but by taking INSD from an earlier counter output, the duration of the win tones can be shortened.

One complication is introduced due to the sound requirement: the synchronisation of the tones with the removal of LEDs during play. To avoid confusion, the tone should not occur before a particular LED is extinguished, and since the state encoder changes as soon as a player's move is completed, this must not cause the immediate 'stunting' of a tone. Figure 19.9 depicts a timing diagram, showing

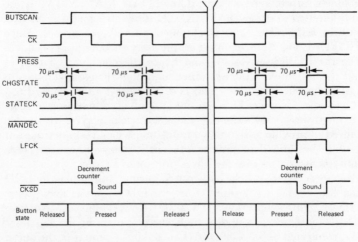

Figure 19.9. Timing diagram showing the relationship between the state encoder and the audio output when decrementing the line counter

how these requirements are met. It is dependent upon the correct timing control of the state encoder in relation to the clocking of the line counters. The left and right-hand portions of the timing diagram show two different situations which may occur with respect to the timing of button depression and the free-running $\overline{CK}$ waveform.

Considering the left-hand side of the timing diagram first, a line button is pressed when $\overline{CK}$ is high, thus STATECK occurs 70 µs later, due to the delayed TRIP signal (see F4). Note that LFCK is the inverse of $\overline{CK}$ when $\overline{MANDEC}$ is low (see F5). The LED is extinguished on the leading-edge of LFCK – since this is when the line counter is decremented – and $\overline{CKSD}$ goes low whilst LFCK is high (see gate IC44d in F8). Thus the tone sounds from the LED going out, for the duration of half a $\overline{CK}$ period. Only one decrement is shown, but several could occur.

The right-hand side of the timing diagram shows two different situations. The line button is depressed when $\overline{CK}$ is low, therefore $\overline{MANDEC}$ does not occur until $\overline{CK}$ goes high (see F4). This timing diagram also shows the situation where the line button is released before a half clock period of $\overline{CK}$ has terminated. Since $\overline{CK}$ must go high to clock the next state at the state encoder, the sound is not cut short, and $\overline{MANDEC}$ does not terminate until the end of the half clock period. This illustrates how important timing can be in a logic circuit, and how difficulties can be overcome by judicious use of particular edges of waveforms.

A design as complicated as this warrants the drawing of other timing diagrams, but space does not permit their inclusion here. The reader may care to tackle this problem for himself if any areas puzzle him!

Pinning-out

The next stage after completing the logic design to your complete satisfaction is to *pin-out* the devices, i.e. to allocate IC numbers. This leads up to possible modifications for optimisation reasons. The suggested method is to use what I have termed an 'IC Usage' table. Since any given device has a maximum of six elements within it (e.g. hex inverter), a good method is to tabulate each gate/element as it is assigned. Once this has been completed, spare gates are readily identified, and optimisation may take place. If the design is divided into identifiable functional areas as this example has been (i.e. F1–F8), then rather than simply ticking off used elements, it is helpful to indicate where they are located by indicating an 'F' number, as shown in the following table. Go through the various functional areas in a fixed and sensible sequence, and for each new gate or element, look to see if an IC already listed has a suitable spare, and use it if so. In this way the number of devices can be optimised.

191

IC usage table for the Autonim circuit

IC Ref.	a	b	c	d	e	f	Description	Used	Type
1	1	1	1	1	–	–	2 i/p OR	√	74LS32
2	1	1	1	1	–	–	2 i/p Schmitt	√	74LS132
3	1	1	1	1	–	–	2 i/p AND	√	74LS08
4	1	–	–	–	–	–	Up/dn bin ctr	√	74LS191
5	1	–	–	–	–	–	Up/dn bin ctr	√	74LS191
6	1	–	–	–	–	–	Up/dn bin ctr	√	74LS191
7	1	1	1	1	–	–	2 i/p NOR	√	74LS02
8	1	1	3	4	–	–	2 i/p NOR	√	74LS02
9	1	8	–	–	–	–	Dual D f/f	√	74LS74
10	1	–	–	–	–	–	4 → 10 dec o/c	√	7445
11	1	–	–	–	–	–	4 → 10 dec o/c	√	7445
12	1	–	–	–	–	–	4 → 10 dec o/c	√	7445
13	1	5	8	8	8	8	6 × buf driver	√	7407
14	2	2	2	8	–	–	2 i/p XOR	√	74LS86
15	2	2	2	8	–	–	2 i/p XOR	√	74LS86
16	2	2	2	2	–	–	2 i/p AND	√	74LS08
17	2	2	2	2	–	–	2 i/p AND	√	74LS08
18	2	3	4	5	–	–	2 i/p AND	√	74LS08
19	3	3	3	–	–	–	3 i/p NOR	√	74LS27
20	3	3	3	3	–	–	2 i/p NAND	√	74LS00
21	3	5	4	6	–	–	2 i/p NAND	√	74LS00
22	3	4	–	–	–	–	4 i/p NAND	√	74LS20
23	3	3	3	3	4	4	6 × inverter	√	74LS04
24	3	–	–	–	–	–	4 → 1 MPX	√	74LS153
25	3	–	–	–	–	–	4 → 1 MPX	√	74LS153
26	4	4	4	4	4	5	6 × inverter	√	74LS04
27	4	4	5	5	8	8	6 × Schmitt	√	74LS14
28	4	6	8	8	–	–	2 i/p OR	√	74LS32
29	4	4	4	4	–	–	2 i/p OR	√	74LS32
30	4	4	6	–	–	–	3 i/p NAND	√	74LS10
31	5	–	–	–	–	–	555 timer	√	NE555
32	5	–	–	–	–	–	555 timer	√	NE555
33	6	6	8	8	–	–	2 i/p NAND	√	74LS00
34	6	7	7	8	–	–	2 i/p NAND	√	74LS00
35	7	–	–	–	–	–	4-bit sync ctr	√	74LS160
36	7	–	–	–	–	–	2 → 4 decoder	√	74LS155
37	4	–	–	–	–	–	4-bit shift reg	√	74LS195
38	7	–	–	–	–	–	4-bit B/S latch	√	74LS75
39	7	–	–	–	–	–	4-bit sync ctr	√	74LS160
40	7	–	–	–	–	–	2 → 4 decoder o/c	√	74LS156
41	8	–	–	–	–	–	AND-OR-INVERT	√	74LS51
42	8	8	–	–	–	–	Dual D f/f	√	74LS74
43	4	8	–	–	–	–	4 i/p NAND	√	74LS20
44	8	4	8	8	–	–	2 i/p NOR	√	74LS02
45	8	4	4	4	4	4	6 × inverter	√	74LS04
46	8	–	–	–	–	–	bin ctr	√	74LS197
47	8	–	–	–	–	–	555 timer	√	NE555

Taking a single example from the table, it may be seen that IC15 is a quad XOR gate, and that gates IC15a, IC15b and IC15c are to be found on F2, and gate IC15d on F8; the type number is 74LS86.

The 'Used' column of the table is ticked off during compilation as soon as all the gates or elements of that IC have all been used. This column then provides a constant check of ICs containing 'spares'. This particular table corresponds to the circuit as finally drawn up, and it will be seen that *there are no spare gates or elements anywhere*. The first table to be drawn up did contain a few spare gates, highlighted by the absence of ticks in the 'Used' column. Subsequent small modifications fully utilised devices with spare gates and freed certain others, resulting in the satisfactory solution with no spare gates. Clearly this cannot always be expected. Note that the judicious use of a transistor driver for the WIN LED obviated the need for a further 7407 buffer driver, as used to drive the PLAY indicator LEDs; had this option been taken, there would have been an extra IC used containing five spare gates.

Calculating power supply current

The power supply cannot be finalised until this stage. Only now can the required current be calculated. For a design this complicated, it is recommended that what I have termed an 'IC Technical Detail' table be used. This not only forms the basis for the power supply current calculation, but serves as a components list, power supply pin indicator, and allows the design to be costed. These factors are very conveniently combined, and the table becomes an invaluable source of reference to go with the design. All ICs of a given type number are now grouped together. The average and maximum supply current can be obtained from Appendix B at the rear of this book. The cost columns have been left blank, since this obviously depends upon supplier and current circumstances.

It may be seen from the table that the total average current drawn from the $+5\,V$ supply is likely to be $423\,mA$, with a maximum of $751\,mA$. Since it is virtually impossible for all the ICs to be drawing maximum current at once, the maximum figure is never likely to be approached, but it is handy to have the figure in mind when designing the power supply.

In addition, the lamp supply must not be forgotten. This must supply three chains of LEDs. If these are driven at a forward current of say $20\,mA$ for good visibility, this will require $3 \times 20\,mA = 60\,mA$, due to the series arrangement shown in F1. The load resistors for these LEDs must vary according to the number of LEDs

IC technical details table for the Autonim circuit

Type No.	IC Refs.	Power pins +5V	Power pins 0V	Qty.	Unit I (mA) av	Unit I (mA) max	Tot I (mA) av	Tot I (mA) max	Unit cost (p)	Total cost (£)
74LS32	1, 28, 29	14	7	3	4	10	12	30		
74LS132	2	14	7	1	7	14	7	14		
74LS08	3, 16, 17, 18	14	7	4	5	9	20	36		
74LS191	4, 5, 6	16	8	3	20	35	60	105		
74LS02	7, 8, 44	14	7	3	2	5.5	6	16		
74LS74	9, 42	14	7	2	4	8	8	16		
7445	10, 11, 12	16	8	3	43	70	129	210		
7407	13	14	7	1	20	40	20	40		
74LS86	14, 15	14	7	2	6	10	12	20		
74LS27	19	14	7	1	3	7	3	7		
74LS00	20, 21, 33, 34	14	7	4	2	4	8	16		
74LS20	22, 43	14	7	2	1	2	2	4		
74LS04	23, 26, 45	14	7	3	6	10	18	30		
74LS153	24, 25	16	8	2	6	10	12	20		
74LS14	27	14	7	1	10	21	10	21		
74LS10	30	14	7	1	0.5	1	0.5	1		
NE555	31, 32, 47	8	1	3	3	6	9	18		
74LS160	35, 39	16	8	2	19	32	38	64		
74LS155	36	16	8	1	6	10	6	10		
74LS195	37	16	8	1	14	21	14	21		
74LS75	38	5	12	1	6	12	6	12		
74LS156	40	16	8	1	6	10	6	10		
74LS51	41	14	7	1	1	3	1	3		
74LS197	46	14	7	1	16	27	16	27		
		Totals		47	–	–	423	751	–	£

in the chain, for the resistor acts as ballast, and must drop the remaining volts. The resistor values will be calculated after the lamp supply voltage has been established.

Designing the power supply (F9)

Clearly the +5 V requirement can be easily met by a 5 V regulator chip such as the μA7805C, which will supply up to 1 A. The circuit shown in F9 is the arrangement settled upon. Transformers usually come with two secondaries the same, and since two separate d.c. supplies are required, this must be taken into account. A bridge rectifier circuit produces just less than 1.4 times the a.c. voltage fed into it. The IC regulator requires *at least* 3 V dropped between input and output terminals, therefore the voltage fed to the I terminal must be greater than +8 V. This calls for a 9 V secondary winding, giving a nominal d.c. voltage after smoothing of around +12 V.

The second secondary winding of the transformer is linked in series with the first, providing an 18 V a.c. signal. It is only possible to single-wave rectify this supply, for anything else will short-circuit the lower bridge rectifier. This leads to the rather unusual arrangement shown, where the return path for the rectified +24 V supply is via the lower left-hand diode of the bridge rectifier to the lower 0 V; this is quite acceptable, since all that this means is an extra 60 mA through that limb of the bridge, and a slight drop in voltage due to the extra series diode. Single-wave rectification also provides just under 1.4 times the a.c. voltage, hence the nominal +24 V from the 18 V a.c. input. Single-wave rectification will contain a fair amount of ripple, but since this supply only drives LEDs, this is of little consequence.

Smoothing capacitors are chosen as large in capacitance value as possible, bearing in mind that excessive capacitance means excessive size and cost. The 0.1 µF ceramic capacitors must be distributed around the circuit board to decouple the +5 V rail at suitable points.

The transformer T1 must have a VA capability of say 12 V × 0.5 A = 6 VA for the 5 V supply. The secondary winding of the transformer used for the 24 V supply will have a similar rating automatically, leading to a 12 VA transformer; note that the actual requirement for the lamp supply is a mere 24 V × 0.06 A = 1.44 VA.*

Calculating the LED load resistor values

If the lamp supply is +24 V, we can now calculate the resistors shown R_A to R_G in F1. Allowing for 2 V dropped by each diode, the following results are obtained, assuming a diode current of 20 mA:

Resistor	No. of LEDs	Voltage across LEDs	V_{res}	Suitable resistor
R_A	1	2 V	22 V	1.1 kΩ
R_B	2	4 V	20 V	1.0 kΩ
R_C	3	6 V	18 V	820 Ω
R_D	4	8 V	16 V	820 Ω
R_E	5	10 V	14 V	680 Ω
R_F	6	12 V	12 V	560 Ω
R_G	7	14 V	10 V	470 Ω

* *The designer capable of designing a more efficient power supply using discrete components can get away with two 6 V windings, and a lamp supply of around +16 V; such a design has a bridge rectifier voltage of only 7 to 8 V, which is sufficient for a +5 V supply if an IC regulator is not used. This can result in a 7 VA transformer, which is considerably smaller.*

The resistor values are rounded up or down to the nearest preferred value. The slight change in current that this causes will not be noticed in terms of LED illumination.

Build and test

The next stage in a conventional project is to build a prototype and to test it. The power supply should be tested on its own before connecting the logic circuitry, suitably loaded with a resistor/s: ICs are expensive to blow up, and a lot of trouble to remove!

It is worth thinking about 'functional build and test' in a complicated design, for this method can simplify commissioning. An example of this might help with the AUTONIM.

Let us consider the building and testing of the portion of circuitry shown in F1, i.e. the display portion of the game. For ease of testing, it is sensible to also build the load logic from F4, and the low frequency clock portion of F5. It is then necessary to make a few temporary connections to replace missing signals. Pin 21–4 or pin 21–5 should be tied to 0 V to force DEC true, thereby enabling the LFCK waveform (see F5). In addition, pins 2, 5, 10 and 13 of IC1 should also be tied to 0 V to replace the missing signals $\overline{\text{SKD}}$–$\overline{\text{SKA}}$. In this condition, the NEW GAME button will initialise the display circuitry of F1, and all the line selection buttons should operate. Depression of any line button should cause that line to decrement to zero, but not beyond. NEW GAME should cause all the LEDs to be illuminated again.

Some other more general steps which can be taken to assist troubleshooting in such a circuit are as follows. The WIN LED can be used very effectively as a general purpose logic level indicator. Simply connect the LED to its transistor drive, and then use a probe connected to the transistor base, instead of linking the base to pin 33–8. The LED is then illuminated for a logic 0, or extinguished for a logic 1 or open-circuit. Investigations around the circuit can be greatly simplified by reducing the clocking rates. The HFCK can be very readily reduced to its slow time-constant by simply linking pin 13-3 to 0 V instead of to the $\overline{\text{LINESCAN}}$ input; this permanently connects in the 2.2 μF capacitor. The LFCK should be slow enough for most purposes, in any case. Connecting pin 30–3 temporarily to 0 V prevents the state encoder from initially being set for a machine start of play in a new game.

Many such tricks can be performed to force particular conditions for test purposes, and these should not be overlooked when faced with a complex circuit containing possible wiring errors. Open-circuiting inputs causes a temporary high at the given inputs without the need of tying the input high, but gate inputs should only be left open-circuit for test purposes.

The final piece of advice, if all else fails to locate the reason for a particularly strange phenomenon, draw timing diagrams for relevant signals. This will generally reveal the reason, and should help in determining a solution.

Final comment

This design is not easy for the novice to understand, but it does represent a complete and tested design. As such, it is an ideal proving ground for the novice. It is expected that the reader will need to read this chapter perhaps several times before the design is completely understood, but the explanation, backed by the rest of the book, is sufficient material for him to come to a full understanding, if he is prepared to work at it. Certainly it is impossible to become a competent designer unless you are prepared to face the necessary application. The mere *fight* of reaching complete understanding will teach more than any of the preceding chapters could on their own.

Fight on until you completely understand this design. This means an appreciation of why *every component* is used; of why *each and every signal* is required. Perseverance can only be rewarded by success, and when that success has been achieved, then you may celebrate! You are then ready to tackle your own *small* design project. My only advice is to make it easy on yourself the first time round. Make it the rule that you will not attempt to use more than *ten* integrated circuits in your first design. Draw full timing diagrams, and then build and test. Where you go from there is up to you!

Exercises

The AUTONIM can be used as the basis of further work. A few ideas for modifications to the design are listed after the circuit diagrams (see page 204). Thinking about these can be rewarding, but it is regretted that readers' solutions cannot be commented upon.

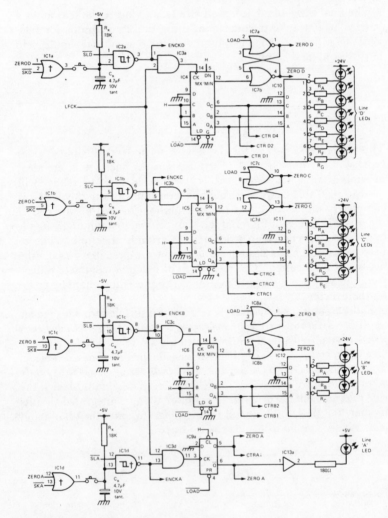

Figure 19.10. AUTONIM display logic (**F1**)

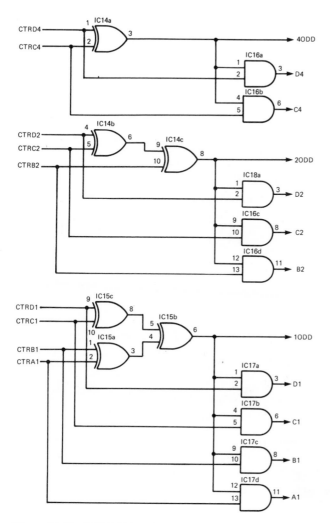

Figure 19.11. AUTONIM position analyser (**F2**)

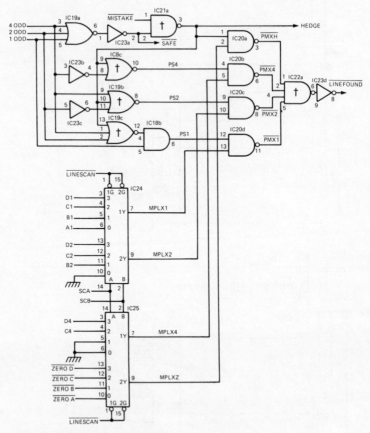

Figure 19.12. AUTONIM priority encoder and line multiplexer (**F3**)

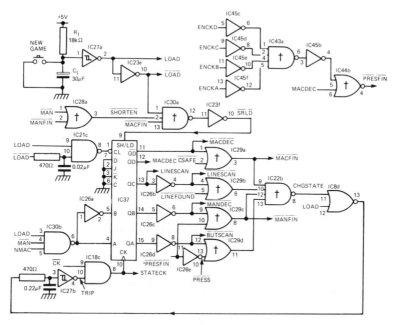

Figure 19.13. AUTONIM state encoder (**F4**)

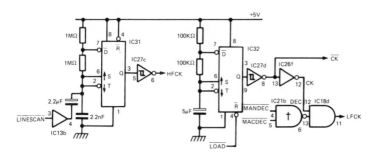

Figure 19.14. AUTONIM clock generators (**F5**)

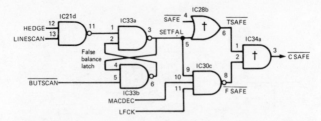

Figure 19.15. AUTONIM false-safe hedge logic (**F6**)

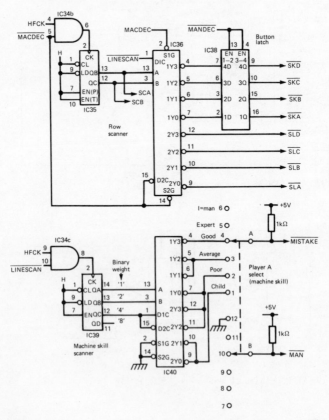

Figure 19.16. AUTONIM line scanner and machine skill scanner (**F7**)

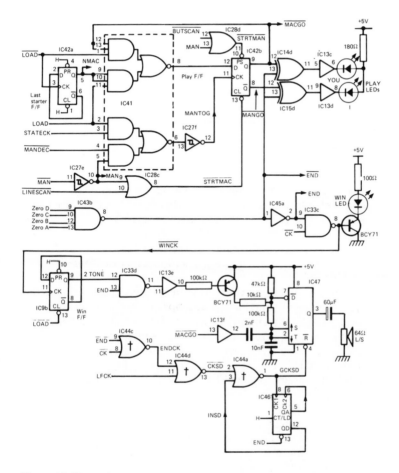

Figure 19.17. AUTONIM move indicator logic and audio stage (**F8**)

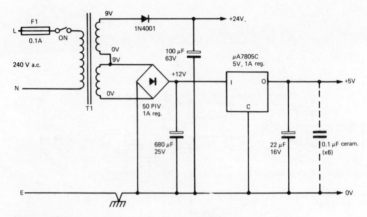

Figure 19.18. AUTONIM power supply (**F9**)

1. Find and eliminate a redundant gate in the audio logic.
2. Design an interface to allow an external display and control panel to be used in place of the normal control panel. This should duplicate all controls, but should be separately powered. Ensure that the interface lines represent the minimum number of lines. The purpose is to provide larger and brighter displays.
3. If a line selection button is very quickly depressed and then released, the machine takes this to be a move, although there has been insufficient time for the appropriate line counter to decrement. Modify the circuit to prevent this. (Not included in the original design because it adds to the complexity.)
4. Modify the circuitry to give an apparently instant reset when the NEW GAME button is pressed.
5. Modify the design to prevent the possibility of the machine taking only one LED from a line when there is only one line left in the game; this can presently occur on low skill settings. This is a worthwhile improvement as it then more nearly simulates a real player who should not miss the obvious; it does, of course, add to the complexity of the circuit.
6. Redesign the control logic to use a counter and decoder in place of the present shift register.

Alternatively, if all this seems a little too daunting, why not try to design an electronic die* using only logic ICs and LEDs?

---

* N.B. 'Dice' is the plural of 'die'.

Part 3 – Microprocessors

A computer provides the most efficient means of
compounding the errors of its programmer.

Author.

20

A 6800 microprocessing system

Once the designer is proficient in the design of ordinary logic – or what can now be referred to as *random logic* – he will do well to at least make himself familiar with the possibilities of microprocessors. This last part of the book is aimed at doing just that, and of showing that a microprocessor is no more than an extremely sophisticated and versatile digital device.

A microprocessor – or MPU – is no more and no less than a *programmable* digital device: the way it responds to particular inputs and affects particular outputs with respect to time is totally programmable by the user. The physical devices employed are termed the *hardware*, and the variable program and associated data are termed the *software*.

The microprocessor is the greatest advance in modern electronics, for it puts real computing power into the size of a small chip, and at a cost which is not a lot more than some complex LSI devices. The only drawback is a human one: the need to *understand* it. There are now countless microprocessors to choose from, ranging from 4-bits and 8-bits up to 16-bits. Of these, 4-bit devices are used for fairly simple control functions where cost is a significant factor (e.g. vending machines). The most common microprocessors are 8-bit devices, for these offer good computing ability, and are suitable for most purposes. The 16-bit devices are rather more specialised, and are more suited to complex arithmetic tasks and certain industrial applications, or where an interface with a minicomputer is required. This book therefore concentrates on 8-bit devices.

The most common 8-bit microprocessors are the 6800, 8080, Z80, SC/MP (8060), and the 6502. These are the devices for which most ready-made software is available. Of these, the 6800 and 8080 are the two most commonly used in industry, for there are several manufacturers offering equivalent devices, and these therefore assure 'twitchy' manufacturers that there is always a 'second source' of supply if their favourite chip manufacturer decides to throw in the towel. Once again, it follows that there is more available software and expertise with these two devices (and their variants in the 6800 and 8080 series) than there is with any other.

The most popular devices for industry need not be the most popular choice for the amateur, since suitability and cost are then more important than second sources. For example, the RCA COSMAC microprocessor has a lot of advantages to offer the experienced random logic designer, and for this reason, is covered in more depth in following chapters.

Although there are numerous microprocessors to choose from, they are all very similar in operation, even though they may differ somewhat in specific architecture and facilities. Because of its widespread use, the 6800 MPU will be considered in this chapter, which discusses typical device architecture and the method of executing instructions.

Microprocessor architecture

A microprocessor requires supporting devices in order to build up a microprocessing system. Figure 20.1* shows the typical architecture of a 6800 based system, although apart from the *internal* detail of the MPU and the peripheral interface adaptor (PIA), it could be said to represent just about *any* microprocessing system. Such a system must comprise:

(a) A microprocessor, for computing and control purposes.
(b) Read only memory (ROM) containing the program instructions (or *code*), and any *permanent data* (constants, etc.).
(c) Random access memory (RAM), for the temporary storage of data.
(d) Input/output interface devices, allowing the microprocessing system to interface with peripheral devices or random logic. The PIA is a support chip available in the 6800 family to allow such interfaces to be programmed as inputs or outputs.

The MPU

A block diagram of the 6800 microprocessor is shown in Figure 20.1. The device is controlled by the block labelled 'instruction decoder & system control'. Timing for all operations is provided by means of an external clock oscillator, which generates the complementary timing signals φ_1 and φ_2. A control bus links the microprocessor control to the control logic of the associated support chips.

Transfer of data within the microprocessor is by means of an internal bus. This bus can output or receive data from the outside world via the bidirectional data buffer. An address buffer is used to

* See page 212.

output a 16-bit *address* for use by support chips; remember that there are only 8-bits of *data*. The remaining registers within the MPU are as follows.

An instruction register (IR) is used to contain the 8-bit code which represents the current instruction; this code informs the control logic what function to perform. A program counter (PC) holds the address of the next instruction to be executed. This means that a particular 8-bit *byte* (or word) from memory (ROM) *contains* the next instruction to be loaded into IR. Once an instruction has been transferred to the IR (via the data bus), the PC is automatically incremented to point to the next instruction (or instruction byte).

All arithmetic and logic functions are performed by the arithmetic and logic unit (ALU). Most MPU operations affect the content of the condition code register (CCR). This comprises 6 bits which signal – or *flag* – certain information about the last operation (e.g. negative result, overflow, etc.).

All MPUs contain some form of accumulator: the 6800 contains two, known as ACC A and ACC B. Arithmetic/logic operations are performed on two operands: one obtained from memory via the data bus, and the other resident within the accumulator. The result of such an operation is loaded into the accumulator; obviously this *overwrites* the original contents of the accumulator.

Microprocessor programs frequently need to temporarily store data in what is termed a *stack*. This stack is made to appear as a last-in first-out (LIFO) memory. Imagine a stack of papers dropped one by one into a wire tray. If they are taken out one by one, they come out in the reverse order, i.e. last-in first-out. This is exactly what happens in a LIFO stack. A stack pointer (SP) contains the address which represents the top of this stack. The stack is allocated a portion of memory (RAM), and the SP moves up and down the addresses within this area of memory such that it always points to the current top of the stack. Simple instructions such as PUSH and PULL transfer a data word to or from the stack, respectively.

An index register (IX) is used to point to data within the memory, and like the program counter, may be incremented after the transfer of data; this enables a string of data words to be transferred with ease. The index register within the 6800 MPU can be used to provide an *offset address* within memory, which is a useful means of shortening the length of address needed. Microprocessor systems usually operate with up to 64 K bytes of memory, which requires 16 address bits (see Chapter 8, page 71). Eight address bits allow for up to 256 addresses, therefore one 8-bit byte added to a 16-bit offset within the IX can address a block of 256 addresses *in one byte*.

The use of offset addressing can be shown by a simple example. Consider the following instruction:

ADD A 7, X

This instruction means: 'add into ACC A the contents of memory location addressed by the index register offset by 7'.

The *address registers* previously mentioned (i.e. PC, SP and IX), are sometimes referred to as *memory pointers*, because they *point* to memory locations.

Memory

A microprocessor requires *software* if it is to operate. Software is stored *within memory*, but the memory chips themselves are naturally referred to as *hardware*.

There are various forms of memory, as follows:

ROM — *Read-only memory*: is factory programmed to contain a permanent binary pattern at every address. Used to contain proven MPU programs for medium and large scale production.

PROM — *Programmable read-only memory*: is user programmed ROM. Programming is usually by means of fusible links, which are 'blown' by passing a high current programming pulse directed to appropriate bits. Each address must be programmed in turn, and the results carefully checked. It is possible to electrically copy one PROM from another, making it suitable for small scale production, or amateur use. Like ROM, once a particular address has been programmed, it cannot be changed.

EPROM — *Erasable programmable read only memory*: is user programmed ROM. Once again, a special programming procedure is required, but it is possible to erase the program by exposing the EPROM device to ultraviolet light for a set time period. EPROM is now available quite cheaply, and its extra versatility makes it an attractive alternative to conventional PROM.

RAM   — *Random access memory*: is usually *volatile* memory, as opposed to the previously listed forms of *non-volatile* memory. This means that RAM memory is programmed/loaded electrically, by the microprocessor itself, but the content of this memory is lost if the power supply is removed. Such memory is used for the temporary storage of data during normal program operation, and is essential for any MPU system. RAM is also useful for testing small programs.

Various types of RAM are available, the most commonly used being known as *static* or *dynamic*. Static RAM will store data written into it for as long as the power supply is maintained, without further attention. Dynamic RAM, on the other hand, is of the type of construction that requires constant refreshing in order to restore a fading charge (as described in Chapter 14*). The extra complication of dynamic RAM, plus the risk of losing data if a fault arises in the clocking or refresh circuitry, means that many engineers prefer not to use it; there are no such risks with static RAM. The particular advantage of dynamic RAM is that it offers far greater storage capacity for a given chip size, and can cost less in large memory systems. Only experienced engineers should consider using dynamic RAM.

Bubble memories offer large memory capacity and *non-volatile* RAM, but they are expensive, and represent a new technology which only a few manufacturers have got to grips with. Many manufacturers consider it risky to use because of the supply situation, and certainly costs make it prohibitive as far as the amateur is concerned. This form of memory is non-volatile because it utilises magnetic 'bubbles' which are circulated around a series of electrodes of minute dimensions. When power is removed, the bubbles simply stay where they are until they get the order to 'march' again.

Getting back to RAM in the microprocessing system, it is of no significance what the actual type is, although it is fairly safe to assume that static RAM is normally used. Limited facilities mean that the amateur is generally forced to try out his programs by manully entering them into RAM, using the MPU system itself. The program must then be proven before the supply is disconnected, or the program must be stored on some form of non-volatile media. A cassette tape recorder provides the answer to this problem, hence

* *Dynamic PMOS.*

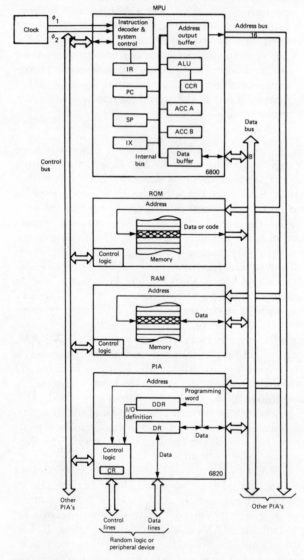

Figure 20.1. Typical architecture of a 6800 microprocessor system

212

the usual need for a tape interface. Once a program has been recorded onto tape, it can be reloaded into RAM from the tape recorder. More ambitious microprocessor systems use *floppy disc* storage – a floppy disc looks rather like a flexible record – but floppy disc drives are rather expensive.

Figure 20.1 shows how memory devices are interconnected with the microprocessor. The illustration shows ROM, but this general term can be taken to equally apply to variants such as PROM or EPROM. 'ROM' signifies memory which is *read-only*. Because it is only possible to read ROM, it can only be used to contain program instructions – or *code* – and *fixed* data. The arrows only show data/code coming *out* of ROM, for this reason. Since RAM can be used to store data, double arrows to the data bus show that data may be written or read by the microprocessor. The MPU controls all data transfers, and is the only source of addresses output onto the address bus.

A typical transfer of data from memory involves sending out an address on the address bus, which is recognised and accepted by only one memory chip, due to internal address decoding logic. The address points to only one 8-bit byte within that memory element, and the contents of this byte are output onto the data bus, under timing control from the MPU via the control bus. Data is received by the MPU data buffer, and is loaded into the appropriate register within the MPU via the internal bus: this is a memory *read* operation.

A similar process is involved in *writing* data to memory, the only difference being that data is routed out from the appropriate MPU register via the internal bus, data buffer, and the external data bus.

The execution of an instruction

Figure 20.2 is provided to make this even clearer, for it is important to understand this basic concept of how a microprocessor works. Before referring to the figure, however, it must be understood that a particular instruction may comprise a varying number of (8-bit) bytes. Certain instructions comprise only one byte, but others are longer. For example, if a memory address must be specified in association with an instruction, it requires one additional byte to specify an address offset relative to IX, or two additional bytes to specify an *absolute address*: since 16 bits are required for a full address. The figure to be discussed shows the case of a 3-byte instruction, where the three bytes are contained in consecutive address locations in a particular *code block* within the memory (it is unimportant what the type of memory is).

Initially the program counter PC is pointing to the beginning of the instruction; the circled numbers within the illustration indicate the successive stages required for this instruction. Thus in stage 1, the contents of PC are routed via the address bus to the memory, and byte 1 of the instruction is transferred via the data bus to the instruction decoder and the IR. Inherent in this code is information telling the instruction decoder that a two-byte address follows.

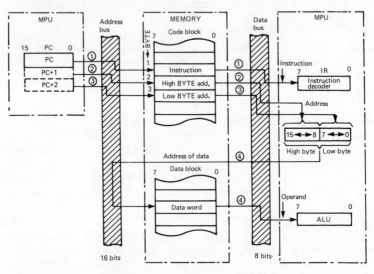

Figure 20.2. Schematic showing the execution of an instruction and the related bus transfers

Immediately after the first transfer has been made, the program counter is incremented (to PC + 1). Thus in stage 2, the PC points at byte 2 of the instruction, which in this case happens to be the high byte of the absolute address which locates required data, i.e. an operand. Thus stage 2 transfers the most-significant 8-bits of the data memory address into the high-byte portion of the MPU's internal address register, again via the data bus.

Once the high byte has been transferred, PC is again incremented (to PC + 2). The address lines now select the third byte of the instruction, which contains the low byte of the data memory address; this is transferred via the data bus into the low byte of the address register. The requisite 16-bit data address has now been built up within the MPU.

Step 4 is to output this address on the address bus, and to transfer the selected data word from the memory data block into the ALU, via the data bus. The MPU then carries out the operation specified within the IR internally.

External data transfers

An interface must be provided between the MPU system and any peripheral devices or random logic. The usual approach with the 6800 family is to utilise a peripheral interface adaptor, such as the 6820. This is actually a dual device, but only one portion of it is shown in Figure 20.1 for simplicity.

Such interfaces between the microprocessor system and the outside world are termed *ports*. Engineers talk in terms of *input ports* and *output ports*, where the former is used to input data to the system, and the latter to output data from the system.

The 6820 PIA is programmable for use as an input port or an output port. Indeed, it is even more versatile than this: each bit may be programmed separately as an input or an output. This is achieved by writing a programming word to the data direction register (DDR); a logic 1 signifies an output, or a logic 0 an input. Data is then transferred to/from the appropriate bit/s in the data register (DR) in accordance with the programmed usage. There are 8 data lines for connection to the outside world (i.e. random logic or peripheral device). There are also two control lines associated with the control logic, which allows external logic to synchronise transfers with the microprocessor signal; an incoming control line may be used to signal that data has been loaded into the DR, or an outgoing signal may be used to indicate to the external logic that the MPU has placed valid data into the DR.

A single 6820 PIA can provide two ports: for simplicity, these will be regarded here as either input or output ports, implying that all the bits in the DDR are identical. Each port represents a unique address within the addressing structure of the microprocessor, therefore within the limits set by the addressing system (i.e. 64 K), and allowing for moderate memory addresses, there is no practical limit to the number of ports which may be used.

The actual transfer of data to/from a PIA register is just like memory transfers: the microprocessor cannot tell the difference, and regards I/O ports purely as memory locations.

The microprocessor and random logic

The microprocessor needs software in order to operate, but once it is operating, it can be regarded as a hardware package. When used in conjunction with random logic, a microprocessor system simply becomes a 'black box' hardware element which interacts sequentially with the random logic, according to a fixed pattern.

The particular advantage of the microprocessor is that it can handle very complex tasks without the need for a lot of special-to-purpose hardware. Its primary disadvantage over random logic is one of speed. A microprocessor operates at similar speeds to random logic elements, but it can only handle one task at once; different tasks must be performed sequentially.

It is interesting to note that design engineers in industry frequently combat the latter limitation by employing several microprocessors in parallel.

21

External data handling

The previous chapter has shown how external data is transferred in and out of a microprocessing system by means of ports, but no mention was made of the precise method of interaction between the hardware and the software: for interaction there must be. It was mentioned that the 6800 microprocessor regards I/O ports as pure memory locations, but this is not always the case if we consider microprocessors in general, as following chapters will show when the COSMAC microprocessor is considered.

We have seen that specific instructions are used to read or write data, therefore normal memory transfers are the result of software commands. This immediately suggests one method of handling external data transfer: direct program control. Obviously this is easy when data is to be output, for the microprocessor system already has the data, and simply initiates the transfer when it is ready. It is not quite so easy when we consider input data, for how is the MPU to know when such data is available?

A method of inputting data under program control involves *polling* input *flags*. When external logic has placed data in a suitable register, it sets a flip-flop, referred to as a *flag*. The program periodically inspects any such flags, and as soon as it finds a flag that is set, it enters a software routine to input the appropriate data word, and to clear the flag (the term *reset the flag* is generally used in this context). The external logic knows that it cannot enter another data word into the register until the flag has been reset, for until this happens, the data has not been read by the MPU.

Interrupts

The above system is all very well, but it lacks speed. It may be that it is important for the microprocessor to react quickly to the presence of input data, or conversely, to the need for external logic to receive an output word quickly. Such needs are generally catered for by *interrupt lines* on the microprocessor in question. External logic may asynchronously assert an *interrupt,* and the microprocessor then rapidly responds by jumping to a special software *interrupt routine,* which performs the special task related to the interrupt. In order to do this, the current task must be suspended until the interrupt service routine has been completed. Before the processor can enter the interrupt routine, however, it must store its current status and point in the program, in order that it may resume in the same status after the interrupt routine. This is one important use for the stack, for this information is 'pushed' onto the stack before entering the interrupt routine, and 'popped' off the stack on leaving the interrupt routine.

It may be that a particular application requires a number of different I/O ports to be serviced on an interrupt basis, therefore the designer must devise a means whereby the processor can establish which particular interrupt service routine is required. The normal method is to set a flag bit at the time of asserting an interrupt, and the initial part of the interrupt routine then polls these flags to find which interrupt service routine to enter.

Direct memory access

The interrupt method enables external logic or a peripheral to obtain a quick response from the microprocessor, but it does not overcome the speed limitation imposed by the inherent nature of program controlled transfers. As we saw in the previous chapter, this may require several steps to be taken, and this can be too time-consuming where it is required to transfer a large amount of data at one time. A peripheral frequently requires the transfer of large blocks of data to or from a block of memory. *Direct memory access* – DMA – is an alternative method offered by most good micro-procesors as a means of overcoming this problem.

The DMA principle takes advantage of the fact that the transfer of a block of data is to *consecutive* memory locations. The processor need only locate the first memory location, and know the number of words to be transferred in the block, and it can then enter another form of transfer, which is not under direct program control: DMA.

There are different methods of accomplishing direct memory access, and different MPUs employ different techniques, some of which follow:

(a) *The halt method.* This method is the simplest but the slowest, for the microprocessor is forced to halt its current program execut-ion at the first suitable point, to vacate the address and data highways, and to then undertake the DMA transfers, not resuming normal program execution until this is completed.

(b) *The cycle stealing method.* This is the most common method, and is medium speed. This involves interposing a DMA cycle in the current program instruction cycle. Thus the program keeps running, but it is effectively slowed down by the DMA stealing otherwise usable cycles.

(c) *The multiplex method.* This is the fastest and most demanding method, for it effectively accomplishes DMA transfers without slowing down normal program execution. Rather than steal whole cycles, this method makes use of time slots when the address/data bus is not in actual use. This method involves critical timing and complicated associated hardware.

Analogue interfacing

Analogue-to-digital (A/D) or digital-to-analogue (D/A) conversion can be accomplished by special devices. These devices are then located in the microprocessor system architecture as input ports (if A/D) or output ports (if D/A), and provide the requisite interface between analogue signal levels and digital data.

Serial interfaces

Some peripheral devices require serial data, as opposed to the parallel data handled by the microprocessor itself. In such cases, a serial/parallel (MPU input) or a parallel/serial (MPU output) converter is required. A suitable device for such purposes is the UART. This device was considered in detail in Chapter 13, and it may be found upon re-examination of Figure 13.6* that such a device contains all the necessary functions to act as a serial interface on either an input or an output port.

* *See page 111.*

22

The 6800 microprocessor

Chapter 20 described a typical microprocessing system with specific reference to the internal architecture of the 6800 microprocessor. This chapter completes a general outline of the 6800 microprocessor by considering its pin-out and hardware facilities.

Like any other microprocessor, entire books are written on the 6800, therefore it must be appreciated that the space available only permits a brief summary. For further details on any microprocessor the reader should turn to such publications, which are readily available from those stockists who specialise in computer and microcomputer components. Most good newsagents stock a variety of monthly magazines intended for amateur micro-users, and the advertisements in these publications often include book lists. If all else fails, the reader should write directly to the manufacturer in question (e.g. Motorola for the 6800 microprocessor).

Pin layout

The pin layout for the 6800 microprocessor is shown in Figure 22.1. The device is TTL compatible, requiring only a single $+5\,$V supply (V_{CC}). Ground is connected to two separate pins (V_{ss}). Like most microprocessors offering TTL compatibility, it is only capable of driving one standard load (sinking up to $1.6\,$mA), although between seven and ten devices of the same family may be driven from a single output.

The data bus comprises eight bidirectional lines (D0–D7), and the address bus 16 lines (A0–A15), giving the capability of addressing up to $64\,$K bytes of memory.

Various other input and output control lines are provided, and these are more easily understood with the aid of the diagram presented in Figure 22.2.

The lines ϕ_1 and ϕ_2 are clock waveforms supplied from an external clock oscillator, as shown in Figure 20.1. These clocking waveforms define the timing for the entire microprocessor system, and hence the speed of execution of instructions. It is normal practice to use crystal controlled oscillators for stability, and this provides the facility of knowing precisely how long given instructions take to execute.

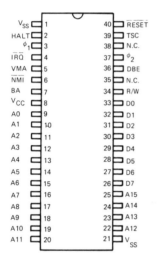

Figure 22.1. Pin layout for the 6800 microprocessor

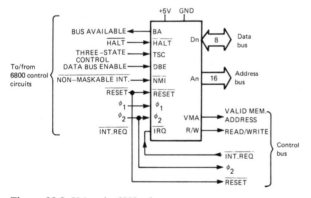

Figure 22.2. Using the 6800 microprocessor

The control bus provides a mixture of signals for use with memory and interface devices: ϕ_2 is used as one of these signals for timing purposes. READ/WRITE (R/W) specifies a data bus read or write operation, and VALID MEMORY ADDRESS (VMA) confirms that the address bus lines have stabilised and present valid memory address data. In a 6800 system, I/O devices (e.g. PIAs) are given discrete memory addresses and are therefore regarded by the MPU

221

as virtual memory. When VMA is low, this disables all family devices by means of chip select inputs.

RESET is used to reset and start the MPU from a power down condition; this signal is also routed to the RESET inputs of PIAs for use during power-on initialisation. INT.REQ (IRQ) is the interrupt request line used by PIAs and I/O devices to signal to the MPU that they need servicing. Software facilities allow the programmer to *mask* such interrupt requests during certain routines: when a software mask is applied, interrupt requests are ignored.

The remaining control signals to/from the 6800 control circuits are of a supervisory nature, and are used for timing and control of the MPU itself. The NON-MASKABLE INTERRUPT signal (NMI) cannot be masked by the software, as the name suggests; this interrupt input will always be serviced by the MPU. The DATA BUS ENABLE (DBE) signal is a three-state control signal for the MPU data bus; normally this signal is derived from ϕ_2. The THREE STATE CONTROL signal (TSC) affects the address bus in the same way that DBE affects the data bus. This signal may be used to accomplish direct memory access by forcing the address bus and the R/W line into the high impedance state.

The HALT signal will stop the MPU from processing; when halted, all three-state outputs go to their high impedance state (i.e. address bus, data bus and R/W line). When the MPU is halted, the VMA line is low, and the BUS AVAILABLE line is high. When BUS AVAILABLE (BA) is high, this indicates that three-state outputs are in the high impedance state, and that external circuitry can take command of these lines. BA goes high as a result of the HALT input being taken low, or due to a WAIT instruction in the program; it is useful as an MPU signal for DMA activity. The BA line remains high until either the HALT input has resumed a high state, or if the halt is the result of a HALT instruction, until an external interrupt occurs.

For further details of the 6800 microprocessor, the reader must turn to alternative publications, and be prepared for an in-depth treatment.

23

The COSMAC microprocessor

Many microprocessor users opt for standard arrangements, using existing hardware configurations, and concentrate upon software design. Many amateur users take this option, and very successfully use microprocessor systems with little or no knowledge of the hardware at all. Since the principal aim of this book is to teach a practical approach to random logic design, it follows that the emphasis with microprocessors should be placed on a micro-processor well suited to complement random logic. It is for this reason that the COSMAC microprocessor will be considered in some detail, for it offers a great flexibility when used in conjunction with random logic.

Before discussing this particular microprocessor, it should be noted that other microprocessors* may offer more comprehensive hardware packages when it comes to general purpose micro-processing systems intended for interfacing with tape, floppy disc or visual display units (i.e. television monitors), but the particular strength of the COSMAC lies in its ease of compatability with TTL or CMOS random logic systems, and also the ease of understanding by a designer experienced in the latter technology.

The COSMAC microprocessor is manufactured by RCA, and is offered in a variety of guises based upon the type number CDP1802. Like the 6800 microprocessor, it is TTL compatible and operates from a single +5V supply. It is worth noting that this can by no means be taken for granted with other microprocessors, a number of which require dual supplies. Whilst more stringent applications might call for a ceramic or high speed version of this device, most users should be satisfied with the plastic encapsulated version branded the CDP1802ACE; this is cheap and versatile, and unlike some other microprocessors, contains all you need on a single chip, except memory. It is even generous in this respect, for it does contain an unusually large number of *scratchpad* registers, i.e. registers available for temporary data storage.

---

* *Readers may care to note that a companion book entitled 'Practical Microprocessor Systems' which concentrates on amateur uses of the INS8060 (SC/MP II) and the 6502 microprocessors, is available from the same publishers.*

Supporting documentation

The importance of good supporting documentation with a product as sophisticated as a microprocessor cannot be stressed too highly. Unfortunately the supporting documentation provided by some manufacturers for their products is little better than abysmal. Small wonder that so many training courses have to be run! If the supporting documentation is not abysmal, it is often so intimidating that the prospective user gets 'chip-fright' even before he starts.

Fortunately RCA have done a splendid job with their supporting documentation, and their publication is thoroughly recommended: 'User Manual for the CDP1802 COSMAC Microprocessor (MPM-201C)'. Remarkably this is quite a slim volume, yet it explains both the hardware and the software in terms that any logic designer can understand. A schematic is used in conjunction with every instruction to ensure that the user fully appreciates its usage*.

The 'User Manual' is supported by a range of other literature and application notes, of which the following small selection might be of interest:

ICAN 6970	Understanding and Using the CDP1855 Multiply/Divide Unit.
ICAN 7032	CDP 1800-Based Video Terminal using the RCA Video Interface System, VIS.
ICAN 6991	A Slave CDP1802 Serial Printer Buffer System.
ICAN 7029	Low Power Techniques for use with CMOS CDP 1800-Based Systems.
ICAN 6934	Cassette Tape I/O for COSMAC Microprocessor Systems.
ICAN 6842	16-bit Operations in the CDP 1802 Microprocessor.
ICAN 6918	A Methodology for Programming COSMAC 1802 Applications Using Higher-Level Languages.
ICAN 6581	Power-on Reset/Run Circuits for the RCA CDP 1802 COSMAC Microprocessor.
ICAN 6611	Keyboard Scan Routines for use with RCA COSMAC Microterminal CDP18SO21.
MPM-206A	Binary Arithmetic Subroutines for the COSMAC Microprocessor.
MPM-207	Floating-Point Binary Arithmetic Subroutines.

* For RCA addresses refer to page 288.

Main features

For most practical (and amateur) purposes, the CDP1802ACE should suffice, with a maximum clock input frequency range of DC to 3.2 MHz, using a single +5 V supply. Provision is made to split the power supply in order to obtain higher speed operation: in this case the interface portion runs off +5 V, and the microprocessing portion runs off +10 V.

It has previously been mentioned that the COSMAC is genuinely self-contained, without the need for supporting devices to furnish it with scratchpad registers, clock drivers, program counters or other memory pointers, which remarkably, are not self-contained on some microprocessor chips. COSMAC only requires an external crystal and your microprocessor is in business.

A 16 × 16 bit matrix of scratchpad memory is available for ease of programming, with the unusual facility of using *any* of these 16 registers as (16-bit) program counters or memory pointers. The device has an inbuilt DMA facility, allowing blocks of data to be transferred on the cycle stealing principle (mentioned in Chapter 21). Thus data may be transferred between memory and a peripheral, or vice-versa, without the need for direct program control. This is the way a program is loaded during development: after initialisation, the program instructions are simply loaded into memory sequentially from address 0000 under automatic DMA control.

A number of different means are available to the user when it comes to input/output (I/O) control, ranging from virtual memory control using the address bus, as described in the previous chapter for the 6800 microprocessing system, to special I/O commands and associated hardware lines. There are also input flags which may be directly tested by the software, an output flip-flop which can also be tested by the software, plus external interrupt and DMA lines. This is best appreciated by details of the pin-out.

Pin layout and functions

Figure 23.1 shows the pin details of the microprocessor. Like the 6800, it is a 40 pin device. This presented the manufacturers with an obvious problem, bearing in mind that it must allow for control lines, 16 address lines, 8 data lines, plus the special input and output lines mentioned above. Reference to Figure 22.1, showing the 6800 layout, shows that a compromise must be made, but this is about the only compromise. RCA solved the problem by only using eight address lines, and by outputting the 16-bit addresses in two 8-bit bytes. This means that the required bits output during the first (high-order) byte must be externally staticised, for subsequent recombination with the second (low-order) byte.

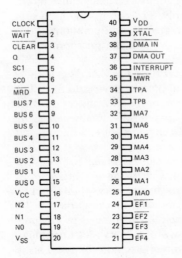

Figure 23.1. CDP1802 pin details (courtesy of RCA)

This method of outputting the address utilises the MPU's two separate timing pulses TPA and TPB. The high-order address byte (A.1) appears on the address bus lines (MA0–MA7) first, and TPA may be used as a strobe to staticise *the required number of address bits* in an external register. An octal register may be used to staticise all eight bits, allowing for addressing a full 64 K bytes of memory, but smaller systems may be contained in a smaller addressing range, and small systems may well only require a few of the high-order bits to be staticised, the rest being redundant. The low-order byte (A.0) of the address is then output on lines MA0–MA7, which are recombined with the high-order byte (effectively lines MA8–MA15), to give the full memory address.

The state of the $\overline{\text{MWR}}$ and $\overline{\text{MRD}}$ lines determines whether a data transfer is to be written to memory, read from memory, or if neither operation is to be performed. The $\overline{\text{MWR}}$ line goes low for a memory write, the $\overline{\text{MRD}}$ line goes low for a memory read, or if neither of these lines goes low, a non-memory operation is performed.

The data bus lines (BUS0–BUS7) are bidirectional, and transfer data in and out of the microprocessor from/to memory or other interface devices. The timing pulse TPB is used to strobe data transfers, and occurs after address and data line settling time, i.e. skew.

226

Four external flag inputs ($\overline{EF1}$–$\overline{EF4}$) are associated with particular flag-testing instructions, leading to branching within the program in accordance with flag status (e.g. SHORT BRANCH IF EF2 = 1). These flags are therefore ideal for polling routines, and for use in conjunction with the $\overline{INTERRUPT}$ line.

The $\overline{INTERRUPT}$ line may be used to make the program jump to an interrupt routine; if the first task in this routine is to poll the flag inputs, up to four separate alternative paths may be determined by direct flag control, or if hardware encoding is used on the flag inputs in order to provide a binary code, after testing all the flags, the service routine could determine up to 16 different interrupt conditions.

The Q output is obtained from an internal Q flip-flop. Since this flip-flop is under software set/reset control, and is also software tested by certain instructions (e.g. SHORT BRANCH IF Q = 0), it is extremely versatile in use. One use is as a means of outputting serial data under direct bit-by-bit program control: each bit must be the result of a separate instruction execution. Another novel application is as a memory bank switch; since the Q output is a hardware flip-flop, it might be set to switch in a second memory bank, offering the possibility of easily controlling up to 128 K bytes of memory!

The three lines N0, N1 and N2 are associated with input/output byte transfers. These allow data to be transferred into or out of memory at the same time that the output lines generate one of seven possible binary codes – there are not eight, because the zero condition is invalid, being the *rest* condition.

For example, the instruction: OUTPUT (N = 6), causes the addressed memory byte to be output onto the data bus coincident with a high on each of the N1 and N2 I/O lines. Similarly, the instruction: INPUT (N = 4), would cause data applied to the data bus to be written into the addressed memory byte coincident with the N2 I/O line being high. The purpose of the I/O lines is to control external logic associated with data bus interface devices; thus in the latter example, the N2 line might be used to enable a three-state register to place data onto the data bus for transfer to memory.

Like the flag inputs, it is possible to use the I/O lines directly — for up to three I/O ports or to decode a binary output to give up to seven ports. By combining these with the Q flip-flop and an extra instruction, this figure can be doubled, providing random logic is used to decode the required N and Q line combinations. Similarly, by including the $\overline{MWR}$ line in external gating, it is possible to utilise the same I/O code for either an input or an output.

So you begin to appreciate the flexibility of the COSMAC

microprocessor, and the reason why this flexibility can only really be exploited by a designer familiar with random logic – *such as yourself!* Just consider the possibilities open with I/O transfers: you can use address lines for selection, the Q flip-flop, or the three I/O lines. Thus the device can be best tailored to a particular application, as Chapter 26 will show.

Two separate direct memory access lines are provided: $\overline{\text{DMA IN}}$ and $\overline{\text{DMA OUT}}$; these request direct memory transfer from or to the data bus respectively.

The remaining lines are concerned with MPU control. The XTAL and CLOCK inputs are linked by the external crystal and a resistor in parallel, and both pins are capacitively decoupled to earth by 20 pF. The $\overline{\text{WAIT}}$ and $\overline{\text{CLEAR}}$ inputs are used to control the mode of operation, where $\overline{\text{CLEAR}}$ alone low causes a general *reset*, $\overline{\text{WAIT}}$ alone low causes a *pause*, both inputs low causes a *load*, and both inputs high specifies *run*. The two remaining lines SC0 and SC1 output a binary state code S0 to S3, where SC0 is the LSB. The meanings of these codes are as follows:

S0 = Fetch.
S1 = Execute.
S2 = DMA.
S3 = Interrupt.

Internal structure

The internal structure of the COSMAC microprocessor is shown in Figure 23.2. It is interesting to contrast this with the internal structure of the 6800 microprocessor, shown in Figure 20.1, for whilst the same basic needs are met, an entirely different approach is used.

The scratchpad registers comprise 16 16-bit registers, with each register divided into a low-order byte and a high-order byte, each of eight bits. These registers are designated R(O) to R(F) using a hexadecimal notation.* Low- or high-order bits are specified by adding the suffix .0 or .1, e.g. R(4).0 refers to the low-order byte of the fourth scratchpad register R(4). These registers may be used as memory pointers, requiring all 16-bits, or to store quite separate 8-bit words.

Where the content of a register is to be used as a memory pointer, the 16-bits are first transferred to the 16-bit Address register (A); a multiplexer (MUX) is then used to output either the low-order or

---

* *Hexadecimal notation is explained in Chapter 8.*

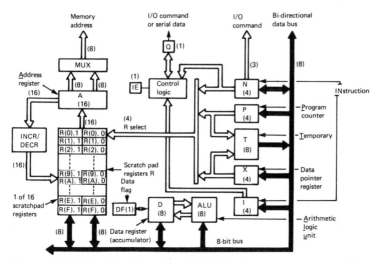

Figure 23.2. Internal structure of the COSMAC microprocessor (courtesy of RCA)

high-order byte on the address lines (MA0–MA7). Any of the 16 registers can be used as a memory pointer, therefore there is no special register designated the program counter. This makes the COSMAC extremely versatile, since the program counter can be changed at the 'drop of an instruction'. The associated INCR/DECR function operates in association with certain instructions to allow any scratchpad register to be incremented or decremented as part of a memory access instruction.

The 4-bit R SELECT (register select) lines specify a particular register from the sixteen available, and these lines may be controlled by any one of the P, X or N registers. The I and N registers form two 4-bit bytes of the INstruction register; the I portion is the high-order byte, and specifies an instruction type, whilst the N portion is the low-order byte, and represents either an operational code, or defines one of the scratchpad registers via the R SELECT lines. For the special INPUT and OUTPUT instructions, the content of the N register is output as the code on the lines N0–N2. The P register specifies which scratchpad register is currently being used as the Program counter, and the X register specifies a scratchpad register to be used as a data pointer. It follows that the P, X and N registers must all comprise four bits.

The Temporary or T register is used to provide temporary storage of the P and X registers when an interrupt takes place. By so doing, it retains information necessary to allow the MPU to resume operation after the interrupt where it left the original part of the program. This register therefore has eight bits.

It may be seen that the 8-bit data bus links all the registers, the arithmetic logic unit (ALU) and the Data or D register; thus all data transfers either within the MPU, or outside the MPU, are via the same data bus. The D register is the equivalent of the usual accumulator, and is used to store the result of all ALU operations, prior to possible transfer to any other memory location or a scratchpad register. The Data Flag DF(1) is a single bit used to indicate overflow conditions within the D register; this bit may be tested directly by program instruction.

Timing

At this point it is worthwhile to consider device timing. The precise timing varies according to the type of instruction, but to illustrate the point, consider a typical *fetch* and *execute* cycle associated with the 'load via N' instruction LDN. This instruction (machine code ON) loads the content of the memory location pointed to by the scratchpad register specified by N into the D register. Figure 23.3 depicts the timing for this operation, and Figure 23.4 is a schematic representation of the entire operation in its two phases: (a) fetch, and (b) execute.

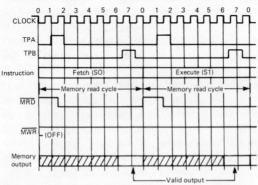

Figure 23.3. Fetch-execute cycle timing for a read-read instruction (courtesy of RCA)

This particular instruction happens to be a read-read instruction, but it could equally well have been an instruction with only one read cycle, read-write, or even three read operations. It should be noted that there must always be an initial read cycle for every instruction, for this is the cycle which fetches the instruction code from memory.

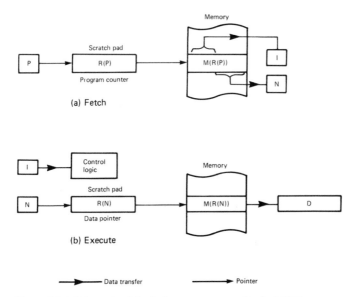

(a) Fetch

(b) Execute

———▶ Data transfer   ———▶ Pointer

Figure 23.4. Schematic of the fetch-execute process for the LDN instruction

In the example, the first read operation is a fetch (state code S0); this has to fetch the next instruction from memory and place it into the I and N registers. The schematic (Figure 23.4) shows the P register pointing to the scratchpad register containing the program counter (represented by the notation R(P)), and the program counter itself points to the instruction within the memory: M(R(P)). The instruction is fetched and is loaded into the I and N registers.

The second read operation is an execute (state code S1); this executes the instruction, which in this case consists of loading the D register from memory. The I register informs the control logic of this requirement, whilst the N register locates the scratchpad register containing the data pointer R(N). The data pointer points to the required data word in memory, M(R(N)), and the latter is loaded into the D register.

So far as timing is concerned during these transfers, TPA signifies that the high-order byte of the address is present on the address bus, and this must be externally staticised. The pulse TPB signifies that the low-order byte of the address is being output on address lines MA0–MA7, and these are combined with the staticised address lines from the high-order byte, which we might call MA8–MA15. The memory read ($\overline{\text{MRD}}$) line goes low well before data is read from the memory, and the pulse TPB is a safe strobe of data from the memory.

For the purposes of comparison, Figure 23.5 shows the timing diagram for a read-write type instruction. The initial memory read cycle is identical to that seen previously, but during the memory

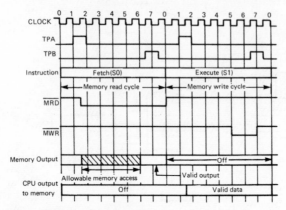

Figure 23.5. Fetch-execute cycle timing for a read-write type instruction (courtesy of RCA)

write cycle (which transfers data from the MPU to a memory location), $\overline{\text{MRD}}$ remains high, and the memory write pulse ($\overline{\text{MWR}}$) goes low for two clock periods during the time that valid data is present on the data bus; the latter is used to strobe data into memory.

Input/output ports

The CDP1852ACE is the plastic encapsulated I/O port device of the same family as the CDP1802CE microprocessor; its input lines provide only a 1 μA drain on the microprocessor outputs, which means there is no practical loading, in view of the MPU's 1.1 mA sink capability. The 74LS series of devices may be coupled to the MPU outputs, but due to their 0.4 mA loading, only two should be used. If it is desired to interface with a number of 74LS devices, one should be used as a buffer, and this then provides the normal fanout of 20 from its output.

Figure 23.6 shows the timing diagram for both input and output instruction timing, and Figure 23.7 depicts how the I/O port may be used in conjunction with the MPU N lines. Note that the polarity of

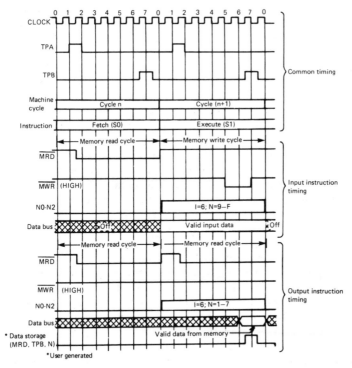

Figure 23.6. Timing diagram for input and output instructions (courtesy of RCA)

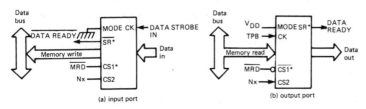

(a) input port

(b) output port

*Polarity depends on mode

Figure 23.7. Methods of using the CDP1852CE I/O port

the chip select 1 line (CS1/$\overline{CS1}$) and the service request ($\overline{SR}$/SR) line is dependent upon the setting of the MODE input.

An input instruction (e.g. INP2) inputs data from an external source and loads it into a memory address specified by the MPU; because read/write terminology refers to *memory*, this is a *memory write* execution. Because data is to be input into the microprocessing system, the I/O port must be configured as an input port, which is achieved by holding the MODE input low. First the input data must be clocked into the internal port register by means of DATA STROBE IN (see Figure 23.7). The negative-going edge of the clock pulse sets $\overline{SR}$ low and latches the data into the register. The $\overline{SR}$ line may be used to signal that data is available by means of the microprocessor interrupt input, or the flag inputs, as $\overline{DATA\ READY}$. The microprocessor subsequently responds with the input instruction, enabling the chip select inputs, and thereby enabling the I/O port's internal three-state outputs to output data onto the data bus; the selected (or decoded) N line is shown enabling CS2, and $\overline{MRD}$ remains high to enable CS1. Note that $\overline{MWR}$ should not be used under these circumstances, for this is the pulse which will write the data from the port into a memory location, and this data must have stabilised on the data bus *before* the write pulse occurs. After the chip enable condition, the $\overline{SR}$ input reverts to the high state, and the port is ready for future transfers.

An output instruction (e.g. OUT2) outputs data from memory to an external destination from a memory address specified by the MPU: it is therefore a *memory read* execution. The unique condition which must be responsible for staticising this data is: MRD.TPB.N. This may require an externally generated data strobe from these conditions, but if the I/O port is used, the procedure is somewhat simpler, as shown in Figure 23.7. In this case, TPB may be used to directly clock the data into the device, which is configured as an output port by taking MODE high; the device is enabled by MRD.Nx, where Nx represents the selected (or decoded) N lines and the signal $\overline{MRD}$ goes low. In this mode, the I/O port has its three-state outputs continuously enabled. The SR line goes high at the termination of the chip select, and remains high until the following rising edge of CK. This line is used as DATA READY by the external circuitry.

The I/O ports may equally well be used with the chip select inputs controlled by address line decode circuitry, in which case the port has a memory address, as with the 6800 microprocessor system previously described. The situation is now very different, since the I/O port now behaves just as if it is part of the memory. In order to avoid confusion, the reader is advised to think of it as *simulated memory*. Input/output instructions are now of no use, and the I/O port is accessed in a normal read/write cycle. When the device is used as an input port, the chip select inputs must enable the chip when the appropriate address lines are asserted, and the $\overline{MRD}$ line is low. When the device is used as an output port, the chip select lines must again be enabled when the address lines are asserted to select the port, and the $\overline{\text{MWR}}$ pulse must be used to clock the device: this entails inverting it to give MWR at the CK input. Because the I/O port is simulated memory, transfers are with respect to the microprocessor D register. It is impossible to transfer data between such an I/O port and memory directly, just as it is impossible to transfer data between two different memory locations directly.

Which method to use depends entirely upon the application, and in general, the best solution is probably the one which minimises the complexity of the hardware.

24
Software

Software is an enormous subject, and this is a small chapter, therefore it is not intended to achieve more than to describe what *software* is, and to introduce some of the relevant terminology.

The structure of software is basically the same whether it is connected with computers or microprocessors: so is the terminology, with the possible exception of the term *firmware*. The latter term evolved to describe standard software packages obtainable in ROM; as such, they are software contained in hardware, hence the term, mid-way between *hard* and *soft*!

Machine code

We have seen that a computer or microprocessor deals purely with words comprising 1's and 0's. *Machine code* (or *machine language*) is the name given to the numeric form of specifying this binary code. It may be a string of 1's and 0's, or it may be octal or hexadecimal numbers which represent distinct bytes of a given word.

An 8-bit microprocessor deals in 8-bit words. If we are programming in machine code, which is the lowest level language possible, we specify the state of every single bit in each word. This may be done bit by bit, but it is more common to use two hexadecimal digits to represent the high-order and low-order 4-bit bytes of this word. Thus the code 2A represents the binary word 0 0 1 0/1 0 1 0*. Sixteen-key keyboards are commonly used to manually enter microprocessor programs in hex notation, and clearly there is less room for error when entering 2A than there is in entering 00101010.

The trouble with machine code is that it is very difficult to work in. When a programmer is trying to think out a problem, he certainly does not want the added burden of having to think in terms of numbers, whether they are binary or hex.

* *Hexadecimal notation is explained in Chapter 8.*

Assembly language

Abbreviated names – *mnemonics* – are given to every type of instruction, where the mnemonic is suggestive of the function performed, and is therefore something that the programmer can soon familiarise himself with and subsequently write from memory. Such a language has a direct one-to-one relationship with machine code, where each mnemonic is directly convertible into machine code. Thus a programmer may write his program in assembler language, and the act of converting it into machine code is carried out as a separate exercise.

The principle advantage of writing in an assembly language is that it is possible to see what the program does: machine code is meaningless to look at. For the amateur or the cost conscious, this is the way that a microprocessor program must be developed: writing it in assembly language and then manually converting it into machine code for manual entry into the microprocessor memory.

Industrial users of microprocessors generally use back-up computers to help them with the development of microprocessor programs, and in such cases, they write the program in assembly language, and then use a software *assembler* program to convert this into machine code automatically.

High level languages

The problem with low level languages – such as assembly languages – is that they are designed specifically for the processor in question, and are all different. You cannot learn 'assembly language' and then immediately program *any* microprocessor in assembler language. The other drawback, in some situations, is that low level languages can be laborious, for they must specify each little step in any process.

For the above reasons, a number of high level languages have been developed which overcome these disadvantages. Such languages offer a fair degree of consistency, and can be operated upon any computers or microprocessors, given the necessary conversion process between that high level language and the appropriate machine code language. This conversion is achieved by means of a special software program known as a *compiler*: a compiler program *compiles* the appropriate sequence of machine code instructions which equate to each high level language instruction.

There are many high level languages. FORTRAN, PASCAL, BASIC, and CORAL are just a few. Each language requires a specific compiler program in order to convert it to a particular machine code. It is therefore implicit that if you wish to write in a high level language such as BASIC, you need the support of a compiler. This either means access to a computer, or a micro-processor with suitable firmware, e.g. a BASIC to machine code compiler in ROM.

The most popular high level language with amateur micro-processor users is BASIC, and BASIC compilers are available with many microprocessors.

Choosing the right language

This is very much a matter of experience and availability. With microprocessors, the choice is usually assembly language, BASIC or PASCAL. Whilst the higher level languages make writing the program simpler, they are not the most efficient, and many exper-ienced programmers prefer to write in assembly language, simply because they can do more within a given size of memory.

Why should this be? A particular high level language instruction might equate to several machine code instructions, and the pro-grammer may not even be aware of precisely how the assembler converts his high level instruction into machine code. When a programmer writes in machine code, he knows precisely what the processor is up to all the time, and he can apply software tricks to minimise the number of instructions.

The structure of programs

The route through a given program may be totally unpredictable if it is dependent upon external stimuli. One thing which you can always be certain of, however, is that the program will always start off on the same route, and until the first optional branch is reached, the same route must always be followed from initialisation.

It has been explained that it is necessary to set up certain initial conditions in hardware circuits (e.g. flip-flop states). So it is with software, and the first task in any program is to *initialise* any variables. The equivalent of flip-flops in software are *flags*: the name given to single bits set to either 1 or 0 according to requirements. Clearly all such flags should be set to known conditions during the *initialisation routine*, at the beginning of every program.

The term *process* is used to describe lengthy pieces of program which undertake a given task. The term *routine* is often similarly used, although this term is sometimes used to imply a block of software that is a sub-program. The term *subroutine* is reserved for a routine which is used by any number of calling routines, and after execution of the subroutine, the processor returns to the next instruction in the calling routine. Rather than repeating a given routine many times in different parts of a program, a single subroutine is written to perform this task, and whenever the task is required, the main program calls up the subroutine.

Since a subroutine may be entered from many different sources, it is sometimes necessary to provide data for the subroutine to work upon. In such cases, the data must be placed in the same portion of store, in order that the subroutine knows where to find it. If the subroutine needs to pass new data back to the calling routine, it places this data in a fixed area of store, and the calling routine subsequently retrieves the data from this area of store once the subroutine task has ended.

Branch instructions provide the means of jumping from one part of a program to another according to variable conditions. Such a jump is dependent upon the results of a comparison test, usually with respect to zero (e.g. less than zero, greater than zero, or equal to zero). Jumps may also be dependent upon the condition of a flag.

The programmer can create as many flags as he wishes. Every RAM word offers him potential flags, i.e. an 8-bit system offers 8 flags per word. Some assembly languages allow individual bits to be tested within a given word, which is ideal for flag testing. Others require the programmer to use a *mask* and a logic operation. A *mask* is the term given to a pre-determined binary pattern such as 00000010.

Some examples of the use of masks will clarify matters. The following 'flag words' are combined with a mask in various ways using logic operations.

If it is desired to reset all the flag bits, a mask of all-ones may be combined with a flag word in a NOR operation, for example:

0 1 0 1 0 1 0 1	Flag word
1 1 1 1 1 1 1 1	Mask for all bits
0 0 0 0 0 0 0 0	Result of NOR

It may be seen that the same word combined with an OR operation would set all the flags. The above example operates on all bits simultaneously, but a single bit, or any number of bits may be operated upon, as desired: it simply depends on adjusting the mask. For example, the following demonstrates how a single bit may be set, irrespective of its original condition:

```
0 1 0 1 0 1 0 1     Flag word
0 0 0 0 0 0 1 0     Mask for bit 1
─────────────────
0 1 0 1 0 1 1 1     Result of OR
```

In the above example, bit 1 is masked, and an OR guarantees to leave bit 1 set; a NOR similarly guarantees to leave the bit reset. Note that the other flag bits remain unchanged. Note also that an exclusive-OR function applied with a similar mask can be used to complement a bit.

In all the above cases, we have been concerned with modifying an existing flag word. Since the result of a logic operation is contained in the accumulator of an MPU, this result must finally be written to the location used to store the flag word, otherwise it remains in its previous state.

If it is desired to examine a flag, it may be extracted in unchanged bit position by applying a mask set to 1 at the required bit, and then applying a logic AND operation; this leaves the flag word unchanged. If a right logical shift is then applied, where the number of places equals the bit position, the flag bit is moved to bit 0. A branching test is then possible, since a numerical value of 1 signifies the flag set, or zero signifies the flag reset.

This just hints at some of the tricks that the programmer can apply using machine code or assembly language. It may be seen that the software manipulations are direct equivalents of possible hardware operations.

One final word about subroutines. It is possible to call one subroutine from another, but each time this occurs, data has to be stored in the microprocessor stack, in order that it may resume operations after each subroutine exit exactly where it left off. Since the size of the stack must be fixed for any given system, this defines the number of times subroutines may be so *nested*.

COSMAC assembly language

The COSMAC assembly language comprises some 91 different instructions. The small selection shown opposite gives some indication of their types. The 'Op Code' is the hex machine code for the instruction. The 'Operation' column gives a description in terms of the notation previously used.

This short extract serves to show typical assembly language instructions, and shows how they are directly replaceable by a machine code. By reference to the figure* of internal structure of the COSMAC microprocessor, it should be possible to work out

* *Figure 23.2 on page 229.*

240

what each instruction does by the operation description. A few random examples are explained below.

Key

R(W): Register designated by W, where W = N or X or P.

M(R(N))→D; R(N)+1 means: the memory byte pointed to by R(N) is loaded into D, and R(N) is incremented by 1.

Instruction	Mnemonic	Op. code	Operation
Increment Reg N	INC	1N	R(N) + 1
Decrement Reg N	DEC	2N	R(N) − 1
Increment Reg X	IRX	60	R(X) + 1
Get Low Reg N	GLO	8N	R(N).0 → D
Put Low Reg N	PLO	AN	D → R(N).O
Get High Reg N	GHI	9N	R(N).1 → D
Put High Reg N	PHI	BN	D → R(N).1
Load Via N	LDN	0N	M(R(N)) → D; FOR N NOT O
Load Advance	LDA	4N	M(R(N)) → D; R(N) + 1
Load Via X	LDX	F0	M(R(X)) → D
Load Immediate	LDI	F8	M(R(P)) → D; R(P) + 1
Output 2	OUT 2	62	M(R(X)) → BUS; R(X) + 1; N = 2
Input 5	INP 5	6D	BUS → M(R(X)); BUS → D; N = 5
Store Via N	STR	5N	D → M(R(N))
OR	OR	F1	M(R(X)) OR D → D
Short Branch	BR	30	M(R(P)) → R(P).0
Short Branch If EF = 1	B1	34	If EF1 = 1, M(R(P)) → R(P).0 ELSE R(P) + 1

GLO places the low-order byte of the scratchpad register selected by N into the D register, leaving the content of the scratchpad register unchanged.

PHI writes the content of the D register into the high-order byte of the scratchpad register selected by N.

LDA reads the memory address specified by the scratchpad register selected by N, and places it in the D register; the scratchpad register selected by N is then incremented by 1, to point to the next memory location.

OUT 2 places the content of the memory location addressed by the scratchpad register selected by X onto the data bus; the scratchpad register selected by X is then incremented to point to the next memory address; whilst the data is output on the bus, the N lines equal binary 2.

B1 requires that if the external flag 1 input is set, the program counter low-order byte is changed to the value contained in the memory address specified by P scratchpad register; if the flag is not set, the program counter is incremented. In other words, if the flag is set – making the condition *true* – then a jump occurs; if the flag is not set – making the condition *false* – then no jump occurs, and the next instruction in sequence is followed.

Flowcharts

Before writing the *code* representing a program, a programmer is well advised to first construct a flowchart. This is a pictorial representation of the software task, and allows him to work out the best methods *before* getting involved in the detail of program instructions. Examples are given in Chapter 26.

Software development

For those with access to a computer, microprocessor software may be developed and tested using special computer programs. For those less fortunate, it is necessary to manually load the microprocessor with the program in machine code, prove it, or debug it as necessary, and to then commit it to some form of ROM. If the program is of any length, a tape recorder interface is necessary, since switching off the supply will otherwise lose the entire program. It is usual to employ a hexadecimal keyboard for the process of entering the program initially.

The most economic way of placing a program into ROM is to use PROM and your own programming circuitry. This must address each memory byte in turn, apply current pulses to the program, and must subsequently check that each word is correctly programmed before proceeding to the next. This can be achieved manually, but long programs are best programmed with some degree of automation. The use of the microprocessor to control a programmer should not be overlooked. Given a programming specification for a given PROM, the reader should be able to design a suitable programmer.

It is worth noting that some stockists of PROM devices do offer a programming service; many also offer a PROM copying service, which is useful where duplication of programs is required.

If the user is prepared to work at it, a PROM programmer may be very simple; it is simply necessary to back it up by labour and care, if automatic versions are out of the question. It is also worth bearing in mind that programs do not have to be placed into ROM if there is a tape recorder facility; it is a simple matter to enter a program from tape.

Naturally a microprocessor needs to know *how* to read in a tape, therefore it must be fed with a small program teaching it how to do this: the equivalent of a computer *bootstrap*. This program should be kept as small as possible, since it must be entered manually. Another option is to put this small bootstrap program into PROM.

Any equipment in which the microprocessor must make itself invisible (i.e. usable by anyone), must have its program put into some form of ROM. It then behaves just like any other random logic circuit.

25
Hard or soft?

Hard or soft? That is the question. It is not a matter of which is 'nobler', but rather a matter of which is the most suitable, and this depends very much upon circumstances. In this chapter the hardware and software approaches will be compared and the various factors involved will be considered.

Of course, the decision is not really between hardware and software, but rather where the emphasis should lie, i.e. the choice between logic and a microprocessor. The following table compares various factors.

Factor	Random logic	Microprocessor
Design	Specific	As general as possible
Design emphasis	Hardware	Software
Flexibility	Low	High
Package count	High	Low
Hardware cost	Depends on quantities	Depends on quantities
Total development cost plus production cost	Depends on quantities	Depends on quantities
Modifications	Difficult	Easy
Speed	Fast	Slower

If the task is relatively simple, and there is no significant difference between the hardware cost of a random logic version and a microprocessor version, the random logic option is probably best. It is only in circumstances where the package count is becoming high with random logic that the microprocessor option begins to look more attractive.

There is very little development time with random logic, unless the design is particularly complex. A microprocessor version, on the other hand, requires both hardware design (relatively simple), and software development, and as we have seen, the latter involves testing, debugging, and subsequent PROM programming.

There is always the speed consideration to take into account. For whilst microprocessors operate at similar frequencies to random logic devices, they must cope with a given task on a sequential basis.

Random logic offers faster solutions because events may happen simultaneously. Very often a hardware/software compromise is possible in circumstances where speed is an important consideration.

For production quantities of anything over about 15 packages, the microprocessor solution begins to look more attractive. The hardware is simpler and cheaper to produce, and since the software becomes firmware, the product reduces to a simple hardware construction exercise.

A random logic design is obviously designed around a specific requirement, and any subsequent modifications required can lead to real problems, and possibly a major redesign. This is where a microprocessor system wins, for such a modification may not even require any change to the hardware: software modifications are easily implemented, and many only reflect a change of ROM in the hardware – but remember that the modified ROM is hardware compatible. Even if the modification calls for a different hardware interface, this is not liable to cause any great problems, and the major changes are still liable to be in the software.

Experience counts

The above arguments are all very well, but they do not take into account experience. When it comes to microprocessor design, *experience* counts. It must be recognised that there is a considerable learning curve associated with microprocessor design, therefore if an engineer is not familiar with microprocessors, his first design is liable to be rather time-consuming. In the short term a complex task might work out cheaper in random logic, but in the long term, if the same engineer is to continue designing new products, the time spent in familiarising himself with microprocessing techniques will pay off.

Once a designer has microprocessing experience, he will approach each new design with the initial aim of using a microprocessor – *by choice*. As he gains more experience, each new design becomes easier, and the use of microprocessors brings with it inherent reliability. Complex tasks are readily handled by microprocessors, and possible modifications to the design are nothing to fear. Once an engineer is competent in microprocessor design, and is used to using standard central processing configurations, the development of microprocessor designs can be shorter than random logic designs.

The enthusiast has different factors to consider, since time does not equate to money. On the other hand, the DIY man is probably only interested in designing one equipment, therefore the inconveniences of developing the software may not seem worthwhile. No one can make the decision for him. All that can be done is to point out the differences, and hopefully, this book does just that.

Which microprocessor?

Since there is a not insignificant learning curve associated with familiarising yourself with any microprocessor, it is worth spending a bit of time researching the differences between them before making your selection. Your choice must depend upon your requirements and circumstances. One approach is to buy a standard microprocessor board, complete with MPU and I/O ports, and preferably a tape interface; this option is likely to be expensive, however, and specific design can work out much more cheaply.

It is worth bearing in mind that whilst microprocessor chips may work out cheaply, the necessary memory to go with them can be very expensive. Always shop around for memory by scanning the advertisements in DIY magazines; prices for the same device can vary fourfold! If you buy a complete board, you can be fairly sure that you are paying for expensive memory.

The reader is particularly recommended to look for the following types of memory, since they are static, popular, widely available, and often offered cheaply:

    2708 PROM   (1 K × 8 bits)
    2114-L2 RAM (1 K × 4 bits)

It is common practice to use memory chips with even lower 'bit-widths' than 4, but this leads to higher package counts, and is therefore more inconvenient. Clearly it is necessary to connect chips in parallel fashion if the bytes offered are less than 8-bits wide, and this leads to more complex gating on the address lines. Remember that RAM is necessary for program development, for the program code must be entered into temporary store. Once the program has been proven, it may be committed to PROM. From the above, it can be seen that each 1 K of final 2708 PROM can be replaced by two 2114-L2 RAM chips during development; there are hardware differences, of course, but nothing drastic.

Smaller RAM devices are useful for normal temporary storage requirements of data, and these are available from 16 and 32 bytes upwards. Since memory is the single most expensive component in such systems, the designer's aim should always be to keep it to a minimum. Some microprocessor chips actually contain some RAM, and this is always worth bearing in mind.

College libraries generally contain a fair selection of material on different microprocessors, and an hour or so browsing may help you decide which microprocessors to find out more about. My only word of warning is to make sure that you look into the hardware implications before becoming too immersed in the software: some microprocessors are much more convenient to use than others.

26

A microprocessor design example – an 'AUTONIM' alternative

It is difficult for anyone without experience in microprocessor design or familiarisation with the intricacies of software to appreciate just how different random logic and microprocessor approaches really are. For this reason, this concluding chapter presents an outline of what is entailed in a microprocessor design.

Since we have already considered a complex random logic design in depth – that of the 'AUTONIM'* – this is most easily achieved by now looking at a microprocessor alternative for the same electronic game. This has the added advantage of assuming familiarisation with the design requirements. This microprocessor alternative must achieve everything that the random logic version did, and should demand no more of the human player.

The COSMAC microprocessor is chosen for this example, because of its particular flexibility with random logic, and because the reader should by now have a reasonable familiarity with its capabilities.

Hardware design

Once it has been decided to use a microprocessor, the designer should aim to keep the hardware to a minimum. This enhances reliability, reduces development time, minimises the cost, and gives maximum flexibility should any modifications be required. The circuit given in Figure 26.1 represents the entire hardware requirement, neglecting only a simple power supply. Compare this with the complexity of the random logic design given in Figures 19.10 to 19.17. The random logic design had a package count of 47, whilst the microprocessor version has a package count of 13, assuming 2 K of memory. (Skilful programming might require less memory than

* *Refer to Chapter 19.*

247

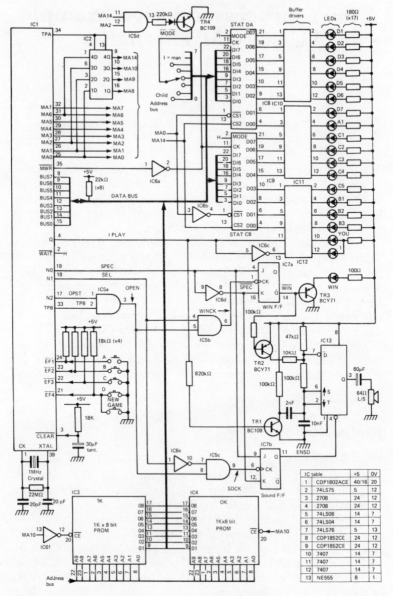

Figure 26.1. A microprocessor version of the AUTONIM

this, but until the software has been worked out, the designer must allow for an adequate amount of memory.)

The circuit given in Figure 26.1 shows two 1 K PROMs; the final design might only need one of them, and the system is equally capable of expanding to use further 1 K blocks of memory.

The line LEDs and the I and YOU MOVE LEDs are all driven by buffer gates (non-inverting), and are all powered directly from the +5 V rail; the I and YOU LEDs again share a common ballast resistor since only one will be illuminated at once.

Three 7407 hex buffer driver devices (ICs10–12) cope with 18 LEDs, which again happens to leave the WIN LED as an odd one out. Rather than wastefully use a further buffer driver device, an emitter-follower transistor TR3 is used.

The line requirements for the game are most economically met with two 8-bit registers, which we shall refer to as *staticisers* (or 'stats') in this design, in order to distinguish them from micro-processor *registers*. It will be recalled that the four lines of the AUTONIM were labelled A–D for convenience, where the number of LEDs in each line was as follows:

Line D	7 LEDs	Now also to be known as Line 4
Line C	5 LEDs	Now also to be known as Line 3
Line B	3 LEDs	Now also to be known as Line 2
Line A	1 LED	Now also to be known as Line 1

These can be combined in the two stats as follows:

STAT DA (IC8) combines Lines D and A.
STAT CB (IC9) combines Lines C and B.

These stats are achieved by means of two CDP1852CE I/O ports; it will be recalled that these devices contain an 8-bit register, and that the three-state gates are always 'open' when configured as output ports*. If any change in the display requirements occurs, the appropriate stat must be loaded with fresh data.

The microprocessor must be able to read which mode the game is working in, i.e. I = man (manual), or the machine skill level: expert/good/average/poor/child. This requires an input port or a simulated memory location. The latter is chosen, where the appropriate address decode (actually a partial decode), biases TR4 on, causing $\overline{\text{MODE}}$ to go low at the switch wiper. The selected line from the six available is therefore taken low during a read cycle, and

---

* *Refer to Chapter 23.*

this is seen as a low on one of the data bus lines BUS0 to BUS5. All the data bus lines have pull-up resistors, and this provides the load for TR4 collector.

The COSMAC microprocessor has a Q flip-flop which is program controllable. Since the MOVE indicator is the single indicator which is changed most frequently, this is ideal for signalling I/YOU. It may be seen that Q true signifies I PLAY, and that Q false signifies YOU PLAY; inverter IC6c ensures the complementary displays.

The only remaining audio/visual outputs are the sound outputs and the WIN indicator LED. Each of these has two possible states – on or off – and is therefore readily controlled by means of a flip-flop. A 74LS76 dual J-K flip-flop provides this requirement (IC7), and associated gating allows the microprocessor to control the state of these two flip-flops.

The COSMAC microprocessor contains 16 scratchpad registers, and this is more than adequate operating RAM for this application, hence there is no need to provide additional external RAM (except for the program code during development). This would seem to rule out the use of the N lines, since I/O instructions are normally relative to memory, i.e. normally RAM. In fact this is not the case, for it is always possible to set up fixed store addresses in PROM which will provide the necessary data output on the data bus, but in this example, even this is not necessary. The three N lines provide sufficient combinations to control the two flip-flops directly, and the data bus is not even required. Output instructions are used to control the flip-flop states, and such instructions must *assume* an output on the data bus; since this output is ignored, it really does not matter what memory address is specified!

The N lines are each given a definite rôle in this case, as follows:

> N2 is designated signal line OPST (output strobe), and must be made to go high for every output instruction. N1 is designated the signal line SEL (select), and is used to select either the WIN flip-flop (IC7a) when true, or the sound flip-flop (IC7b) when false. N0 is designated the SPEC (specify) signal line, and specifies the required state of the selected flip-flop.

It therefore follows that particular output instructions have specific hardware functions, as follows:

N2	N1	N0	Hardware function	Instruction
1	1	1	Set WIN	OUT 7
1	1	0	Reset WIN	OUT 6
1	0	1	Set ENSD	OUT 5
1	0	0	Reset ENSD	OUT 4

250

Note that the K input must always be complementary to the J input, hence inverter IC6d. The strobe OPST is combined with the timing pulse TPB to provide an output enable strobe OPEN; the latter is ANDed with SEL to clock the WIN flip-flop, or with $\overline{\text{SEL}}$ (from the output of inverter IC6e), to clock the sound flip-flop.

When the WIN flip-flop is set, Q goes low to produce $\overline{\text{WIN}}$, which biases TR3 on, and hence illuminates the WIN LED. When the sound flip-flop is set, the ENSD (enable sound) signal goes true, and this enables a 555 timer connected as an audio oscillator in a similar fashion to that used in the random logic version.

The 555 circuitry is the same as in Figure 19.17, although the control inputs vary. Transistor TR1 is used to provide the alternative tones for the two players, and is therefore driven from the I PLAY line. Transistor TR2 is used to provide the alternative tone used during a win sequence, and is therefore driven from the $\overline{\text{WIN}}$ line.

The inputs from the four line selection buttons (A–D) are conveniently connected directly to the four flag inputs of the microprocessor, and must therefore be polled by the program. Since a different routine will be entered in the event of a win, no confusion arises if the NEW GAME button also uses one of the same flag inputs, hence the economic version shown. It is true that the D line button would double as a NEW GAME selection, but who knows? and who cares! Never confuse the user with penny-pinching economies.

The next thing to consider is the *address map* for the system. This is shown in Figure 26.2. The memory address lines MA0–MA7 from

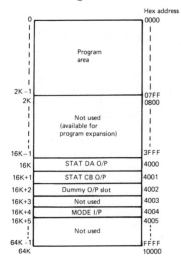

Figure 26.2. Memory map of the system

the microprocessor output the high byte of the 16-bit memory address when TPA is true, hence latch IC2 latches the four bits required for this application: MA8, MA9, MA10 and MA14. These output memory address lines are combined with the low-order address byte on lines MA0–MA7 when TPB goes true. The lines MA0–MA10 are sufficient to address up to 2 K of memory. A space is then allowed in the map for possible memory expansion. If it is found that more than 2 K of programming space is required, it is only necessary to staticise MA11 in order to provide a doubling of available program memory (up to 4 K). Similarly, further memory up to the 16 K − 1 point can be addressed by also taking into account lines MA12 and MA13. The MA14 line is used to locate the two external output ports, designated STAT DA and STAT CB. Note that a dummy output slot is provided for the OUT instructions; any address would do, but this is tidier, and requires no actual memory!

The memory address at 16 K + 4 is used as an input port to read the mode switch setting; 16 K + 4 is chosen because a partial decode is possible, decoding only two address bits: MA14 and MA2. This leaves memory address 16 K + 3 unused, plus the addresses from 16 K + 5 and above.

Note that it is easy to express memory locations in terms of 'K'. The third table in Chapter 8 shows the binary weighting of the address line bits, and a further table is provided later in the same chapter of hexadecimal/binary equivalents. The latter may be used to derive the hex address, if the full 16-bit binary address is broken down into four 4-bit bytes, where each byte is represented by a hex digit. Two examples are given below.

15 14 13 12	11 10 9 8	7 6 5 4	3 2 1 0	
0 0 0 0	1 0 0 0	0 0 0 0	0 0 0 0	2 K in binary
0	8	0	0	2 K in hex
0 0 0 0	0 1 1 1	1 1 1 1	1 1 1 1	2 K − 1 in binary
0	7	F	F	2 K − 1 in hex

Memory addressing beyond the capacity of the memory address lines of the chip is simply achieved by decoding the more significant address lines and using this to enable appropriate chips via the chip enables. The lower significance address lines must always go to *every* memory device.

Because the output ports are given discrete memory locations, they are treated as memory, and are written to by means of an MWR pulse.

This design assumes prior debugging of the software in RAM, and shows the final circuit where program is contained in PROM. Since it is no longer necessary for the user to manipulate the MPU, it is always required to start in the initialised state at power-on; this is ensured by applying a $\overline{\text{CLEAR}}$ pulse via pin 3 of the MPU. The XTAL and CK inputs show the connection of a crystal and associated components to provide the clocking requirements.

Software design

Firstly, let us consider the assembly language instructions needed for the I/O requirements.

The instructions OUT 7–OUT 4 cause the N lines to output the requisite binary code which is combined with TPB to set or reset the two flip-flops. The memory byte addressed by the scratchpad register specified by X is output on the bus during this operation, but this is ignored. For convention, according to the memory map, the address selected for all these output instructions is X4002.*

The instructions required to load the external stats must be *write* instructions, therefore the data to be written must first be loaded into the D register of the MPU. A STORE VIA N (STR) instruction (see COSMAC assembly language in Chapter 24) can then be used to load the external stats from the D register, where the N register points to a scratchpad register which contains the address of the required stat (i.e. X4000 for STAT DA or X4001 for STAT CB).

The instruction required to read the mode switch must be a *read* instruction, such as LDX; this requires that the X specified scratchpad register contains the address of the MODE I/P port, i.e. X4004. Such an instruction loads the D register. A further instruction must then transfer this data word from the D register to R(B).1. This register is shown in the map of scratchpad registers presented in Figure 26.3.

The MOVE indication is controlled by the two instructions: SEQ to set Q (for I PLAY), and REQ to reset Q (for YOU PLAY).

The input flags are polled very conveniently by a SHORT BRANCH instruction such as B1; this causes a program branch if the flag $\overline{\text{EF1}}$ is asserted by pressing line button A, or no branch if the flag is not asserted. For software purposes, the lines are more conveniently referred to as lines 1–4, as mentioned earlier.

Thus it is a simple matter to interface software and hardware. What must next be considered is what software registers or flags are required to achieve our aim.

---

* Note that the prefix 'X' denotes a hexadecimal number.

Registers and flags

Certain requirements for registers and flags will be known at the outset; others will become obvious as our involvement in the flowcharting or programming itself becomes deeper. The scratchpad register map shown in Figure 26.3 shows some of the requirements which can be established at an early stage. These are filled up from the bottom of the available space for convenience; certain of the upper registers are conventionally used for other purposes (e.g. program counter, stack pointer, etc.).

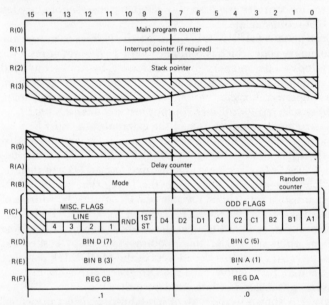

Figure 26.3. Scratchpad register map

The R(F) register serves to contain the 16-bits required by the external staticisers, where R(F).1 is REG CB, the data source for STAT CB, and R(F).0 is REG DA, the data source for STAT DA. These register bits must be set to a 0 for every LED that is required to be illuminated, bearing in mind that the buffer drivers are non-inverting, and must be low to drive the LEDs.

Registers R(D) and R(E) are used to contain the binary values of the four line counters; the number in brackets indicates the maximum count in equivalent decimal. Thus each time a line counter is decremented, the appropriate counter in these two registers is decremented. A separate REFRESH DISPLAY subroutine must be

254

written to examine the binary registers, to format this into the revised form for display in R(F), and subsequently to output the content of R(F) to the external stats, via the D register. For example, the instruction GHI gets the high-order byte of the register specified by N and places it into the D register; thus if N is set equal to F (i.e. 15_{10}), this transfers REG CB to D.

The so-called ODD FLAGS are the software equivalent of odd binary bits in the various lines, labelled A1, B1, etc., in the random logic version (see Figure 19.11). The MISC. FLAGS portion of R(C).1 contains four LINE FLAGS, the random flag (RND) and the first start flag (1ST). Their purpose will be outlined in the following flowchart description.

A RANDOM COUNTER is provided in R(B); this counter is initialised at 4, and is decremented to 1, thereafter reverting to 4. This counter replaces the hardware equivalent in Figure 19.16 (IC35), and is used to provide a random starting point for the program during the LINESCAN routine. A DELAY COUNTER is provided to generate a time delay, and effectively is the software equivalent of the low frequency clock previously used.

Other flags or registers may be required. If they are, the COSMAC still has plenty of empty scratchpad registers to choose from.

Flowcharting

The next step is to draw a high level *flowchart* of the program. This is a simple pictorial representation of the requirements, and is shown in Figure 26.4. At this stage, the flowchart must be kept as simple as possible. It may be seen that the basic concept of four main routines still applies, i.e. BUTSCAN, MANDEC, LINESCAN and MAC-DEC. A guided tour through the flowchart follows.

After ENTRY, block 10 indicates that the 1ST START flag is set; this is the first *initialising* procedure. Block 20 then shows that other initialising steps must be taken, i.e. reset all the flags by setting flag words R(C).0 and R(C).1 to zero. The binary registers must then be initialised for the start counts, i.e. BIN D = 7 (R(D).1 = 07), etc.

Block 30 is then entered, and the 1ST START flag is complemented. This part of the program is subsequently passed through after a NEW GAME has been called, and the 1ST START flag has decided which player starts play; this action of complementing it gives players alternate chances of starting. Block 40 calls up the REFRESH DISPLAY subroutine, which formats R(F) from R(D) and R(E), and outputs data to STAT DA and STAT CB, to give the correct line displays.

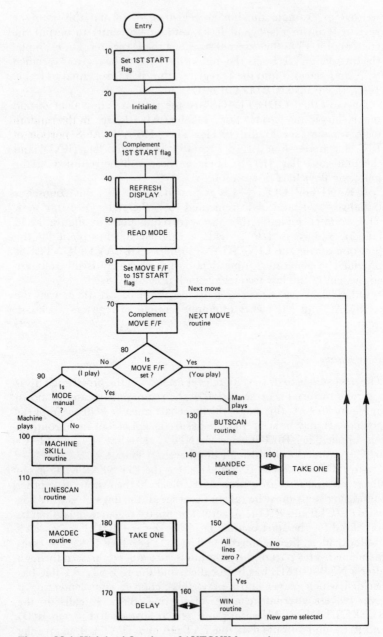

Figure 26.4. High level flowchart of AUTONIM procedure

256

Block 50 reads the mode switch by means of a read instruction, and stores this in the MODE scratchpad register byte. Block 60 makes the move flip-flop (i.e. the Q flip-flop) equal to the 1ST START flag; this sets up for the correct player at the start of play.

From block 70 onward, we will have entered that portion of the program which is looped through many times during a single game; for every new move, the program returns to block 70. The block itself complements the Q flip-flop, thereby setting up for the 'other' player's move. Block 80 is a decision, asking if the move flip-flop is set or not. If the answer is no, this indicates the I PLAY situation, or if it is yes, this indicates the YOU PLAY situation.

Block 90 asks if the mode is manual, and if the answer is yes, it diverts the program to BUTSCAN; if not, it enters the machine's reply sequences.

Thus block 130 is entered if a manual move is required, and a routine called BUTSCAN is employed. This is the software equivalent of BUTSCAN in the random logic design, and is responsible for polling the input flags in order to locate a depressed line button. Once a button is found depressed, the software must lock onto this button, ignoring any others.

The program then passes into block 140, and the MANDEC routine, to decrement the appropriate line counter for as long as the line button is depressed, but stopping at zero. This routine calls upon a TAKE ONE subroutine to reduce the line counter at a set rate, and to provide the audible tone that goes with it, and the REFRESH DISPLAY subroutine* to update the line display via the stats.

The alternative path for the machine's play is through Block 100, a MACHINE SKILL routine, which examines the MODE register, and establishes whether a hedge move is required or not; this must make use of the RANDOM COUNTER. Block 110 is then entered to provide the software equivalent of LINESCAN, finding a suitable line to take from, and block 120 is the MACDEC routine, to decrement the chosen line. As before, the TAKE ONE subroutine is called upon.

After the machine or player's move, block 150 is entered, to check if all the lines are zero. If they are not, NEXT MOVE takes the program back to block 70. If all lines are zero, the WIN routine is entered. This makes use of the DELAY subroutine to provide the time delay associated with the flashing WIN LED and the win tones. The program loops within this routine until NEW GAME is selected, whereupon it returns to block 20.

Unfortunately, space does not permit much more analysis of the software, but example flowcharts are provided for the BUTSCAN

*Called up by the TAKE ONE subroutine.

and MANDEC routines, plus the TAKE ONE and DELAY subroutines. These take the flowcharting down a level in detail, but they still do not represent equivalence with single assembly language instructions.

If the reader cares to work through these additional flowcharts, he will begin to understand the techniques necessary. The following brief notes associated with these flowcharts may help.

BUTSCAN routine (Figure 26.5)

Each input flag is tested in turn in loop fashion until one is found set. When one is found set, a check is made to see if the relevant line counter is zero; if it is, this button is ignored, and looping continues,

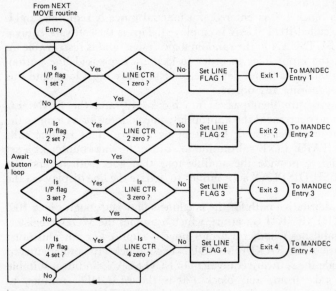

Figure 26.5. Flowchart of BUTSCAN routine

but if not, a LINE FLAG is set as a line indicator to other routines, and the routine is exited from one of four different exits. Different exits are used since the separation established according to line selected is of use in the following MANDEC routine.

MANDEC routine (Figure 26.6)

The appropriate line counter is decremented, the TAKE ONE subroutine is entered to refresh the line display and control the

258

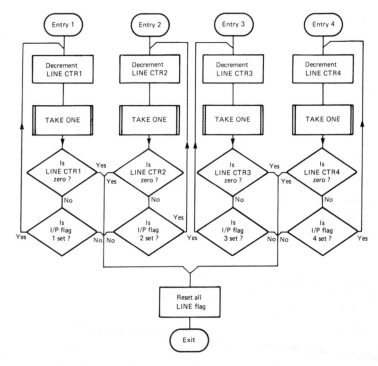

Figure 26.6. Flowchart of MANDEC routine

tones, and then two checks are made. The first checks if the line counter is now zero, and if so prepares for exit; the second checks if the input flag is still set, signifying that the button is still depressed, and if so, the program loops back to take out a further LED. If the line counter is zero, or if the line button is no longer depressed, all the line flags are reset, and the routine is exited.

TAKE ONE subroutine (Figure 26.7)

This subroutine calls up two other subroutines, namely REFRESH DISPLAY and DELAY. The sequence is as follows. REFRESH DISPLAY is called to reformat the R(F) registers and to refresh the hardware staticisers. Enable sound sets the sound flip-flop, which then stays on. The RANDOM FLAG is set, causing the RANDOM COUNTER to be 'rotated' within the DELAY subroutine. The DELAY subroutine then ensures that the tone is sounded for a

259

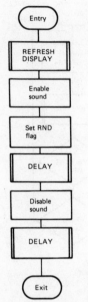

Figure 26.7. Flow-chart of TAKE ONE subroutine

reasonable time, before it is disabled. A further delay ensues to provide a gap between tones, and the subroutine is then exited, return being made to the next block in the calling routine.

DELAY subroutine (Figure 26.8)

This subroutine provides a time delay by a standard looping technique. A counter is initially loaded with a value, and the subroutine then continues to decrement the counter and loop until the counter reaches zero. The time delay expires when the counter reaches zero.

This particular delay subroutine also incorporates the random counter routine, providing that the RND flag is set before entry. If this flag is set, it is 'rotated' from 4 down to 1, and then back to 4. If the RND flag is not set, a dummy time load branch causes no action, but takes the same time to pass through as does the branch rotating the random counter; this maintains the same time interval through the routine whether the RND flag is set or not.

After the random counter section of the subroutine, each line flag is checked; one (and only one) will have been set by the BUTSCAN routine. When the set line flag is found, the related input flag is

260

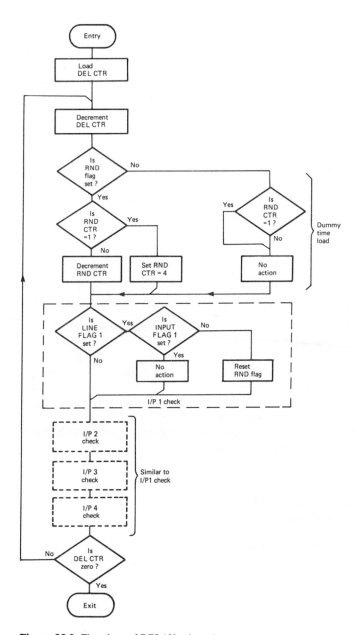

Figure 26.8. Flowchart of DELAY subroutine

261

checked, to see if the button is still depressed; this technique means that other buttons are ignored. If the button is still depressed, no action occurs, but if it is no longer pressed, the RND flag is reset. This ensures that the RANDOM COUNTER stops as soon as the line button is released, and introduces a random element into where the RANDOM COUNTER stops. The RANDOM COUNTER is subsequently used by the LINESCAN routine to establish where it starts its scan for a suitable line, and thereby maintains the random line selection previously achieved with the random logic.

Since the delay subroutine must loop many times to provide the required delay, it is most important that if the path through the routine differs in any way, it must still have the same number (and type) of instructions, so that it takes the same time to execute. Hence the dummy time load and no action boxes, which ensure that all routes through the subroutine are always equal.

Conclusion

Figures 26.5 to 26.8 represent flowcharts at one level lower than the high level flowchart shown in Figure 26.4; each box on the high level flowchart can be broken down into similar lower level flowcharts.

It is then possible to break each of these lower level flowcharts into assembly language level flowcharts, although many programmers forego this stage and go straight to writing the code. If you have any problems, it is always sensible to draw flowcharts representing every instruction.

Remember that the hardware design assumes that the software has been proven and committed to PROM. If this is not the case, you must bear in mind the added complications associated with a microprocessor design:

(a) You need RAM large enough to take the entire program for software development. (Later replaced by PROM.)
(b) You need greater control of the MPU for program development.
(c) You need a tape recorder interface for such a long program, during development.
(d) You need a PROM programmer to commit the proven program to PROM – or to provide anyone offering a programming service with an appropriate data input (e.g. punched tape or marked cards).

Postscript

It is hoped that this practical approach to random logic design is adequate to give the reader sufficient confidence to embark upon his own design projects. Always remember to plant acorns at first, and leave the large oaks until you have gained more experience. Design, like any other creative pursuit, requires considerable practice. You are sure to learn a lot from your own mistakes.

Too much ambition in the early stages can lead to great disappointment. Remember the suggested limit of about ten integrated circuits until you have had a number of successes. After that, it is still wise to try to break larger designs down into smaller sized modules which can be independently tested.

The part of the book given over to microprocessors is only intended to inform the reader what kind of options they offer him. Do not attempt to design the hardware for a microprocessor system until you have gained considerable experience in conventional random logic system. If you wish to experiment with microprocessors before then, restrict yourself to the ready-made microprocessor systems.

If you failed to completely understand the design examples presented in Chapters 18 and 19, it is advisable to reread them until you do. If this proves a struggle, it will be a worthwhile struggle, for real learning will be the final reward. Suddenly everything will gel. Everything you need is within the covers of this book. Once you understand these designs, your knowledge will be adequate for you to undertake your own simple design projects with confidence.

The appendices which follow should be of great assistance when undertaking your own designs, but it is strongly recommended that you supplement this information by more detailed device data published by one of the larger manufacturers. It is wise to stick to TTL logic until you are fairly experienced. Probably the most useful book to start with is: 'The TTL Data Book for Design Engineers', published by Texas Instruments.

Appendices

Appendices – brief details

Appendix A – abridged TTL data
Appendix B – selected TTL pinout details and supply currents
Appendix C – electrical characteristics
Appendix D – ASCII code
Appendix E – a note on drawing standards

The following appendices are provided in order that the prospective designer may have enough data to enable him to attempt simple design exercises. It should be noted that whilst all device data included is as accurate as possible, no responsibility can be taken by the publishers or author for any errors therein. Whilst different manufacturers generally attempt to produce directly compatible devices where these are given the same numerical identification, this must not be assumed. The data which follows is not related to any single manufacturer, therefore the user should check manufacturers' data before using any of the devices included. The purpose of each appendix is outlined below.

Appendix A – abridged TTL data

This appendix provides pinout details for some of the most common TTL devices, plus more detailed information on certain devices.

Appendix B – selected TTL pinout details and supply currents

This appendix provides pinout details and information on device supply currents for most of the TTL devices mentioned in this book. Space restrictions necessitate that this information is presented in tabular form.

Appendix C – electrical characteristics

This appendix includes absolute maximum ratings and representative characteristics for 54/74 series TTL devices and 4000 series COS/MOS devices. Also included is information on the switching characteristics of TTL flip-flops.

Appendix D – ASCII code

This appendix provides details of the ASCII code.

Appendix E – a note on drawing standards

This appendix provides information on various drawing standards concerned with logic symbols.

Appendix A – abridged TTL data

This appendix contains pinout information on a selection of the most commonly used 74 series TTL devices. These devices are allocated reference numbers (e.g. 'A2') for use within this book. Text references of the form: 'App. A2' refer to the reference numbers used within *this particular appendix*. The divisions used are as follows:

A   Common gates, page 271
B   Special gates, page 272
C   Flip-flops, page 274
D   Registers, page 275
E   Counters, page 276
F   Decoders, page 278
G   Data selectors, page 279
H   Comparator, page 280
J   Monostable multivibrators, page 281
K   555 type timer, page 282
L   Memory, page 283

The devices on a particular page are ordered according to usage rather than in numerical order. The following table lists all the devices in numerical order, and provides their reference number within the appendix.

Each device is also listed with a *cost factor* (C.F.). The designer should always bear in mind the cost of the devices he is using, in order that the design may be cost-effective. In order that this information may be provided in a manner that will be universally applicable despite different currencies and inflation, the C.F. rating is a relative indication. The cost factors are based upon the cost of the most common device of them all – the 7400 quad 2 I/P NAND gate, which is normalised such that its C.F. is 1.0. All other prices are relative to this price.

The cost factors were compiled at the time of writing, and should not differ *greatly* between different suppliers, or at different times. This information is only provided as a guide. By checking the current price for a 7400 device, the approximate cost for another device may be obtained by multiplying this price by the appropriate C.F. For example, if the price for a 7400 is 10p in the U.K., a 7404 (App. A2) should cost around 13p.

Numerical listing of devices included in this appendix

Type	Appendix ref.	Description
555	K	Timer
2114L	L2	1024 × 4 bit static RAM
2708	L1	1024 × 8 bit static EPROM
7400	A1	Quad 2 I/P NAND gate
7402	A6	Quad 2 I/P NOR gate
7403	B6	Quad 2 I/P NAND gate (O/C)
7404	A2	Hex inverter
7405	A2	Hex inverter (O/C)
7408	A7	Quad 2 I/P AND gate
7410	A3	Triple 3 I/P NAND gate
7414	A4	Hex Schmitt inverter
7416	B2	Hex buffer inverter (O/C)
7417	A2	Hex buffer (O/C; non-inverting)
7420	A5	Dual 4 I/P NAND gate
7430	B1	8 I/P NAND gate
7432	A8	Quad 2 I/P OR gate
7451	B3	Dual AND-OR-INVERT gate
7474	C1	Dual D-type flip-flop
7475	C3	4-bit bistable latch
7476	C2	Dual J-K type flip-flop
7485	H1	4-bit magnitude comparator
74121	J1	Monostable multivibrator
74122	J2	Re-triggerable monostable multivibrator
74125	B7	Quad bus buffer (L 3-S)
74LS125	B7	Quad bus buffer (L 3-S)
74126	B7	Quad bus buffer (H 3-S)
74LS126	B7	Quad bus buffer (H 3-S)
74LS138	F1	3–8 decoder
74LS139	F1	2–4 dual decoder
74150	G3	16–1 line data selector
74153	G2	Dual 4–1 line data selector
74154	F2	4–16 decoder
74157	G1	Quad 2–1 line data selector
74190	E3	Decade counter (sync. up/down)
74191	E3	Binary counter (sync. up/down)
74196	E1	Presettable decade counter
74197	E1	Presettable binary counter
74198	D3	8-bit bidirectional shift register
74199	D2	8-bit single direction shift register
74LS240	B8	Octal buffer/line driver/receiver (INV L 3-S)
74LS241	B8	Octal buffer/line driver/receiver (NON-INV H/L 3-S)
74273	D1	Octal D-type flip-flops
74279	C4	Quad $\bar{S}$ $\bar{R}$ latch

270

A1   C.F. 1.0

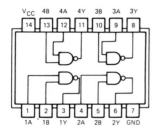

7400   QUAD 2 I/P NAND

A2   C.F. 1.3
1.6
2.7

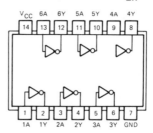

7404   HEX INVERTER
7405   HEX INVERTER (O/C)
For non-inverting buffer
with o/c use 7417

A3   C.F. 1.4

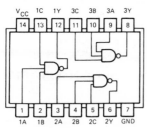

7410   TRIPLE 3 I/P NAND

A4   C.F. 3.7

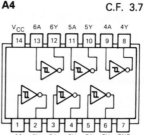

7414   HEX SCHMITT INVERTER

A5   C.F. 1.6

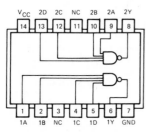

7420   DUAL 4 I/P NAND

A6   C.F. 1.1

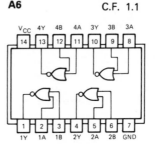

7402   QUAD 2 I/P NOR

271

COMMON GATES (contd)

A

A7   C.F. 1.6

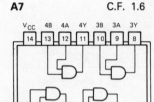

7408   QUAD 2 I/P AND

A8   C.F. 2.7

7432   QUAD 2 I/P OR

SPECIAL GATES

B

B1   C.F. 1.6

7430   8 I/P NAND

B2   C.F. 2.5

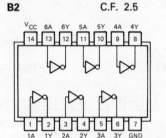

7416   HEX BUFFER INVERTER (O/C)

B3   C.F. 1.5

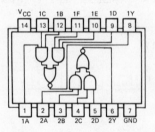

7451   DUAL AND-OR-INVERT

B4   C.F. 3.1

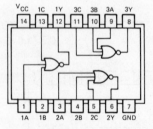

7427   TRIPLE 3 I/P NOR

B5   C.F. 3.1

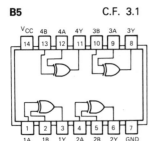

7486   QUAD 2 I/P XOR

B6   C.F. 1.3

7403   QUAD 2 I/P NAND (O/C)

B7   C.F. 4.5

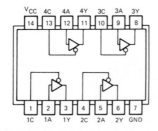

74125
74LS125   QUAD BUS BUFFER (L 3-S)* (type shown)

74126
74LS126   QUAD BUS BUFFER (H 3-S)

B8   C.F. 15.0

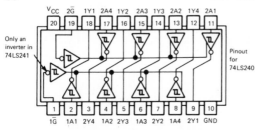

74LS240   OCTAL BUFFER/LINE DR/RX
(INVERTED L 3-S)* (type shown)

74LS241   OCTAL BUFFER/LINE DR/RX
(NON-INVERTED 3-S WITH
×4 = L & ×4 = H CONTROL)

*3-S signifies 3-state outputs; H or L indicates
requirement for control output to enable gates.
The 74LS241 has four gates with each form of control.*

273

FLIP-FLOPS

C

C1 C.F. 2.7

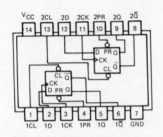

7474 DUAL D-TYPE FLIP-FLOP
WITH PR & CL*

C2 C.F. 2.9

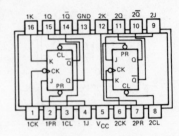

7476 DUAL J-K TYPE FLIP-FLOP
WITH PR & CL*

C3 C.F. 3.5

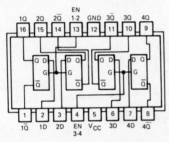

7475 4-BIT BISTABLE LATCH

C4 C.F. 10.0

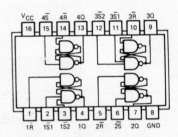

74279 QUAD S̄R̄ LATCH

* Unused PR or CL inputs should be held high

274

REGISTERS

D

D1 C.F. 24.0

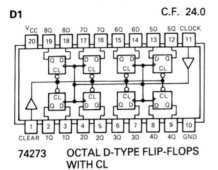

74273 OCTAL D-TYPE FLIP-FLOPS
WITH CL

D2 C.F. 13.6

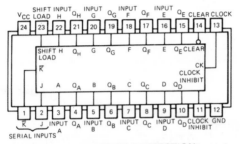

74199 8-BIT SINGLE DIRECTION
SHIFT REGISTER
(PARALLEL IN & OUT)

D3 C.F. 13.6

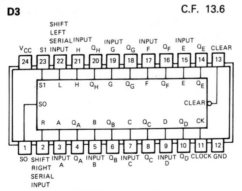

74198 8-BIT BIDIRECTIONAL
SHIFT REGISTER
(PARALLEL IN & OUT)

275

E1

C.F. 9.0
8.0

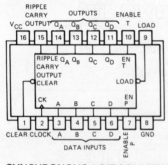

74196	DIVIDE BY 2 (CLOCK 1 – Q_A) & DIVIDE BY 5 (CLOCK 2 – Q_D) (LINKED FOR DIVIDE BY 10)
74197	DIVIDE BY 2 (CLOCK 1 – Q_A) & DIVIDE BY 8 (CLOCK 2 – Q_D) (LINKED FOR DIVIDE BY 16)

PRESETTABLE DECADE OR BINARY COUNTERS/LATCHES

Performs BCD, Bi-Quinary or Binary counting

E2

C.F. 9.0

	COUNTER TYPE	CLEAR TYPE
74160	DECADE	ASYNC
74161	BINARY	ASYNC
74162	DECADE	SYNC
74163	BINARY	SYNC

SYNCHRONOUS 4-BIT COUNTERS

E3

C.F. 12.0
11.0

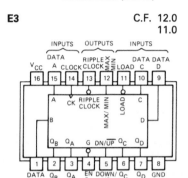

SYNCHRONOUS UP/DOWN COUNTERS

74190   DECADE COUNTER
74191   BINARY COUNTER

ASYNCHRONOUS LOAD INPUT

POSITIVE-EDGE TRIGGERED

MAX/MIN FOR OVERFLOW/UNDERFLOW
RIPPLE CLOCK FOR OVERFLOW/UNDERFLOW

SAMPLE WAVEFORMS FOR 74191 BELOW

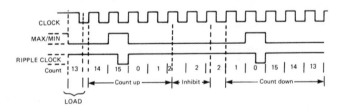

F1

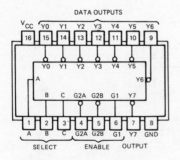

74LS138   **3 → 8 DECODER**

Inputs				Outputs							
ENABLE	SELECT										
G1	G2*	C	B	A	Y0	Y1	Y2	Y3	Y4	Y5	Y6	Y7
X	H	X	X	X	H	H	H	H	H	H	H	H
L	X	X	X	X	H	H	H	H	H	H	H	H
H	L	L	L	L	L	H	H	H	H	H	H	H
H	L	L	L	H	H	L	H	H	H	H	H	H
H	L	L	H	L	H	H	L	H	H	H	H	H
H	L	L	H	H	H	H	H	L	H	H	H	H
H	L	H	L	L	H	H	H	H	L	H	H	H
H	L	H	L	H	H	H	H	H	H	L	H	H
H	L	H	H	L	H	H	H	H	H	H	L	H
H	L	H	H	H	H	H	H	H	H	H	H	L

*G2 = G2A + G2B

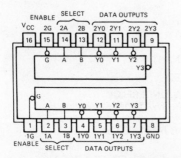

74LS139   **2 → 4 DUAL DECODER**

Inputs			Outputs			
Enable	Select					
G	B	A	Y0	Y1	Y2	Y3
H	X	X	H	H	H	H
L	L	L	L	H	H	H
L	L	H	H	L	H	H
L	H	L	H	H	L	H
L	H	H	H	H	H	L

EACH DECODER

F2

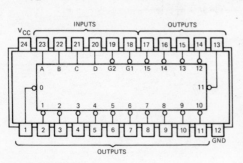

74154   **4 → 16 DECODER**

WHEN ENABLED, ONLY ONE
OUTPUT GOES LOW

A, B, C, & D INPUTS ARE BINARY
SELECTION OF OUTPUT

EXAMPLES

D	C	B	A	Selected output
L	L	L	H	1 (PIN 2)
L	H	L	H	5 (PIN 6)
H	H	H	H	15 (PIN 17)
L	L	L	L	0 (PIN 1)

DATA SELECTORS

G

G1

C.F. 6.4

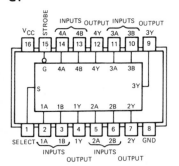

INPUTS		
STROBE	SELECT	Output Y
H	X	L
L	H	AS B I/P
L	L	AS A I/P

X = Don't care

74157   QUAD 2 → 1 LINE DATA SELECTOR

G2

C.F. 6.4

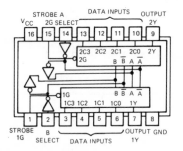

IF STROBE IS HIGH, OUTPUT Y IS LOW

IF STROBE IS LOW, OUTPUT Y IS AS
DATA INPUT SPECIFIED BY BINARY
SELECT INPUTS (SEE BELOW)

Select inputs		Selected data I/P
B	A	
L	L	C0
L	H	C1
H	L	C2
H	H	C3

74153   DUAL 4 → 1 LINE DATA SELECTOR

279

DATA SELECTORS (contd)

G3

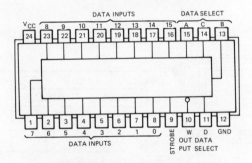

IF STROBE IS HIGH, OUTPUT W IS HIGH

IF STROBE IS LOW, OUTPUT W IS AN
INVERSION OF THE DATA INPUT
SPECIFIED BY THE BINARY SELECT
INPUTS.

EXAMPLES

D	C	B	A	Selected input
L	L	L	H	1 (PIN 7)
H	L	H	L	10 (PIN 21)

74150   16 → 1 LINE DATA SELECTOR

COMPARATOR

H1

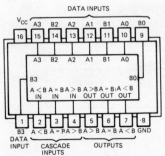

Comparing inputs				Cascading inputs			Outputs		
A3, B3	A2, B2	A1, B1	A0, B0	A > B	A < B	A = B	A > B	A < B	A = B
A3 > B3	X	X	X	X	X	X	H	L	L
A3 < B3	X	X	X	X	X	X	L	H	L
A3 = B3	A2 > B2	X	X	X	X	X	H	L	L
A3 = B3	A2 < B2	X	X	X	X	X	L	H	L
A3 = B3	A2 = B2	A1 > B1	X	X	X	X	H	L	L
A3 = B3	A2 = B2	A1 < B1	X	X	X	X	L	H	L
A3 = B3	A2 = B2	A1 = B1	A0 > B0	X	X	X	H	L	L
A3 = B3	A2 = B2	A1 = B1	A0 < B0	X	X	X	L	H	L
A3 = B3	A2 = B2	A1 = B1	A0 = B0	X	X	H	L	L	H
A3 = B3	A2 = B2	A1 = B1	A0 = B0	H	H	L	L	L	L
A3 = B3	A2 = B2	A1 = B1	A0 = B0	L	L	L	H	H	L

7485   4-BIT MAGNITUDE COMPARATOR

280

J1

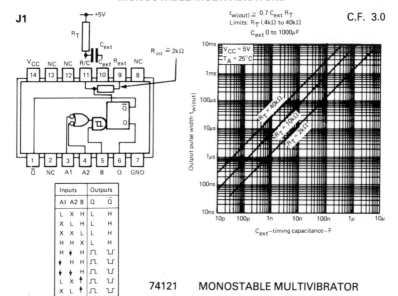

$t_{w(out)} \cong 0.7\, C_{ext}\, R_T$
Limits: R_T 1.4kΩ to 40kΩ
C_{ext} 0 to 1000μF

C.F. 3.0

Inputs			Outputs	
A1	A2	B	Q	Q̄
L	X	H	L	H
X	L	H	L	H
X	X	L	L	H
H	H	X	L	H
H	↓	H	⊓	⊔
↓	H	H	⊓	⊔
↓	↓	H	⊓	⊔
L	X	↑	⊓	⊔
X	L	↑	⊓	⊔

74121   **MONOSTABLE MULTIVIBRATOR**

J2   C.F. 4.5

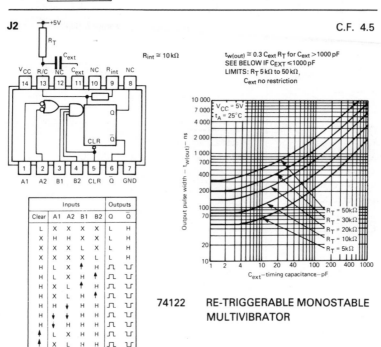

$t_{w(out)} \cong 0.3\, C_{ext}\, R_T$ for $C_{ext} > 1000$ pF
SEE BELOW IF $C_{EXT} \leqslant 1000$ pF
LIMITS: R_T 5 kΩ to 50 kΩ,
C_{ext} no restriction

Inputs					Outputs	
Clear	A1	A2	B1	B2	Q	Q̄
L	X	X	X	X	L	H
X	H	H	X	X	L	H
X	X	X	L	X	L	H
X	X	X	X	L	L	H
H	L	X	↑	H	⊓	⊔
H	L	X	H	↑	⊓	⊔
H	X	L	↑	H	⊓	⊔
H	X	L	H	↑	⊓	⊔
H	H	↓	H	H	⊓	⊔
H	↓	↓	H	H	⊓	⊔
H	↓	H	H	H	⊓	⊔
↑	L	X	H	H	⊓	⊔
↑	X	L	H	H	⊓	⊔

74122   **RE-TRIGGERABLE MONOSTABLE MULTIVIBRATOR**

555 TYPE TIMER

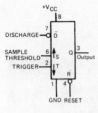

Symbol used in text
(See page 50)

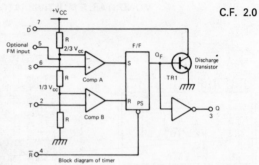

Block diagram of timer

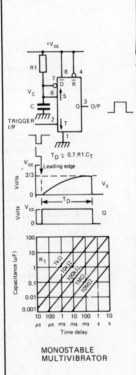

$$T_m \cong 0.7 \ (R1+R2) \ C_T$$
$$T_s \cong 0.7. \ R2. \ C_T$$

Initial start-up only

ASTABLE
MULTIVIBRATOR

See also page 52

$$T_D \cong 0.7.R1.C_T$$

MONOSTABLE
MULTIVIBRATOR

MAXIMUM RATINGS
$V_{CC \ MAX} = 18V$
DEVICE DISSIPATION:
UP TO $T_{AMB} = 55°C$
        600 mW
**THEREAFTER DERATED
LINEARLY   5 mW/°C**

**AMBIENT TEMP. RANGE:
0 – 70°C
(PLASTIC ENCAPS).
MAX O/P CURRENT
200 mA (HIGH OR LOW)**
NOTE: $V_{cc \ min} = 4.5V$

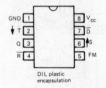

DIL plastic
encapsulation

**DEVICE IS
TTL COMPATIBLE**

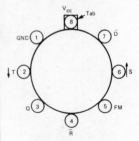

**TO-5 STYLE
PACKAGE**

L1

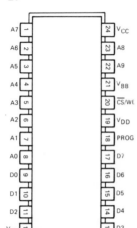

2708   EPROM
1024 bytes of 8-bits
INPUT LOAD CURRENT   10µA max.
TTL COMPATIBLE
Automatic programming is required

NOMINAL SUPPLY VOLTAGES

V_{CC}	$+5V$
V_{DD}	$+12V$
V_{BB}	$-5V$

PROGRAMMING NOTES

After completion of an erase
operation (by shortwave high-
intensity ultra-violet light),
all bits are set to the 1 state.
Manufacturer's data should be
consulted for programming details.
This requires pin 20 to be raised
to +12V, and programming data to
be applied on the data lines for
each address in turn; a programming
pulse is applied to pin 18. Only
one pulse may be applied at once for
any given address. Programming requires several loops to be made
through all addresses.

ERASABLE PROGRAMMABLE READ ONLY MEMORY (STATIC)

L2

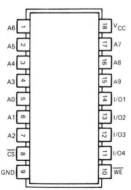

2114L   STATIC RAM
1024 bytes of 4-bits

$\overline{CS}$	$\overline{WE}$	I/O	Mode
H	X	Hi-imp	Not selected
L	L	H	WRITE 1
L	L	L	WRITE 0
L	H	D_{out}	READ

SINGLE +5V SUPPLY
TTL COMPATIBLE
SUPPLY CURRENT 70mA max.
INPUT LOAD CURRENT 10µA max.

283

Appendix B – selected TTL pinout details and supply currents

This appendix contains information on most of the TTL devices mentioned in this book. This information is tabulated in numerical order for the type numbers, and is principally intended to provide the following:

(a) Description of the output type (T-P for totem-pole; O-C for open-collector; 3-S for three-state).
(b) Supply current (in mA) for standard and LS types.
(c) The number of pins.
(d) Page references to where the device is mentioned in the text.
(e) Pinout details. This is in coded form, and a key is provided at the bottom of the right-hand page.

If the reader experiences any difficulty in using this table, the App.A column provides a cross-reference to Appendix A for devices listed therein. Comparison between these two appendices should clarify usage of this table.

Type 74-	No. Per pack	Description	Notes	App. A	Type of O/P	Standard typ*	Standard max	LS-type typ*	LS-type max	No. pins	Page refs.
						Supply currents (mA)					
00	4	2 I/P NAND		A1	T-P	8	22	2	4	14	22, 89, 100, 194
02	4	2 I/P NOR		A6	T-P	11	27	2	5.5	14	22, 194
03	4	2 I/P NAND		B6	O-C	8	22	1.5	4.5	14	
04	6	Inverter		A2	T-P	12	33	4	6	14	22, 33, 53, 194
05	6	Inverter		A2	O-C	12	33	2.5	6.5	14	
07	6	Buffer driver	30 V O/P	–	O-C	20	40	–	–	14	194
08	4	2 I/P AND		A7	T-P	15	33	5	9	14	22, 25, 33, 194
10	3	3 I/P AND		A3	T-P	6	17	2	3	14	25, 194
13	2	4 I/P Schmitt	NAND	–	T-P	17	32	3.5	7	14	23
14	6	Scmitt inverter		A4	T-P	30	60	10	21	14	22, 53, 143, 194
17	6	Buffer driver		–	O-C	25	41	–	–	14	22, 25
20	2	4 I/P NAND		A5	T-P	4	11	1	2	14	194
27	3	3 I/P NOR		–	T-P	13	26	3	7	14	194
30	1	8 I/P NAND		B1	T-P	2	6	0.5	1	14	143
32	4	2 I/P OR		A8	T-P	30	38	4	10	14	22, 143, 194
37	4	2 I/P NAND buffer		–	T-P	21	54	4	12	14	
45	1	BCD → dec. decoder	80 mA sink	–	O-C	43	70	–	–	14	194
47	1	BCD → 7-seg dec/dr	47A 40 mA sink LS47 24 mA sink	–	O-C	64	103	7	13	16	92
51	2	2 (AND)-OR-INVERT	LS51 only ‡ NCA for '51	B3	T-P	5.5	14	1	3	14	22, 194
74	2	D-type F/F	↑ clock	C1	T-P	17	30	4	8	14	44, 56, 194
75	1	4 bit bis latch		C3	T-P	32	53	6	12	16	44, 56, 194
76	2	J-K type F/F	Neg-edge clock	C2	T-P	20	40	4	6	16	46, 56, 84, 140, 155
85	1	4-bit mag. comp.		H1	T-P	55	88	10.5	20	16	80
86	4	2 I/P XOR		–	T-P	30	50	6	10	14	22, 155, 194
97	1	6-bit bin rate mplr		–	T-P	70	120	–	–	16	86
121	1	Monostable	(L121)	J1	T-P	18	40	8	20	14	48
122	1	Retrig. mono		J2	T-P	46	66	12	20	14	48
125	4	Bus buffer		B7	3-S	32	54	11	20	14	22
132	4	2 I/P Schmitt		–	T-P	21	40	7	14	14	194
138	1	3 → 8 decoder		F1	T-P	–	–	7	11	16	101, 143
153	2	4 → 1 MPX		G2	T-P	36	60	6	10	16	101, 194
154	1	4 → 16 decoder	(L154)	F2	T-P	34	56	17	28	24	101
155	2	2 → 4 decoder		–	T-P	25	40	6	10	16	101, 140, 194
156	2	2 → 4 decoder		–	O-C	25	40	6	10	16	194
157	2	2 → 1 MPX		G1	T-P	30	48	5	8	16	102
160	1	4-bit sync. ctr	Decade – async. CL	–	T-P	61	101	19	32	16	194
163	1	4-bit sync. ctr	Binary – sync. CL	–	T-P	61	101	19	32	16	87, 143
164	1	8-bit par'l o/p s/r	Ser'l I/P	–	T-P	37	54	16	27	14	58
165	1	8-bit ser'l o/p s/r	Par'l I/P	–	T-P	42	63	21	36	14	58
190	1	UP/DN decade ctr	Sync.	E3	T-P	65	105	20	35	16	87
191	1	UP/DN binary ctr	Sync.	E3	T-P	65	105	20	35	16	87, 194
195	1	4-bit S/R	Par'l I/P & O/P	–	T-P	39	63	14	21	16	194
197	1	P/S binary ctr	Par'l I/P	E1	T-P	48	59	16	27	14	87, 194
279	4	S̄-R̄ latch		C4	T-P	18	30	4	7	16	55

* Typical supply currents are only approximate, and assume half I/P's high and half low – these figures not given by manufacturer and have been suitably rounded.

T-P = Totem-pole
3.5 = 3-state
O-C = open circuit
'L' type given if no 'LS' version

				Pin details												Type 74-
1	*2*	*3*	*4*	*5*	*6*	*7*	*8*	*9*	*10*	*11*	*12*	*13*	*14*	*15*	*16*	
1A	1B	1Y	2A	2B	2Y	GND	3Y	3A	3B	4Y	4A	4B	V$_{CC}$	–	–	00
1Y	1A	1B	2Y	2A	2B	GND	3A	3Y	3B	3Y	4A	4B	4Y	V$_{CC}$	–	02
←							AS '00						→	–	–	03
1A	1Y	2A	2Y	3A	3Y	GND	4Y	4A	5Y	5A	6Y	6A	V$_{CC}$	–	–	04
←							AS '04						→	–	–	05
←							AS '04						→	–	–	07
←							AS '00						→	–	–	08
1A	1B	2A	2B	2C	2Y	GND	3Y	3A	3B	3C	1Y	1C	V$_{CC}$	–	–	10
1A	1B	NC	1C	1D	1Y	GND	2Y	2A	2B	NC	2C	2D	V$_{CC}$	–	–	13
←							AS '04						→	–	–	14
←							AS '04						→	–	–	17
←							AS '13						→	–	–	20
←							AS '10						→	–	–	27
A	B	C	D	E	F	GND	Y	NC	NC	G	H	NC	V$_{CC}$	–	–	30
←							AS '00						→	–	–	32
←							AS '00						→	–	–	37
0	1	2	3	4	5	6	GND	7	8	9	D	C	B	A	V$_{CC}$	45
B	C	LT	RBO	RBI	D	A	GND	e	d	c	b	a	g	f	V$_{CC}$	47
1A(1)	2A(1)	2B(1)	2C(2)	2D(2)	2Y	GND	1Y	1C(2)	1D(2)	1E(1)‡	1F(2)‡	1B(1)	V$_{CC}$	–	–	51
1$\overline{CL}$	1D	1CK	1PR	1Q	1$\overline{Q}$	GND	2$\overline{Q}$	2Q	2$\overline{PR}$	2CK	2D	2$\overline{CL}$	V$_{CC}$	–	–	74
1$\overline{Q}$	1D	2D	EN 3–4	V$_{CC}$	3D	4D	4$\overline{Q}$	4Q	3Q	3$\overline{Q}$	GND	EN 1–2	2Q	2$\overline{Q}$	1Q	75
1CK	1PR	1$\overline{CL}$	1J	V$_{CC}$	2CK	2$\overline{PR}$	2CL	2J	2$\overline{Q}$	2Q	2K	GND	1$\overline{Q}$	1Q	1K	76
B3	I(A<B)	I(A=B)	I(A>B)	O(A>B)	O(A=B)	O(A<B)	GND	B0	A0	B1	A1	A2	B2	A3	V$_{CC}$	85
←							AS '00						→	–	–	86
B	E	F	A	$\overline{Z}$	Y	$\overline{EN(0)}$	GND	CK	$\overline{ST}$	$\overline{EN(I)}$	UN/CAS	CL	C	D	V$_{CC}$	97
$\overline{Q}$	NC	A1↓	A2↓	B↑	Q	GND	NC	R$_{int}$	C$_{ext}$	CR$_{ext}$	NC	NC	V$_{CC}$	–	–	121
A1↓	A2↓	B1↑	B2↑	$\overline{CL}$	$\overline{Q}$	GND	Q	R$_{int}$	NC	CR$_{ext}$	NC	CR$_{ext}$	V$_{CC}$	–	–	123
1C	1A	1Y	2C	2A	2Y	GND	3Y	3A	3C	4Y	4A	4C	V$_{CC}$	–	–	125
←							AS '00						→	–	–	132
A	B	C	$\overline{G2A}$	$\overline{G2B}$	G1	Y7	GND	Y6	Y5	Y4	Y3	Y2	Y1	Y0	V$_{CC}$	138
1$\overline{ST}$	B	1C3	1C2	1C1	1C0	1Y	GND	2Y	2C0	2C1	2C2	2C3	A	2$\overline{ST}$	V$_{CC}$	153
GND = P12; V$_{CC}$ = P24; $\overline{G1}$ = P18; $\overline{G2}$ = P19; I(A→D = P23–21); Ō(0→10 = P1–11); Ō(11→15 = P13→15)																154
1D	1$\overline{ST}$	1Y3	1Y2	1Y1	1Y0	GND	2Y0	2Y1	2Y2	2Y3	A	2$\overline{ST}$	2D	V$_{CC}$		155
←							AS '155						→	–	–	156
SB/$\overline{A}$	1A	1B	1Y	2A	2B	2Y	GND	3Y	3B	3A	4Y	4B	4A	$\overline{ST}$		157
$\overline{CL}$	CK	A	B	C	D	EN(P)	GND	$\overline{LD}$	EN(T)	QD	QC	QB	QA	RCO	V$_{CC}$	160
←							AS '160						→	–	–	163
A	B	QA	QB	QC	QD	$\overline{GND}$	CK	$\overline{CL}$	QE	QF	QG	QH	V$_{CC}$	–	–	164
SH/$\overline{LD}$	CK↑	E	$\underline{F}$	G	H	$\overline{QH}$	GND	QH	SER-I	$\underline{A}$	B	$\underline{C}$	D	CK-I	V$_{CC}$	165
DB	QB	QA	$\overline{EN}$	DN/$\overline{UP}$	QC	QD	GND	D	C	$\overline{LD}$	MX/MN	$\overline{ORC}$	CK	DA	V$_{CC}$	190
←							AS '190						→			191
$\overline{CL}$	J	$\overline{K}$	A	B	C	D	GND	SH/$\overline{LD}$	CK↑	$\overline{QD}$	QD	QC	QB	QA	V$_{CC}$	195
CT/LD	QC	$\underline{C}$	A	QA	CK2	GND	CK1	QB	$\underline{B}$	D	QD	$\overline{CL}$	V$_{CC}$	–	–	197
1$\overline{R}$	1$\overline{S}$(1)	1$\overline{S}$(2)	1Q	2$\overline{R}$	2$\overline{S}$	2Q	GND	3Q	3$\overline{R}$	3$\overline{S}$(1)	3$\overline{S}$(2)	4Q	4$\overline{R}$	4$\overline{S}$	V$_{CC}$	279

NC = no connection
LT = lamp test
NCA = no connection allowed
RBO = ripple blanking O/P
RBI = ripple blanking I/P
I = input
O or Q = output

A–H = inputs
Y, Z = output
a–f = 7 segments
(Numerals) = gate/function identity
LD = load
SH = shift
DN = down
CT = count

PR = preset
CL = clear
G = enable
CK = clock
S = select
P = pin
MX = max
MN = min

‡ See notes col.

287

Appendix C – electrical characteristics

This appendix contains representative characteristics for the 54/74 series of TTL devices and the 4000 series of CMOS devices. TTL data is based upon information from Texas Instruments, and CMOS data is based upon information from RCA. Although every care has been taken to ensure that this information is correct, no responsibility can be taken for any errors which might occur, or for the results of such errors. This information is supplied for guidance purposes only, and it is the user's responsibility to check individual device data sheets. The representative characteristics are provided to give a general indication of typical parameters, but these characteristics do vary from device to device, therefore individual data sheets should be consulted for positive information on other than the indicated types.

For further information, the reader should contact appropriate manufacturers. The following addresses are provided for the reader's use:

> RCA Solid State, Division, Somerville, N.J., 08876, USA.
> RCA Limited, Sunbury-on-Thames, Middlesex TW16 7HW, England.
> RCA s.a., 4400 Herstal, Liege, Belgium.
> Texas Instruments Ltd., Manton Lane, Bedford, England.
> Texas Instruments Inc., 13500 North Central Expressway, Dallas, Texas, 75265, USA.

The amateur will find that enthusiast magazines in the electronics field contain a large number of advertisements for 74 series plastic DIL devices (standard and LS are the most common, with only a few L and S types usually listed), and 4000 series CMOS devices.

See Chapter 14 for general information about logic families. Refer to Appendix A for abridged TTL data, or Appendix B for TTL pinout details and supply current figures.

54/74 family characteristics

ABSOLUTE MAXIMUM RATINGS

Characteristic		*54 54H 74 74H*	*54L 74L*	*54LS 74LS* *Diode inputs*	*54LS 74LS* *Emitter inputs*	*54S 74S*	*Unit*
Supply voltage V_{CC}		+7	+8	+7	+7	+7	V
Input voltage max		+5.5	+5.5	+7	+5.5	+5.5	V
Inter-emitter voltage max		+5.5	+5.5		+5.5	+5.5	V
Voltage at open-collectors (max)	'06, '07	+30					V
	'16, '17, '26	+15					
	others		+8	+7	+7	+7	
Voltage at disabled 3-state O/P (max)		+5.5		+5.5	+5.5	+5.5	V
Free air temperature range	54 family	−55 to +125 (All types)					°C
	74 family	0 to +70 (All types)					
Storage temperature range		−65 to +150 (All types)					°C

STANDARD INPUTS – ONE LOAD (MAXIMUMS)

Characteristic		*54 74*	*54H 74H*	*54L/74L* *Diode inputs*	*54L/74L* *Emitter inputs*	*54LS 74LS*	*54S 74S*	*Unit*	74HC
High level input current	I_{IH}	40	50	10	20	20	50	µA	1µA
Low level input current	I_{IL}	−1.6	−2	−0.18	−0.8	−0.4	−2	mA	1µA
Input pull-up resistor		4	2.8	40	8	18	2.8	kΩ	← MAX PULL-UP RES

REPRESENTATIVE CHARACTERISTICS ('00 DEVICE)

Characteristic				54 / 74	54H / 74H	54L / 74L	54LS / 74LS	54S	Unit
High level	I_{OH}	54 family	max	−0.4	−0.5	−0.1	−0.4	−1.0	mA
output current		74 family	max	−0.4	−0.5	−0.2	−0.4	−1.0	mA
Low level	I_{OL}	54 family	max	16	20	2	4	20	mA
output current		74 family	max	16	20	3.6	8	20	mA
High level input voltage	V_{IH}		min	2	2	2	2	2	V
Low level	V_{IL}	54 family	max	0.8	0.8	0.7	0.7	0.8	V
input voltage		74 family		0.8	0.8	0.7	0.8	0.8	
High level	V_{OH}	54 family	min	2.4	2.4	2.4	2.5	2.5	
output voltage			typ	3.4	3.5	3.3	3.4	3.4	
		74 family	min	2.4	2.4	2.4	2.7	2.7	V
			typ	3.4	3.5	3.2	3.4	3.4	
Low level	V_{OL}	54 family	typ	0.2	0.2	0.15	0.25		
output voltage			max	0.4	0.4	0.3	0.4	0.5	
		74 family	typ	0.2	0.2	0.2	0.25		V
			max	0.4	0.4	0.4	0.5	0.5	
Propagation delay	t_{pLH}	L → H level	typ	11	5.9	35	9	3	ns
		output	max	22	10	60	15	4.5	ns
	t_{pHL}	H → L level	typ	7	6.2	31	10	3	ns
		output	max	15	10	60	15	5	ns
test conditions		C_L		15	25	50	15	15	pF
(load C & R)		R_L		400	280	4000	2000	280	Ω

TTL · BISTABLE SWITCHING CHARACTERISTICS

Parameter		From I/P	To O/P	7474 dual D-type			7476 dual J-K type			Unit
				min	typ	max	min	typ	max	
Maximum frequency	f_{max}			15	25		15	20		MHz
Preset to output	t_{pLH}	PS	Q			25			25	ns
delay	t_{pHL}	PS	$\overline{Q}$			40			40	ns
Clear to output	t_{pLH}	CL	Q			25			25	ns
delay	t_{pHL}	CL	$\overline{Q}$			40			40	ns
Clock to output	t_{pLH}	CK	Q/$\overline{Q}$	14	25		16	25		ns
delay	t_{pHL}	CK	Q/$\overline{Q}$	20	40		25	40		ns

4000 series CMOS characteristics

ABSOLUTE MAXIMUM RATINGS

Characteristic				Values	Unit
Supply voltage range	V_{DD}		A series	−0.5 to +15	V
			B series	−0.5 to +20	V
Input voltage range (all inputs)				−0.5 to (V_{DD} + 0.5)	V
Free air temperature range	T_A	ceramic	Types D, F, K	−55 to +125	°C
		plastic	Type E	−40 to +85	
Storage temperature range	T_{stg}			−65 to +150	°C
Power dissipation per package	P_D	ceramic	Types D, F, K	500	mW
		plastic	Type E	500	mW
Power dissipation per output transistor				100	mW

ELECTRICAL CHARACTERISTICS

Characteristic		Conditions		A series			B series			Unit
		V_{IN}	V_{DD}	min	typ	max	min	typ	max	
Supply voltage operating range	V_{DD}			3	10	12	3	15	18	V
Low level output voltage	V_{OL}	+5	+5	0	50		0			V
		+10	+10	0	50		0			
		+15	+15	N/A			0	0.05		
High level output voltage	V_{OH}	0	+ 5	4.95			5	4.95	5	V
		0	+10	9.95			10	9.95	10	
		0	+15	N/A				14.95	15	
Input leakage current	I_{IL}		+15	$\pm 10^{-5} \pm$ 1						µA
	I_{IM}		+20				$\pm 10^{-5} \pm 1$			
3-state output leakage	I_{OL}		+20				$\pm 10^{-4} \pm 2$			µA
	I_{CH}									

REPRESENTATIVE CHARACTERISTICS (CD4001A) – QUAD 2I/P NOR

Characteristic		Conditions V_O (V)	V_{DD} (V)	Ceramic packages typ	max	Plastic packages typ	max	Unit
Sink current (N-channel)	I_{DN} min	+0.4	+ 5	1	0.4	1	0.3	mA
		+0.5	+10	2.5	0.9	2.5	0.6	
Source current (P-channel)	I_{DP} min	+2.5	+ 5	−2	−0.5	−2	−0.3	mA
		+9.5	+10	−1	−0.5	−1	−0.25	
Propagation delay H → L	t_pHL	–	+5	35	50	35	80	ns
		–	+10	25	40	25	55	
Propagation delay 1 → H	t_pLH	–	+ 5	35	95	35	120	ns
		–	+10	25	45	25	65	

$V_{SS} = 0\,V$

Appendix D – ASCII code

The American Standard Code for Information Interchange – or the 'ASCII code' – is widely used in digital and computer engineering. It comprises seven bits, and codes a total of 128 alphanumerics, punctuation marks, and machine codes.

ASCII is divisible into convenient subsets determined by the three most significant bits (bits 5 to 7); thus subsets not required in a particular application may be excluded. The table below is arranged to clearly show these subsets. There are 64 characters used for upper-case letters, numerals, common punctuation marks, and space (SP). A further 32 characters specify lower-case letters, and less commonly used punctuation marks. The remaining 32 characters specify machine commands such as line-feed (LF), ring bell (BEL), and an ineffective character (NUL); note that the latter is chosen for the code 0000000.

Bit numbers

7 6 5 4 3 2 1	0 0 0	0 0 1	0 1 0	0 1 1	1 0 0	1 0 1	1 1 0	1 1 1
0 0 0 0	NUL	DLE	SP	0	@	P		p
0 0 0 1	SHO	DC1	!	1	A	Q	a	q
0 0 1 0	STX	DC2	"	2	B	R	b	r
0 0 1 1	ETX	DC3	#	3	C	S	c	s
0 1 0 0	EOT	DC4	$	4	D	T	d	t
0 1 0 1	ENQ	NAK	%	5	E	U	e	u
0 1 1 0	ACK	SYN	&	6	F	V	f	v
0 1 1 1	BEL	ETB	'	7	G	W	g	w
1 0 0 0	BS	CAN	(	8	H	X	h	x
1 0 0 1	HT	EM	)	9	I	Y	i	y
1 0 1 0	LF	SUB	*	:	J	Z	j	z
1 0 1 1	VT	ESC	+	;	K	[	k	{
1 1 0 0	FF	FS	,	<	L	\	l	|
1 1 0 1	CR	GS	–	=	M	]	m	}
1 1 1 0	SO	RS	.	>	N	∧	n	~
1 1 1 1	SI	US	/	?	O	—	o	DEL

Note how conveniently the subsets are grouped. For example, there is only one bit difference between lower-case and upper-case (i.e. bit 6), and the upper three bits can be hard-wired if only the numerals are required. If certain upper bits remain unchanged, they may be ignored, thereby reducing the number of bits. An eighth parity bit is normally used in a full code.

Appendix E – a note on drawing standards

The logic symbols used throughout this book are drawn in general compliance with the American MIL-STD-806B. The reason for this choice is that these symbols are recognised by engineers worldwide, and need little explanation. The majority of digital devices originate from American manufacturers, and in consequence, the data sheets relating to these devices generally comply with this MIL standard. This standard utilises distinctively shaped curved symbols for logic gates, and more complex devices are generally represented by rectangles with appropriate labelling.

The standards relating to logic symbols have been in a state of flux over the past decade. The International Electrotechnical Commission (IEC) has concentrated on producing an internationally recognised standard for logic symbols, and this has led to the development of various standards in interested countries of the world, based upon rectangular symbols. The American version of these symbols from the American National Standards Institute is ANSI Y.32.14-1973 (IEEE Std 91-1973), which officially superseded MIL-STD-806B as an industry standard in 1973, but engineers and manufacturers seem to prefer the MIL standard, which lives on! Thus whilst military documentation in America may follow the ANSI standard, commercial literature generally still uses the older and more familiar MIL standard used within this book.

British Standards issued BS 3939: Section 21, on binary logic elements, which follows the general principles set out in the IEC standards. At the time of publication of this book, Issue 2 of BS 3939 is in force, being based upon IEC 117, but this is out of date and is due for revision. This standard is only currently being introduced into military documentation, and poses certain problems since it is still incomplete, and is far from being as comprehensive as the ANSI standard. The present IEC 117 standard is to be replaced by IEC 617, of which Part 12 deals with binary logic elements, and BS 3939 is to be revised in accordance with the revised IEC document, which will introduce a selection of new symbols.

The author is currently involved in documentation for the services in the U.K., and is therefore familiar with the latest British Standard and the problems it imposes by its lack of definition for many logic devices, ranging from simple functions such as a three-state gate, to common devices such as multiplexers and decoders. He is also familiar with the problems that engineers find with the new symbols, for they do mean a new learning exercise. Bearing in mind that this book is intended for a worldwide market, it was not considered appropriate to use the current BS 3939 or an equivalent standard, since this would have introduced many difficulties:

(a) Most engineers are not familiar with the 'new' logic symbols.
(b) Most engineers dislike the new logic symbols.
(c) Most data books use MIL-STD-806B symbols.
(d) Since many devices have not been allocated symbols, the newer standards cannot be used exclusively.
(e) The use of the newer style symbols necessitates considerable explanation, and sufficient space is not available.
(f) It is easier to become familiar with the symbols most commonly used in manufacturers' literature, or conversions will be necessary.

Having said all this, it is only fair to state that the author recognises the advantages offered by the new style symbols *once everyone understands them and they are sufficiently comprehensive.* It is worth

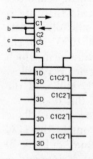

Figure 1. Bidirectional shift register
(BS 3939, Issue 2, Section 21)

noting that these symbols do allow logic diagrams to be significantly condensed where it is not important to show actual devices; this allows block diagrams to be replaced by logic diagrams which tell an *au-fait* engineer all he needs to know about the logic functions performed without the need for amplifying text.

Figure 1 is provided as an example of the new style symbols, and depicts a bidirectional shift register. It may be appreciated that

296

symbols such as these require considerable familiarity before they may be used without further explanation, hence the reason for avoiding them in this book.

In the example shown, input *a* provokes a shift action from top to bottom, input *b* provokes a shift from bottom to top, and input *c* controls the parallel action. Input *d* is a common reset. The 'D' indicates D-type flip-flops, and the '⌐' symbol indicates a postponement of the change of state of the output.

Equivalent logic symbols in different standards

Figure 2 is provided to show the equivalent logic symbols between standards for simple logic gates.

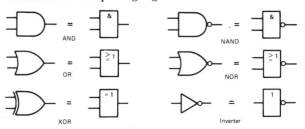

Figure 2. Equivalent logic symbols: left-hand examples are MIL-STD-806B; right-hand examples are BS 3939 or ANSI Y.32.14-1973 or IEC 117.

Special symbology used within this publication

It is explained elsewhere within this book that the logic symbols used are restricted to the symbols normally used on data sheets for particular devices. Where the symbol is not truly representative of the purpose of a gate (although it is logically equivalent), a '†' symbol is used inside the gate to indicate that it is not performing its expected function. The symbols shown in Figure 3 with a 'dagger' symbol are as they might appear in this book; adjacent to these symbols are the true logical equivalents of the functions they represent.

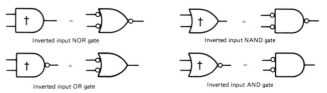

Figure 3. Logic symbols used in this book with dagger symbols and their equivalent logic functions

Index